Introductory Physical Geology
Laboratory Manual for Distance Learning

GREG P. GARDINER

Coast
LEARNING·SYSTEMS

Kendall Hunt
publishing company

Kendall Hunt Book Team:
Mark C. Falb, Chairman and Chief Executive Officer
Chad M. Chandlee, President and Chief Operating Officer
David L. Tart, Vice President, Higher Education
Paul B. Carty, Director of Publishing Partnerships
Georgia Botsford, Editorial Manager
Lynne Rogers, Senior Editor
Timothy J. Beitzel ,Vice President, Operations
Christine E. O'Brien Assistant Vice President, Production Services
Mary Melloy, Senior Production Editor
Colleen Zelinsky, Senior Permissions Editor

Coast Learning Systems Book Team:
Ding Jo H. Currie, Chancellor, Coast Community College District
Loretta Adrian, President, Coastline Community College
Dan C. Jones, Executive Dean, Office of Instructional Systems Development
Lynn M. Dahnke, Director, Marketing & Publisher Partnerships
Robert D. Nash, Director, Instructional Design & Faculty Support
Sylvia E. Amito'elau, Educational Media Designer
Judith M. Garvey, Director, eMedia & Publishing
Wendy Sacket, E-Media & Publishing Project Coordinator
Linda Wojciechowski, Senior E-Media & Publishing Assistant
Thien Vu, E-Media & Publishing Assistant

Figures 5.4, 5.5, 5.6, 6.2, 6.3, 7.6, 7.7, 8.3, 8.4, 11.4
From *Geology: Laboratory Manual for Distance Learning* by James L. Ruhle. Copyright © 2000 by Coast Community College District. Reprinted by permission of Kendall Hunt Publishing Company.

Figures 12.1, 12.2, 12.8, 12.11, 12.15, 12.17
From *Planet Earth* by John J. Renton. Copyright © 2002 by John J. Renton. Reprinted by permission of Kendall Hunt Publishing Company.

Cover design by Don Vierstra; cover images © iStock, Inc., and Shutterstock, Inc.
All Shutterstock images used under license from Shutterstock, Inc.

ISBN-13: 978-0-7575-6320-1

Coast Learning Systems
Coastline Community College
11460 Warner Avenue
Fountain Valley, CA 92708
telephone: (800) 547-4748
e-mail: CoastLearning@coastline.edu

fax: (714) 241-6286
website: www.CoastLearning.org

Printed in the United States of America
10 9 8 7 6 5 4 3 2
Kendall Hunt
publishing company

Contents

Acknowledgments

Several of the individuals responsible for the creation of this course are listed on the copyright page of this book. In addition to these people, appreciation is expressed for the contributions of the following individuals:

The author of this laboratory manual, Greg P. Gardiner, M.S., has more than 12 years experience as an educator teaching geology and earth science. He has a teaching credential in biological sciences, a supplemental credential in geological sciences, and holds a Master's degree in Environmental Science from California State University, Fullerton. Greg has presented a paper at the California Academy of Sciences. He has a passion for geologic sciences and has worked diligently to coordinate the instructional content of these lab lessons by linking the exercises to real-life activities in order to help students understand the concepts and processes of this fascinating subject. Greg has also conducted field study programs at Yosemite National Park and Catalina Island, California.

Sylvia E. Amito'elau. M.S., has overseen the instructional design of this lab manual, as well its accompanying textbook and online course, from concept to completion. She is an instructional designer for Coast Learning Systems, a division of Coastline Community College in Fountain Valley, California. She has assisted in design and development on several educational projects, including online courses in accounting, Arabic, chemistry, Chinese, education, math, and student success for more than 8 years. At Coastline Community College, Sylvia is responsible for providing instructional design, training, and support for all faculty, particularly in areas related to distance learning. As a member of the Senate Academic Standards Committee, she participated in the development of the Coastline Academic Quality Rubric. She is also a part-time faculty member teaching computer application courses and has experience teaching courses in various delivery modalities such as classroom, hybrid, and online. In addition, Sylvia has worked on the California Virtual Campus project, training and assisting Southern California community college faculty in the design, development, and delivery of online instruction. Sylvia holds a Master of Science degree in Instructional Technology and a Bachelor of Arts degree in Mathematics.

We would like to express our thanks to the members of the Academic Advisory Team whose names appear on page viii. Special thanks are also owed to the graphic design contributions made by Bob Dixon, Marie Hulett, Don Vierstra, and Mark Worden.

Preface: How to Take This Lab Course

To the Student

Welcome to the *Introductory Physical Geology Laboratory Manual for Distance Learning*. The first lab lesson in this manual deals with how to read and use topographic maps. The remaining lessons follow a sequence that progresses through the basics of plate tectonics, seismology, minerals and rocks, and geologic time and concludes with such overarching topics as Earth's major geologic features and economic geology resources.

Learning Outcomes

The designers, academic advisors, and producers of this lab manual have specified the following learning outcomes for students using the *Introductory Physical Geology Laboratory Manual for Distance Learning*. After successfully completing the lab exercises, you should be able to:

1. Effectively apply the concepts, principles, and theories of geology to make accurate observations and to identify and distinguish among samples/structures/landscapes.
2. Gather and analyze data, formulate and test hypotheses, solve problems, and come to supportable conclusions given various scenarios and research topics.

Features

This manual and laboratory kit are part of an intensive laboratory course that explores the basic concepts and principles of physical geology. Each lesson includes specific learning objectives that students should use to prepare for the lab. The lab manual includes exercises and procedures that illuminate the central principles of physical geology. Each lab lesson includes questions designed to help you analyze, review, and apply your knowledge of the material covered in the lab course. Reading this lab manual, watching the video clips and completing the activities in the online component, and completing the lab exercises will provide you with information that you would receive in the classroom if you were taking this lab course on campus.

The laboratory kit contains most of the materials and mineral samples necessary to conduct the lab exercises contained in each lesson.

Each lesson in the lab manual contains the following elements:

➤ Overview

This section introduces the topics covered in the lab exercises, explains why they are important, and makes connections to previous lesson concepts that you'll need to remember.

➤ Learning Objectives

These objectives outline the significant goals to be achieved after completing each lesson. (Note: Instructors often design test questions after learning objectives, so use them to help focus your study.)

➤ Materials

This section provides a list of materials that will be needed to complete the lab exercises. Some items will be provided in the accompanying lab kit, and others may need to be purchased or borrowed if they are not readily available in your home.

➤ Illustrations

These drawings and photographs have been included to amplify your understanding of specific concepts or to illustrate particular steps and procedures within the course of various lab experiments.

➤ Online Activities

This section involves using the Internet to access the course website, where you will participate in a variety of interactive games and simulations, watch videos, view images, and complete quizzes based on these activities.

➤ Quiz

This section includes a variety of questions designed to verify your comprehension of the lab exercises and will help you make connections to and apply the principles covered within the course.

How to Take This Distance Learning Lab

If this is your first experience with distance learning, welcome. Distance learning courses are designed for busy people whose situations or schedules do not permit them to take a traditional on-campus course.

This lab manual has been designed to be used as a tool to help reinforce topics and concepts on which you will later be tested. To complete this lab course successfully, you will need to complete exercises that:

- provide you with information that you can apply to your everyday experiences.
- provide visual reinforcement to help you understand and appreciate the complexity of the various physical geologic processes that occur above and beneath the surface of the earth as you know it.
- provide you with the opportunity to practice what you have learned.

- help make the study of physical geology more organized, systematic, and enjoyable. Since you are required to assimilate a large amount of information in a short period of time, a lot of your dedicated time is required. You should be prepared to set aside time when you can tackle and complete an entire lab exercise so that you can master the concepts involved and be prepared for assessment.

Even though you do not have scheduled classes to attend each week on campus, please keep in mind that this is a college-level course. It will require the same amount of work as a traditional, classroom version of this lab course and at the same level of difficulty. As a distance learner, however, it will be up to you alone to keep up with your deadlines. It's important that you schedule enough time to read, study, review, and reflect. Also, take some time immediately after completing a lab lesson to reflect on what you have just learned. This is an excellent time to discuss the lesson with a friend or family member. Your active thinking and involvement will promote your success.

Academic Advisory Team

Robert Altamura, Ph.D., Florida Community College at Jacksonville Open Campus, Urban Resources Center

Edward (Erik) Bender, M.S., Orange Coast College

Theodore Erski, M.A., McHenry County College

Roberto Falero, M.S., DPRA, Inc.

Gail Gibson, Ph.D., Florida Community College at Jacksonville—Kent Campus

Jonathan Kuespert, M.S., M.B.A., BreitBurn Energy Management Company

Michael Leach, M.S., M.A., New Mexico State University

James McClinton, M.S., Eastern New Mexico University—Roswell

Joseph Mraz, M.S., Santa Fe Community College

Jay P. Muza, Ph.D., Broward College

Douglas Neves, Ph.D., Cypress College

Kathy Ann Randall, M.S., Lincoln County Campus of the Flathead Valley Community College

Kelly Ruppert, M.S., California State University, Fullerton, and Coastline Community College

Richard Schultz, Ph.D., C.P.G., Elmhurst College

Debbie Secord, M.S., Coastline Community College

William H. Walker, Ph.D., Thomas Edison State College

Curtis Williams, M.S., California State University, Fullerton

Jan Yett, M.S., Orange Coast College

TOPOGRAPHIC MAPS

Lesson 1

AT A GLANCE

Purpose

Learning Objectives

Materials Needed

Overview

> **Topographic Quadrangle Maps**
>
> **Compass Bearings**
>
> **Public Land Survey System**
>
> **Scale**
>
> **Scale Conversion**
>
> **Map Symbols**
>
> **Contour Lines**

Online Activities

Lab Exercises

> **Lab Exercise #1:** *Contour Exercises*
>
> **Lab Exercise #2:** *Topographic Profiles*

Quiz

Purpose

The activities in this lesson will lay the foundation for the use of topographic maps. Knowing how to read and interpret a topographic map is essential for understanding geological features in any area. Furthermore, hikers, campers, geologists, and engineers use the topographic map as a three-dimensional tool to interpret the land surfaces for their scientific studies or recreational use.

Learning Objectives

After completing this laboratory lesson, you will be able to:

- Understand how specific elevation points relate to the overall topography of a broad area.
- Understand how different landforms are depicted on maps.
- Understand how to interpret map symbols and scales.
- Construct a topographic map by drawing contour lines based on points of elevation.
- Construct a topographic profile.
- Read and interpret topographic maps.

Materials Needed

The activities will be performed using the following materials provided in the lab kit, as well as materials readily available in your home. If you do not already have them in your home, you may need to purchase some of the materials. Be sure you have all listed materials before starting the activity.

- ❑ A USGS topographic quadrangle map of Yosemite Valley, California (included in your laboratory kit)
- ❑ USGS topographic map symbols pamphlet (included in your laboratory kit)
- ❑ Protractor or compass (included in your laboratory kit)
- ❑ Ruler (included in your laboratory kit)
- ❑ Pencil
- ❑ Eraser
- ❑ Calculator

Overview

A topographic map is a flat, two-dimensional representation of a three-dimensional land surface, otherwise known as the topographic relief. Such a map depicts the topographic relief by means of contour lines that are configured to show the hills and valleys and variations in surface elevation. A topographic map differs significantly from the more familiar planimetric map. A planimetric map does not show contour lines nor does it express topographic relief, an example of planimetric map would be a highway map. Most topographic maps also depict many features that are commonly found on planimetric maps, such as bodies of water, vegetation, roads, buildings, political boundaries, and place names.

Topographic Quadrangle Maps

Most topographic maps of areas within the United States are published by the United States Geological Survey (USGS), and most of these topographic maps depict rectangular sections of the earth's surface known as quadrangles. A quadrangle is a section of the earth's surface that is bound at the top or north side of the map and the bottom or south side of the map by lines of latitude, whereas the left or west side of the map and the right or east side of the map is bounded by lines of longitude. Lines of latitude, or parallels, are parallel to the equator. The equator is an imaginary great circle that surrounds the earth's surface and it is equidistant from the poles and perpendicular to the earth's axis of rotation. The equator divides the carth into two equal hemispheres, which is the northern and southern hemisphere. They extend from the equator, which is zero latitude, to both the North Pole—90 degrees north latitude— and the South Pole—90 degrees south latitude. The north-south orienting lines of longitude, or meridians, start at the Greenwich meridian in England (known as the prime meridian) and extend westward (west longitude) and eastward (east longitude) by 180 degrees to the International Date Line situated approximately in the middle of the Pacific Ocean. Lines of longitude are not parallel but converge at the North Pole and the South Pole. Since North America is north of the equator and west of the prime meridian, all latitudes in the continental United States are north latitudes and all longitudes are west longitudes. Refer to **Figure 1.1** which visually describes latitude and longitude grid and coordinate system.

Latitude and longitude are expressed in degrees, minutes, and seconds, as follows:
1 degree (°) = 60 minutes (')
1 minute = 60 seconds (")

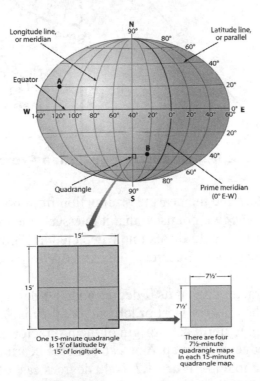

Figure 1.1 Latitude and Longitude Grid and Coordinate System. Illustration by Don Vierstra

Quadrangle maps are published in several sizes, but two of the most common are 15-minute quadrangle maps and 7.5-minute quadrangle maps. The laboratory activity for this lesson will feature a 7.5-minute quadrangle map representing an area that measures 7.5 minutes of latitude by 7.5 minutes of longitude—or one-eighth of a degree of latitude by one-eighth of a degree of longitude.

Compass Bearings

A bearing is the direction from one point on a map to another. If it is expressed in degrees east or west of true north or in degrees east or west of true south, it is a quadrant bearing. If it is expressed in degrees between 0 and 360, it is an azimuth bearing, where true north is 0 degrees or 360 degrees, east is 90 degrees, south is 180 degrees, and west is 270 degrees.

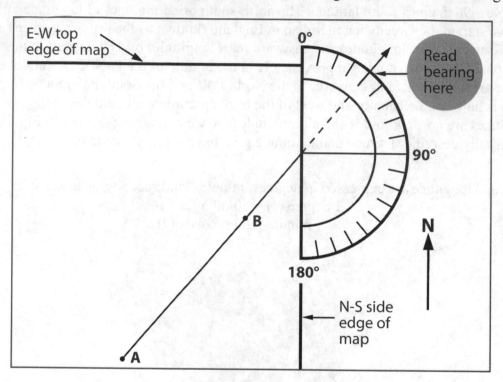

Figure 1.2 Reading Bearings with a Protractor

Refer to Figure 1.2. To determine the bearing or direction from point A on the map to point B, draw a line through the two points so that it intersects the map border, either the left (west) edge or the right (east) edge. In the example depicted in **Figure 1.2**, a line was drawn through points A and B so that it also intersects the east edge of the map.

One must then orient a protractor so that its 0-degree and 180-degree marks are on or parallel to the east or right edge of the map (or west or left edge of the map), with the 0 degree end toward true north or geographic north. The origin of the protractor is placed at the point where the A-B line intersects the edge of the map. You can read the bearing directly from the protractor, which, in the example in **Figure 1.2**, is 40 degrees east of north. This is expressed as North 40 degrees East or N40E.

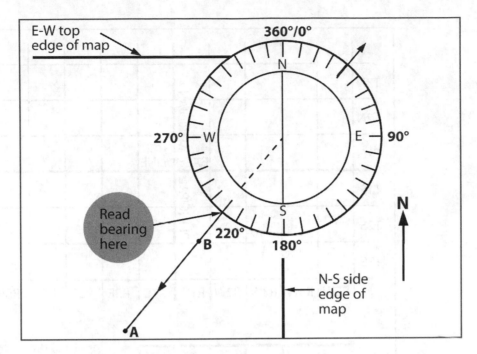

Figure 1.3 Reading Bearings with a Compass

One may also use a compass to read bearings, as depicted in **Figure 1.3**. Ignore the compass needle and use the compass as if it were a 0–360 degree circular protractor. Bearings can also be expressed with respect to south. For example, if one were to express the compass direction from point B to point A, the bearing would be expressed as 40 degrees west of south. This is expressed as South 40 degrees West (S40W) or an azimuth bearing of 220 degrees.

Public Land Survey System

The U.S. Public Land Survey System (PLSS) is used in most parts of the United States west of the original thirteen states. The PLSS is depicted in **Figure 1.4**. It was established in each state by surveying *principal meridians* (north-south lines) and *base lines* (east-west lines). Once the initial principal meridians and base lines were established, additional parallels and meridians were surveyed. Strips of land called "township strips" run parallel to the base line and are numbered north and south of it (T1N, T2N, . . . or (Township 1 South) T1S, T2S, . . .). Strips of land called "range strips" run parallel to the principal meridian and are numbered east and west of it (R1E, R2E, . . . or R1W, R2W, . . .). Each intersection of a township strip with a range strip forms a square, called a township. Each township square measures 6 miles by 6 miles and therefore contains 36 square miles. Each square mile (640 acres) is a numbered section.

Sections are numbered from 1 to 36, beginning in the upper right corner, zig zagging back and forth, and ending in the lower right corner of the township square. Often, the PLSS boundary lines are depicted as a red grid on topographic quadrangle maps. Any points can be located precisely within a section by dividing the section into quarters (labeled NW, NE, SW, SE). Each of these quarters can be subdivided into quarters and labeled accordingly. For example, point X in **Figure 1.4** is in the southeast one-quarter of the southwest one-quarter of the southeast one-quarter of Section 22 in Township 2 South, Range 3 West, which is written in shorthand as:

$$\text{SE} \tfrac{1}{4}, \text{SW} \tfrac{1}{4}, \text{SE} \tfrac{1}{4}, \text{Sec. 22, T2S, R3W}$$

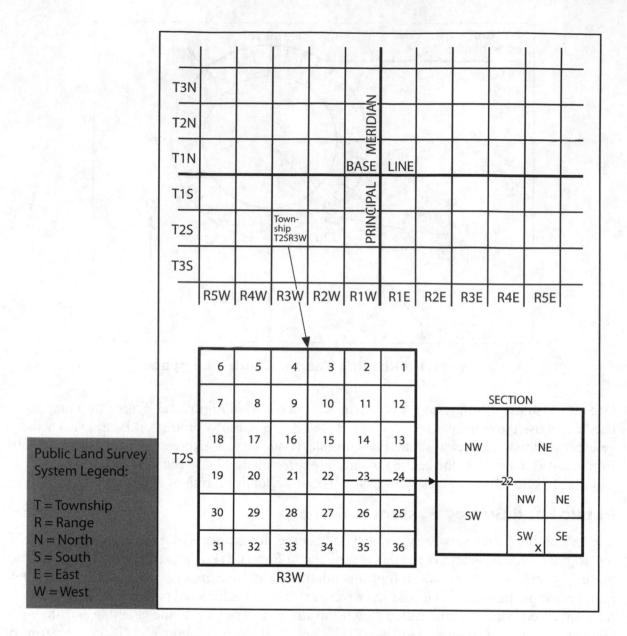

Public Land Survey
System Legend:

T = Township
R = Range
N = North
S = South
E = East
W = West

Figure 1.4 The Public Land Survey System

Scale

Maps are scale models similar to the way a child's toy boat or car are scale models of the real thing. To make a model, one must first establish a model scale or ratio that is the proportion by which one reduces the object to the model size. Topographic maps model the surface of the earth—often large portions of it—so the ratio scale might be considerable, such as 1:24,000, which may also be expressed as the fractional scale 1/24,000. This indicates that the portion of the earth represented has been reduced to 1/24,000 of the actual size. Also, any unit of measurement (centimeter, inch, foot, etc.) on the map is equal to or represents 24,000 of the same units of measurement on the ground. For example, 1 centimeter (cm) on the map represents 24,000 cm on the ground. Remember that the smaller the fractional scale (i.e., 1/250,000), the larger the area covered, but the lesser the detail. On the other hand, the larger the fractional scale (i.e., 1/24,000), the smaller the area covered but the greater the detail.

A map with a 1/24,000 fractional scale provides useful detail. But knowing that 1 inch on the map is equal to 24,000 inches on the earth's surface is not very convenient, since no one measures big distances in inches. Therefore, if one divides 24,000 inches by 12 to get 2,000 feet, the scale becomes useful—1 inch on the map equals 2,000 feet on the earth's surface. This is known as a verbal scale.

A graphic scale or bar scale is also printed in the margin of topographic quadrangle maps. It usually includes three scales: miles, feet, and kilometers.

Scale Conversion

Scale conversions are important to comprehend for a topographic map, because they provide the reader of the map an idea of the distance between two points on the map.

Example 1: One inch on 1:24,000 scale represents what distance on the ground?

Solution:
Using these conversions: 1 foot = 12 inches; 5,280 feet = 1 mile; and 1 mile = 1.609 km,

$$24{,}000 \text{ inches} \times \frac{1 \text{ foot}}{12 \text{ inches}} \times \frac{1 \text{ mile}}{5{,}280 \text{ feet}} = 0.378 \text{ miles}$$

$$0.378 \text{ miles} \times \frac{1.609 \text{ km}}{1 \text{ mile}} = 0.608 \text{ km}$$

Example 2: A mile on the ground would be what distance (in inches) on a 1:24,000 scale topographic map?

Answer:

$$1 \text{ mile} \times \frac{5{,}280 \text{ feet}}{1 \text{ mile}} \times \frac{12 \text{ inches}}{1 \text{ foot}} \times \frac{1 \text{ inch on topographic map}}{24{,}000 \text{ feet}} = 2.64 \text{ inches on the map}$$

Map Symbols

Topographic maps provide remarkably detailed information about natural and cultural features. The map symbols are located in the USGS Topographic Map Symbols pamphlet in the lab kit, which identifies all the features shown on a topographic map. Township, range, and section lines are always shown in red; topographic contour lines are always shown in brown; rivers, streams, bodies of water, swamps, marsh, etc., are always shown in shades of blue; and vegetation is always shown in green.

Additional information in the margins of topographic maps includes the revision date, since people are forever changing the man-made features and because the earth's surface changes from events such as earthquakes, landslides, and floods. A photo-revision is when aerial photographs are taken to discover new changes in the land surface features, and the changes are overprinted on the maps in a standout color of purple and red. Other information in the map margins includes the names of the topographic map, an index map showing the location within the state of the mapped area, the names of adjacent topographic maps, latitude and longitude coordinates of the four corners of the map, and the contour interval. The contour interval is the vertical difference in elevation between the contour lines and is used to show the general shape of the terrain.

Since the geographic true north (i.e., always at the top of topographic map—north pole) and the magnetic north pole (i.e., magnetic compasses are not attracted to true geographic north, but instead they are attracted to magnetic north pole, which is 450 miles northwest of Hudson Bay in Northern Canada) do not coincide, most topographic maps also include in the map margin the magnetic declinations, the angle formed between the direction of true geographic north and magnetic north pole. However, the magnetic declination is exact for only the year listed on the topographic map because of the slow migration of the magnetic north pole. On topographic maps, magnetic declination for a specific year can be found within the margin of the map.

Contour Lines

The configuration of the land surface on a topographic map is shown by contour lines, often called contours. Contours represent lines of equal elevation on the earth's surface and appear as thin brown lines on topographic quadrangle maps. All topographic maps use mean sea level as their reference datum or plane of zero elevation. To aid in counting contour lines on topographic maps, every fifth contour line—an index contour—is darker and generally identified by its elevation above sea level. The contour interval selected by the cartographer depends on the configuration of the land surface. All contour lines are multiples of the contour intervals. For example, if in mountainous areas such as the Sierra Nevada, a 100-foot contour interval might be the most suitable because of the steep slopes where the contour lines are 0, 100, 200, 300 feet, and so on. However, in the mid-continent area of the United States, a 20-foot contour interval might be the most useful because of the gentle sloping of hills and valleys, the contour lines represent 0, 20, 40, 60, 80 feet, and so on. Most of the USGS topographic maps use the smaller contour interval because it allows for easier readability and provides necessary detail to understand the geologic features in the area.

Most topographic maps contain bench marks, where the elevation and position have been surveyed to the nearest foot. Bench marks are identified by symbols such as "BM" or "X," followed by the elevation. The BM symbol denotes a permanent marker (such as a metal plate embedded in concrete) placed in the field by the USGS or Bureau of Land Management at the point indicated on the map.

Topographic relief is the difference in elevation between two points on a map. Local relief refers to adjacent hills and valleys, whereas total relief is the difference in elevation between the highest and lowest points on the map.

Rules for Contour Lines
1. Evenly spaced contour lines depict a uniform slope.
2. Closely spaced contour lines depict a steep slope.
3. Widely spaced contour lines depict a gentle slope.
4. Contour lines may merge to form a single contour line where there is a vertical cliff.
5. Contour lines never split or branch.
6. Contour lines never end at a point, but may end at the margin of the map.

7. A concentric series of closed contours represents a hill or mountain. These concentric series of closed contour lines do not have hachure marks (tick marks), which create a depression contour.
8. Depression contours have hachure marks (tick marks) on the downhill side, which are concentric series of closed contour lines that represent a closed depression.
9. Contour lines form a V pattern when crossing a stream valley or canyon. The apex of the V always points upstream (the rule of "Vs").

Online Activities

As per your instructor's directions, go to the online lesson for this lab and complete the activities assigned. *Note:* You will need to view the videos in this online lesson in order to complete the Lab Exercises included in this lesson.

Lab Exercises

Lab Exercise #1: *Contour Exercises*

- Dixie Mine contour exercise
- Prospect Hill contour exercise

Dixie Mine Contour Exercise
To better understand the meaning of contour lines, you will begin this laboratory exercise by contouring the set of spot elevations in the Dixie Mine contour activity (**Figure 1.5**). Watch the video *How to Create Contour Lines for a Topographic Map* and then follow the steps listed below.

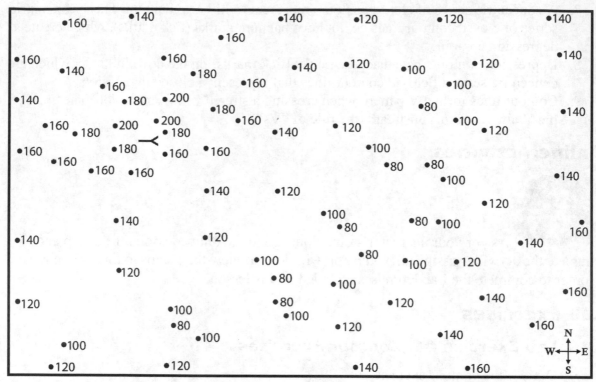

Figure 1.5 Dixie Mine Contour. Illustration by Don Vierstra

Instructions and Observations

Step 1: Look at the Dixie Mine contour (**Figure 1.5**) and note areas that are surrounded by lower and upper elevations.

Step 2: Use a contour interval of 20 feet with sea level as your reference datum so that you will have contour lines for 20 feet, 40 feet, 60 feet, and so forth, above sea level. Begin by locating the highest contour line on the map. Draw contour lines by connecting points that have the same elevation.

Step 3: Continue drawing contour lines for the hill around the Dixie Mine site and continue this same contour activity for the intermittent pond/lake area. Since many of the spot elevations do not fall on a contour line, it will be necessary to interpret between known points. For example, the 180-foot contour line would lie about midway between spot elevations of 160 feet and 200 feet.

Step 4: Locate the highest elevation point and write in the label "hill." Locate the lowest area and write in the label "depression."

The Dixie Mine exercise is a way for you to practice making a contour map and will help you for the next assignment.

Prospect Hill Contour Exercise

Use what you learned from the Dixie Mine exercise and complete the Prospect Hill contour exercise (**Figure 1.6**). Follow the same instructions from the Dixie Mine contour exercise (**Figure 1.5**) to complete the Prospect Hill contour exercise. Submit your work as directed by your instructor.

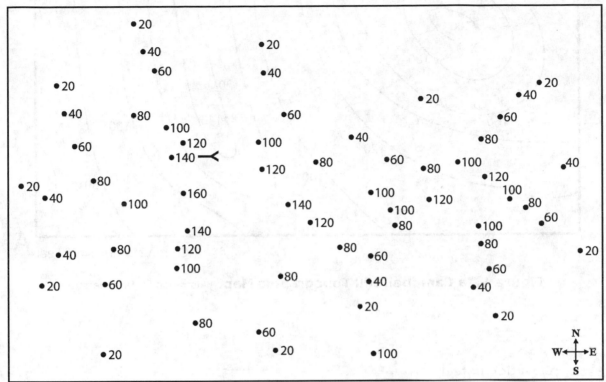

Contour Interval= 20 Feet
≺ Tunnel or mine

Figure 1.6 Prospect Hill Contour. Illustration by Don Vierstra

Lab Exercise #2: *Topographic Profiles*

Topographic maps present an aerial view of the earth's surface, depicting topographic features by means of contour lines and symbols. To view the shape of the earth's surface, however, it is useful to adopt a side-view perspective, as would be viewed against the horizon. This perspective is accomplished by constructing a topographic profile.

- Campbell Hill Topographic Profile
- Yosemite Valley exercise

Campbell Hill Topographic Profile Exercise

In this exercise, you will learn how to produce a side view or cross-section of the land surface (**Figure 1.7**). Watch the video *Creating a Topographic Profile of a Land Surface Area* and then follow the steps listed for this Lab Exercise.

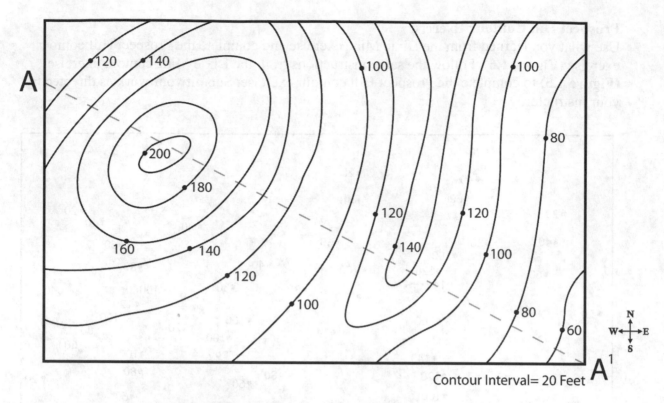

Figure 1.7a Campbell Hill Topographic Map. Illustration by Don Vierstra

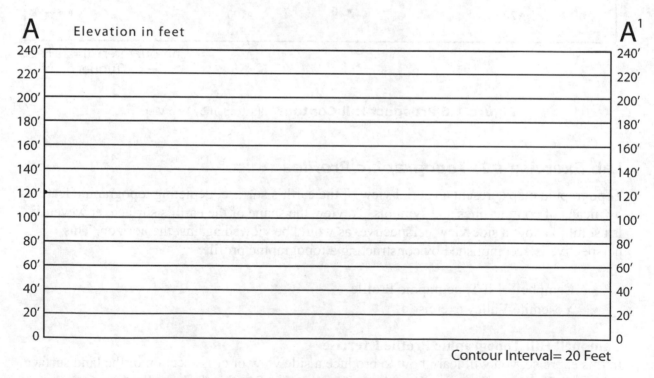

Figure 1.7b Campbell Hill Topographic Profile. Illustration by Don Vierstra

Instructions and Observations

Step 1: Locate line A-A^1. For this exercise, line A-A^1 in **Figure 1.7a** Campbell Hill Topographic Profile has been drawn for you.

Step 2: Lay a strip of paper along line A-A^1 and make tick marks at each place where a contour line intersects the line of section, noting the elevation of the tick marks. Also, identify on the strip of paper the locations of major geologic features such as mountain tops and valleys.

Step 3: Identify the elevations of the evenly spaced horizontal lines on the graph in **Figure 1.7b** using a scale of 1 inch = 100 feet. In this case the elevations on the graph must include the highest and lowest elevations along the line of section. Remember also that each horizontal line on the graph represents a constant elevation corresponding to a contour line on the map.

Step 4: Lay the strip of paper along the bottom of the graph. Above each tick mark on the paper strip, place a dot on the graph at the proper elevation.

Step 5: Complete the **Figure 1.7b** Campbell Hill Topographic Profile by drawing a smooth line connecting all of the points on the graph.

The topographic profile for Campbell Hill is a way for you to practice making a topographic profile and will help you for the next assignment.

Yosemite Valley Topographic Profile Exercise

Use what you learned from the Campbell Hill exercise to complete the Yosemite Valley–Yosemite National Park Topographic Profile (**Figure 1.8**). Follow the same instructions as you did for creating the Campbell Hill Topographic Profile. Identify and write the names of the peaks on **Figure 1.8b**. Submit your work as directed by your instructor.

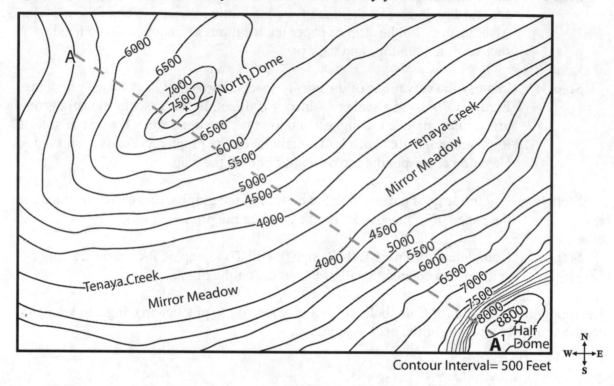

Figure 1.8a Yosemite Valley–Yosemite National Park Topographic Map. Illustration by Don Vierstra

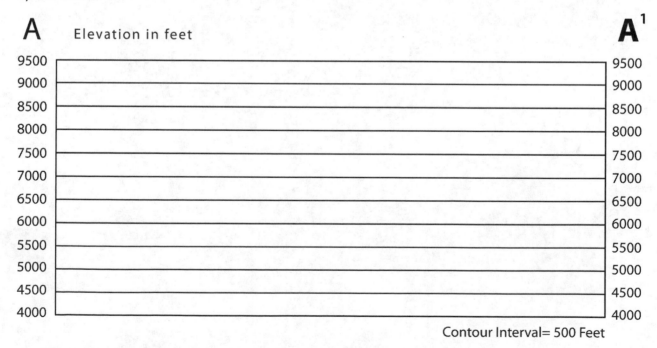

Figure 1.8b Yosemite Valley–Yosemite National Park Topographic Profile.
Illustration by Don Vierstra

14

Lesson 1/ Topographic Maps

In **Figure 1.8**, the graph was drawn using a vertical scale of 1 inch = 100 feet or 1 inch = 1,200 inches (1:1,200). This is quite different from the horizontal scale of the map in **Figure 1.8**, which is 1:12,000. This difference causes a vertical exaggeration, which is nearly always necessary to construct a readable topographic profile. Without the vertical exaggeration, the profile might be so shallow that only the highest peaks would be visible. The vertical exaggeration is calculated by dividing the fractional vertical scale (1:1,200) by the ratio horizontal scale (1:12,000), giving a value of ten. A 10X vertical exaggeration on a topographic profile results in slopes that are 10 times steeper than the real slopes on the ground surface.

Quiz

Questions 1 and 2 are based on **Lab Exercise #1:** *Contour Exercises.*

1. According to the Prospect Hill topographic profile in **Figure 1.6**, the land surface could be
   a. a valley.
   b. a hill.
   c. two valleys with a hill in the middle.
   d. two hills with a valley in the middle.
   c. two closed depressions with a flat-topped plateau in the middle.

2. In **Figure 1.6**, what is the elevation of the mine (locate the mining symbol) on Prospect Hill?
   a. 100 feet
   b. 120 feet
   c. 130 feet
   d. 140 feet
   e. 150 feet

Question 3 is based on **Lab Exercise #2:** *Topographic Profiles.*

3. What answer below represents the profile in **Figure 1.8** between point A and point A[1]?

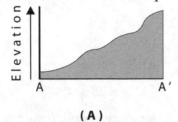

(A)

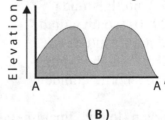

(B)

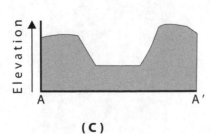

(C)

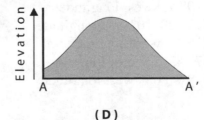

(D)

For questions 4 and 5, you will want to refer to information found in the Scale Conversion section of this lesson.

4. On a 1:125,000-scale map, one inch represents what distance on the ground in miles? Record your answer from *Lab Exercise #1, step 13*.
   a. 1.65 miles
   b. 1.79 miles
   c. 1.86 miles
   d. 1.97 miles
   e. 2.20 miles

5. A mile on the ground would be what distance (in inches) on a 1:50,000 scale topographic map?
   a. 1.15 inches
   b. 1.26 inches
   c. 1.38 inches
   d. 1.44 inches
   e. 1.57 inches

Questions 6 through 23 are based on the 7.5-minute topographic quadrangle map of Yosemite Valley, Yosemite National Park, California (found in the lab kit).

6. Using the USGS Topographic Map Symbols pamphlet in the laboratory kit, what type of lake is Starr King Lake on the USGS Yosemite Valley topographic map?
   a. annual lake
   b. perennial lake
   c. intermittent lake
   d. dry lake
   e. narrow wash

7. What parallel (latitude line) marks the northern limit of the topographic quadrangle map?
   a. 119° 45' north latitude
   b. 119° 29' 10" south latitude
   c. 37° 42' north latitude
   d. 37° 42' 30" south latitude
   e. 37° 47' 05"north latitude

8. What meridian (longitudinal line) is the eastern limit of the topographic quadrangle map?
   a. 119° 45' west longitude
   b. 119° 29' 10" east longitude
   c. 37° 42' west longitude
   d. 37° 42' 30" east longitude
   e. 37° 47' 05" west longitude

9. What is the magnetic declination of the topographic quadrangle map?
   a. 10.5° west
   b. 10.5° east
   c. 15.5° west
   d. 17.5° east
   e. 20.5° west

10. In what year was the magnetic declination measured?
   a. 1955
   b. 1958
   c. 1961
   d. 1964
   e. 1967

11. This topographic quadrangle map was compiled from aerial photographs taken from
   a. 1951.
   b. 1952.
   c. 1953.
   d. 1954.
   e. 1955.

12. What is the fractional scale of the topographic map?
   a. 1/12,000
   b. 1/24,000
   c. 1/62,500
   d. 1/250,000
   e. 1/1,000,000

13. How can the ratio scale (1: 24,000) of this map be expressed as a verbal scale?
   a. 1 inch = 1,000 feet
   b. 1 inch = 2,000 feet
   c. 1 inch = 1 mile
   d. 1 inch = 4 miles
   e. 1 inch = 12 miles

14. Using the bar scale provided in the map margin, measure the length of the southern boundary of the topographic quadrangle from El Portal (El Portal topographic quadrangle) to Merced Peak (Merced Peak topographic quadrangle). The distance in miles is
   a. about 3/4 of a mile.
   b. about 5 miles.
   c. about 9 miles.
   d. about 14.5 miles.
   e. about 18.5 miles.

15. What direction does the Merced River flow through the valley floor from Sentinel bridge to El Capitan Bridge?
    a. northwest
    b. northeast
    c. east
    d. southeast
    e. southwest

16. Identify the section, township, and range for the Big Oak Flat on the Yosemite Valley Topographic map?
    a. Sec. 35, T.2S, R20E
    b. Sec. 35, T.2S, R21E
    c. Sec. 2, T.3S, R20E
    d. Sec. 2, T.3S, R21E
    e. southwest

17. What is the contour interval of the topographic quadrangle map?
    a. 5 feet
    b. 10 feet
    c. 20 feet
    d. 40 feet
    e. both 10 feet and 40 feet

18. What mountain, peak or dome has the highest elevation point on the topographic map?
    a. Glacier Point
    b. Half Dome
    c. Clouds Rest
    d. Basket Dome
    e. Sentinel Peak

19. What is the elevation of the highest point on the topographic quadrangle map?
    a. 7,542 feet above sea level
    b. 7,779 feet above sea level
    c. 8,842 feet above sea level
    d. 9,926 feet above sea level
    e. 8,122 feet above sea level

20. What is the elevation of the lowest point benchmark "BM" on the topographic quadrangle?
    a. 3,332 feet above sea level
    b. 3,438 feet above sea level
    c. 3,513 feet above sea level
    d. 3,908 feet above sea level
    e. 4,400 feet above sea level

21. What is the total relief within the topographic quadrangle map?
   a. 5,008 feet
   b. 5,514 feet
   c. 6,018 feet
   d. 6,030 feet
   e. 6,488 feet

22. The approximate distance from Yosemite Lodge to Mirror Lake is _____
   miles. (Use your ruler or protractor to measure and calculate the approximate distance
   in miles. Remember 1 inch equals 2,000 feet.)
   a. 2.02 miles
   b. 2.66 miles
   c. 3.26 miles
   d. 3.84 miles
   e. none of the above

23. What is the azimuth bearing from the "L" in Lost Lake to the "Q" in Quarter Domes
   near the east end of Yosemite Valley topographic map?
   a. 30 degrees
   b. 35 degrees
   c. 40 degrees
   d. 45 degrees
   e. 50 degrees

***Questions 24 and 25 refer to the geology history of Yosemite Valley, which can be found on
the back of the USGS 7.5-minute topographic map.***

24. On the back of the USGS Yosemite Valley topographic map is the history of how
   Yosemite Valley was formed. Locate Figure 4. What period of time did the Merced
   River begin to carve out the valley?
   a. Cambrian period
   b. Jurassic period
   c. Cretaceous period
   d. Tertiary period
   e. Quaternary period

25. On the back of the USGS Yosemite Valley topographic map is the history of how
   Yosemite Valley was formed. Locate Figure 6. What is the shape of the Yosemite
   Valley?
   a. V shape
   b. U shape
   c. W shape
   d. X shape
   e. S shape

PLATE TECTONICS

Lesson 2

Purpose

This laboratory lesson will provide you with a foundation and understanding of plate tectonics.

Learning Objectives

After completing this laboratory lesson, you will be able to:

- Explain the hypothesis of continental drift.
- Explain how Earth's magnetism, paleomagnetism, and magnetic reversals aided development of the theory of plate tectonics.
- Describe how plates interact at the three basic types of plate boundaries.
- Explain the formation of volcanic islands like those formed at hotspots compared to those formed at convergent plate boundaries.
- Describe the Wadati-Benioff zone.
- Describe the Wilson cycle.

Materials Needed

- ❏ Pencil
- ❏ Eraser

Overview

The theory of plate tectonics revolutionized the science of geology. However, before the advent of plate tectonics, scientists presented several hypotheses in an attempt to explain questions concerning the apparent jigsaw puzzle–like fit of the continents and their modern positions. Plate tectonics is the modern theory that the Earth's rigid outer layer, called the lithosphere, is broken in to large moving sections or plates. Many of the features found at plate edges, such as folded mountain ranges, volcanoes, trenches, rift valleys, island arcs, and so forth have been created by plate tectonic activity.

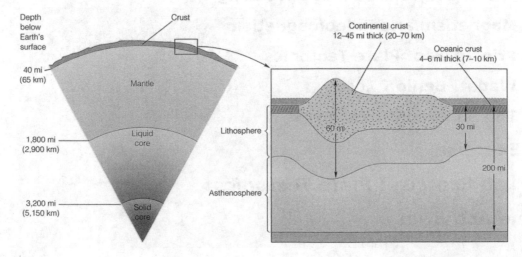

Figure 2.1 Earth's Interior. The three major subdivisions of Earth are the core, mantle, and crust. The crust and the outer brittle portion of the mantle are combined in the lithosphere, which in turn overlies a plastic portion of the mantle called the asthenosphere. From *Planet Earth* by John J. Renton. Copyright © 2002 by John J. Renton. Reprinted by permission of Kendall Hunt Publishing Company.

History of Plate Tectonics

In the late 1700s and early 1800s, the early geologists began to investigate the earth by applying the scientific process of collecting data, then proposing and testing explanations based on that data. One of their first conclusions was that the Earth was originally molten; as it cooled, rocks solidified into the continents we know today, locked into position for all time. This model dominated much of geological thinking for well over a century.

Other explanations, however, continued to emerge. Around the early 1900s, the contracting earth model was proposed. This model was based on the idea that Earth does not have a constant size but is actually shrinking due to the cooling of its interior. The shrinking has caused Earth's crust to form hills, valleys, and even mountain ranges in the same way that the skin of a dried up fruit withers and cracks.

Once scientists were aware that the interior of the earth is not cooling down but is actually quite hot, a different idea was proposed: the expanding earth model. Because substances expand when heated, this model suggested that Earth's interior heat was causing it to expand, breaking up the crust in the same way the skin or a lemon might tear apart if the fruit inside expanded. The expansion, according to the model, has separated the continents, created oceans and formed major land features such as mountain ranges. Even as geologists pondered whether the evidence supported an Earth that changed sizes, another idea was under formulation: continental drift.

Ever since cartographers produced maps with a sufficient degree of accuracy to portray the shapes of the continents realistically, individuals have noticed the matching coastlines on opposite sides of the Atlantic Ocean. As early as 1620, the English philosopher, statesman and scientist, Francis Bacon, commented on the similarity of the Atlantic coastlines of South America and Africa. The similarity had caused him and others to wonder whether the two continents once been joined like two pieces of a giant jigsaw puzzle or if the apparent match was just a coincidence.

Most scientists at the time were convinced that it was indeed just a coincidence, but one prolific geologist, Edward Suess, made a different suggestion. In the early 1800s, Suess noted not only the fit between the continents, but also the discovery of identical *Glossopteris* fern fossils in South America, Africa and Australia. He wondered how the same plants had ended up on different continents. The only explanation that made sense to him was that all the southern continents, including Antarctica, had once been joined into one larger continent that he called Gondwana or Gondwanaland. Suess' ideas were not at all taken seriously and were discarded. However, in the early 1900s, several geologists took a second look, the most noteworthy of which was the German climatologist, Alfred Wegener.

Wegener went further than Suess, both in his hypothesis and in the evidence he gathered to develop it. He noted other identical sets of fossils that appeared on different continents separated by oceans, and wondered by what means these animals might have traveled overseas (**Figure 2.3**). He observed that the striations, long scratches in rock left behind by glaciers, appeared in areas that are now tropical.

Wegener proposed that not only had South America and Africa once been joined, but that the northern continents had also been joined together to form a larger continent, Laurasia. In fact, his evidence seemed to indicate that *all* of the continents had once been connected together into one supercontinent he called Pangaea (**Figure 2.2**).

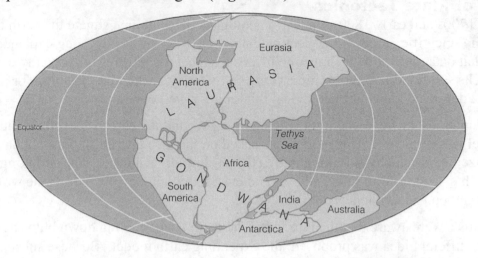

Figure 2.2 Supercontinent. Alfred Wegener proposed that all of the present continents were once joined into a supercontinent he called Pangaea. From *Planet Earth* by John J. Renton. Copyright © 2002 by John J. Renton. Reprinted by permission of Kendall Hunt Publishing Company.

Wegener demonstrated how mountain ranges, rock types, the distribution of fossils, and glacial deposits told a common story of the existence of a supercontinent some 250 million years ago, and the subsequent break up of that continent into the present day continental configuration. His careful record of the directions of glacial striations, and other features from the eastern margin of South America demonstrated the match of the western margin of Africa (**Figure 2.3**). Wegener first published his hypothesis on continental drift in 1912. A few years later, while recuperating from wounds suffered during World War I, he wrote his famous paper, "The Origin of Continents and Oceans," which was published in 1915.

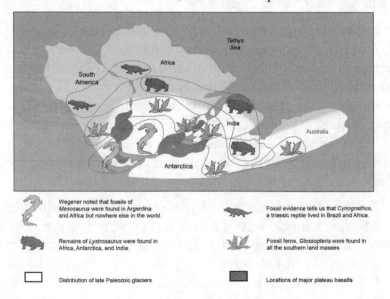

Figure 2.3 Gondwana. Various kinds of data exist to support the idea that the southern continents were once joined into a supercontinent some 200 million years ago. From *Planet Earth* by John J. Renton. Copyright © 2002 by John J. Renton. Reprinted by permission of Kendall Hunt Publishing Company.

Lesson 2/Plate Tectonics

In the paper, he postulated the existence of the supercontinent he called Pangaea, which based on fossil evidence, began to break up about 200 million years ago to eventually give rise to our present continents. The major shortcoming of Wegener's proposal was that he could not identify a scientifically defensible source of energy and a mechanism to move the continents. An active and changing environment clearly caused the Earth's dynamic surface features. From the time Wegener introduced the concept of continental drift, he was able to offer scientifically sound explanations for many common observations.

The Theory of Seafloor Spreading

In 1928, Arthur Holmes (1890–1965) proposed what he called seafloor stretching, where the upwelling of a mantle (the part of Earth between base of the crust and the top of the core) convection cell near the surface of the Earth would result in the continents moving away from each other. Rather than having the continents plow through the oceanic crust (the crust that underlies the ocean basin and it is denser than the continental crust) as Wegener had proposed, continents were simply being carried along as the underlying crust was being stretched. In the 1950s, magnetometers were first used collect data on the strength of the magnetism of the seafloor. This magnetic data, called paleomagnetism (the prefix *paleo* means "old"), was collected from the basalts of the oceanic crust and suggested that new oceanic crust was being added at the oceanic ridges.

Collection of the magnetic zonation data from ocean surveys increased after World War II, and it greatly puzzled geologists. So Princeton University geologist, Harry Hess, undertook the task of explaining how such striping could occur. According to Hess, the only possible explanation for the banding patterns was that the rocks of the ocean floor were constantly spreading away from the oceanic ridge. Hess asserted that outflow of magma at the rift zones is continually forming new oceanic crust, and that its addition to existing crust actually widens the seafloor, a concept called seafloor spreading (**Figure 2.4**). As newly erupted magma solidified into new crust, it recorded Earth's magnetic field and then moved away from the rift as more rock formed at the rift. When a magnetic reversal occurred, the basalts that formed after the reversal then recorded the altered magnetic field, with the iron crystals in that rock pointing to the new north pole. The longer the time between magnetic reversals, the wider the magnetic stripe that was created. Hess conjectured that if seafloor spreading were a fact, there should be two such patterns of magnetic striping, one on each side of the rift, that are mirror images of each other.

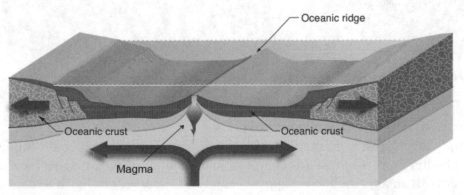

Figure 2.4 Seafloor Spreading. Magma makes its way to the surface where new oceanic crust is being formed. In doing so, newly formed rock is moving the oceanic crust in opposite directions from the mid-oceanic ridge. Illustration © Kendall Hunt Publishing Company.

Oceanic Ridges

It was soon discovered that every ocean had an oceanic ridge and that all of the oceanic ridges connected create a total length of about 65,000 km (40,000 miles) (**Figure 2.5**). Not only are the oceanic ridges the most dominant feature on the ocean bottom, it is said that if one were approaching Earth from space and the ocean basins were empty, the oceanic ridges would be the first surface feature to be identified, even before major mountain ranges such as the Rockies, the Alps, and the Himalaya. With the advent of plate tectonics, the oceanic ridges were identified as the site where new oceanic lithosphere (the layer of Earth consisting of the crust and the outer rigid portion of the mantle) is being created.

Deep-Sea Trenches

Another major discovery of the ocean bottoms was the finding of long, narrow, deep trenches—referred to as deep-sea trenches—that paralleled some continental margins. The advent of plate tectonics showed the deep-sea trenches to be the sites of the zones of subduction. This process, where the denser oceanic crustal plate collides against and moves beneath other less-dense crust is called subduction. The prefix *sub* means "under" and a duct is a channel, so the term *subduction* describes the motion of this crust as it slides underneath. Deep-sea trenches formed parallel to the continental margins as the oceanic lithosphere was initially subjected to compressive forces.

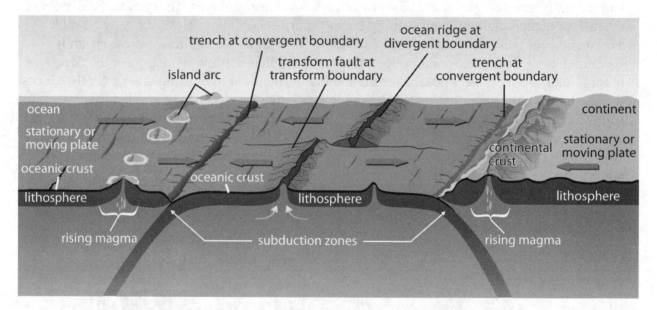

Figure 2.5 Oceanic Ridges and Deep-Sea Trenches. Illustration by Don Vierstra

Magnetism and Paleomagnetism

According to theory, Earth's magnetic field is the result of rotation and convection within Earth's liquid outer core. The result is comparable to having a dipole magnet located at Earth's center with an axis inclined at approximately 11.3 degrees to Earth's rotational axis (**Figure 2.6**).

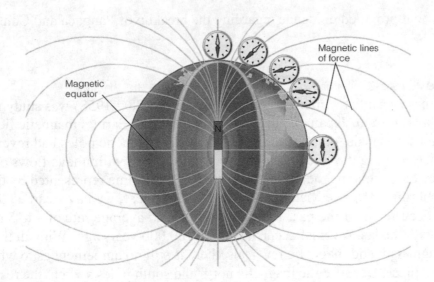

Figure 2.6 Magnetic Lines of Force. The needle of the dipmeter (i.e. a compass in which the needle can move vertically as well as horizontally) also aligns parallel to Earth's magnetic lines of force, but in a vertical plane. Note that at the magnetic equator, the needle is parallel to Earth's surface (no dip angle). At the locations closer to the magnetic poles, the angle between the needle and Earth's surface increases with increasing latitude until, over the magnetic pole, the needle is vertical (90º angle of dip). From *Planet Earth* by John J. Renton. Copyright © 2002 by John J. Renton. Reprinted by permission of Kendall Hunt Publishing Company.

The north and south magnetic poles are not static but wander about 15 km (9 miles) per year. In 1838, the north magnetic pole was located on the west coast of the Boothia Peninsula in the Arctic (95° West longitude. and 70° North latitude). Paleomagnetic data have shown that the location of the north magnetic pole remained relatively stable until about 100 years ago when it began to wander at an uncharacteristic high rate. Since then, the north magnetic pole has moved about 1,100 km (690 miles) into the Arctic Ocean. This means that, from the point of view of a compass needle, the direction of magnetic north has changed; it points in a slightly different direction now than it did in 1838, because the location of magnetic north has changed. The orientation of Earth's magnetic field is constantly being recorded within newly extruded basaltic lava flows on the seafloor.

As the liquid basalt cools, one of the minerals that forms is magnetite, a black magnetic mineral, found in igneous and metamorphic rocks and as a separate deposit. As magnetite cools intrusively tiny crystals are being formed into permanent magnets, but not at the high temperatures at which it first crystallizes.

The orientation of Earth's magnetic field, called its magnetic alignment, is frozen in rocks that contain magnetic minerals like iron. Basalt, which composes the oceanic lithosphere, has large amounts of iron, but there are also some rocks in the continental lithosphere that contain magnetic minerals. When the iron crystals in these rocks solidify from the magma, they capture alignment of magnetic north and south. A magnetometer is an instrument that can detect the direction of that magnetic alignment. This new technology allowed geologists to determine the orientation of the Earth's magnetic field at the time the rock formed, a capability that has launched the field of paleomagnetism, the study of the changes that have occurred in Earth's magnetic field. The rocks have stored the story of Earth's magnetic history, a story that provided evidence regarding the breakup of Pangaea and Continental Drift.

Magnetic Reversals

In 1920, a Japanese scientist named Motonori Matuyama (1884–1958) was studying the magnetism of lava flows in Japan and discovered the fact that Earth's magnetic field appeared to have undergone reversals—that is, the north and south magnetic poles had reversed locations. By determining the orientation of the magnetic field within lava flows of different ages, the history of Earth's magnetic field over the period of time represented by the lava flows can be determined. Since Matuyama's original discovery, we have learned that magnetic reversals have occurred over the past 10 million years at an average rate of 4 to 5 reversals per million years, with the last reversal occurring about 780,000 years ago. With all that we know about Earth magnetism and magnetic reversals, there is still no agreement as to what causes reversals to take place. Because the magnetic north and south poles switch, the resulting record in the rocks is called normal and reverse polarity.

Once a magnetic reversal occurred, the basalts that formed after the reversal recorded Earth's new magnetic field, and all of the magnetite crystals pointed to the new north pole. The newly formed oceanic crust would form a new set of bands of rock that all had widths of the same magnetic orientation. Which pole is north and which pole is south is called magnetic polarity. Today, the north pole is in the Arctic region while the south pole is in the Antarctic region. This is called normal polarity. Reverse polarity occurs when poles switch places so that what a compass points to as the north pole is in the Antarctic and the south pole is in the Arctic.

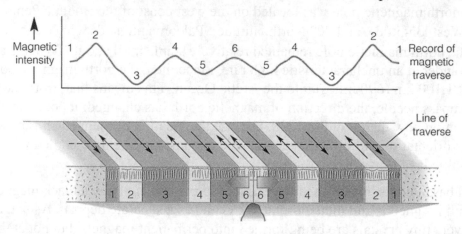

Figure 2.7 Magnetic Striping. A traverse perpendicular to the trend of the oceanic ridge shows a systematic variation in the magnetic intensity of the magnetic stripes. From *Planet Earth* by John J. Renton. Copyright © 2002 by John J. Renton. Reprinted by permission of Kendall Hunt Publishing Company.

Principles of Plate Tectonics

Alfred Wegener's hypothesis about a supercontinent called Pangaea had many details about how the continents had fit together, but his theory lacked a mechanism that could explain how the continents moved to their present locations. Discovery of young rocks on the seafloor with alternating magnetic polarity could finally serve to explain Wegener's Continental Drift hypothesis.

Plate Boundaries

The dividing line between two plates is called a plate boundary. There are three types of plate boundaries: (1) divergent boundaries, where two plates are moving apart from each other, (2) convergent boundaries where the plates are moving toward each other, and (3) transform boundaries where the plates are sliding past each other. Each type of boundary has distinctive features associated with it (see **Figure 2.8**).

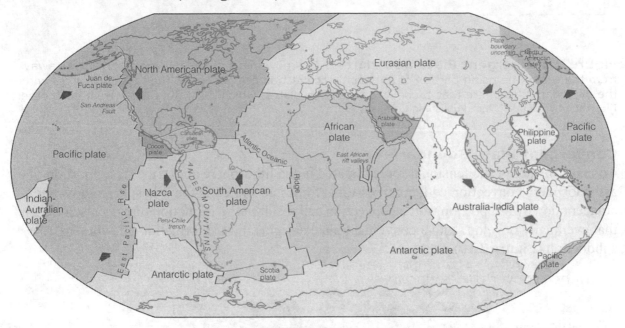

Figure 2.8 Plate Boundaries. The lithosphere is broken into about a dozen large plates and many smaller plates. The number of plates change with time as large plates break apart and smaller plates collide and weld together. Sawtooth lines indicate a convergent boundary, the double lines indicate divergent boundaries, and transform boundaries are shown with single lines. From *Planet Earth* by John J. Renton. Copyright © 2002 by John J. Renton. Reprinted by permission of Kendall Hunt Publishing Company.

Divergent Plate Boundaries

Tensional forces generated in lithosphere immediately above the rising portion of a convection cell results in rifting of the lithosphere and the ultimate formation of divergent plate boundaries. This results in the sequential development of rift zones, rift valleys, linear oceans, and finally an opening ocean (**Figure 2.9**). The best example of a rift valley on Earth today is the East African Rift Valley, while an example of a linear ocean is the Red Sea.

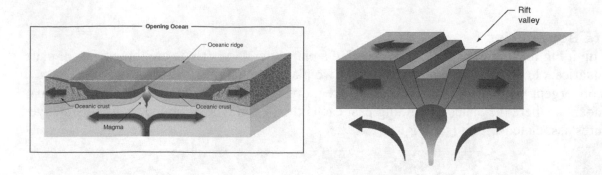

Figure 2.9 Divergent Plate Boundaries. The movement of the asthenospheric rocks away from the top of the rising portion of the mantle convection cell generates the tensional forces within the overlying lithosphere that cause it to break into plates, which then move away from each other. Illustration © Kendall Hunt Publishing Company.

Convergent Plate Boundaries

To compensate for the tensional forces created in the lithosphere above the rising portion of an asthenosphere convection cell, compressional forces generated in the lithosphere above the adjacent downward portion of the convection cell result in the formation of a deep sea trench that eventually develops into a convergent plate margin, and the formation of a zone of subduction **(Figure 2.10)**.

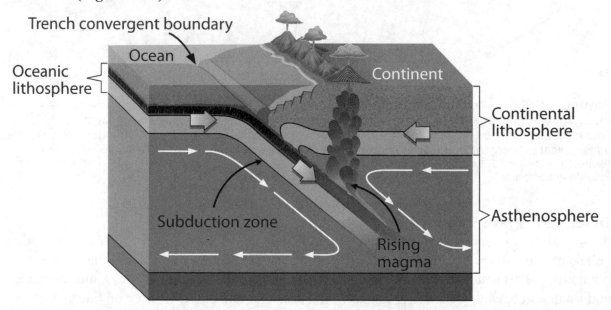

Figure 2.10 Convergent Plate Boundaries. Illustration by Don Vierstra

Transverse Plate Boundaries

The third type of plate boundary is the transform boundary, where two tectonic plates slide past each other. The San Andreas Fault that extends from Mexico to northern California is a transform boundary at the meeting of the Pacific and North American tectonic plates. Here, the Pacific Plate is moving northwest relative to the North American Plate; the stresses that are involved account for the large number of earthquakes in California (see **Figure 2.11**).

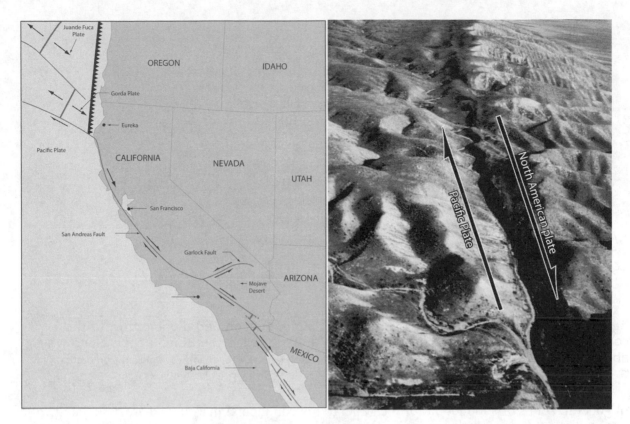

Figure 2.11 Transform Plate Boundary The best-known fault in North America is the San Andreas Fault, which is a transform plate boundary between the Pacific and North American lithospheric plates. Map (left): From *Planet Earth* by John J. Renton. Copyright © 2002 by John J. Renton. Reprinted by permission of Kendall Hunt Publishing Company; photo (right): Courtesy R. E..Wallace/USGS.

Wadati-Benioff Zone

During the 1940s, Hugo Benioff, a seismologist and professor at the California Institute of Technology, and Kiyoo Wadati, a seismologist at the Central Meteorological Observatory of Japan were studying intermediate and deep focus earthquakes. The plane of earthquakes, now called the Wadati-Benioff zone, represents the contact between the upper surface of the subducting oceanic plate and the rocks of the overlying asthenosphere. The point at which the zone of deep focus earthquakes terminated was interpreted to be the depth at which the rocks of the oceanic lithosphere were completely assimilated into the plastic asthenosphere, offsetting the volume of asthenosphere rocks that were converted to lithospheric rocks at the oceanic ridges.

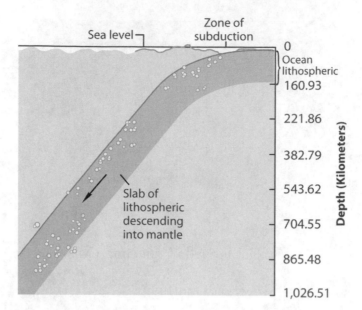

Figure 2.12 Benioff Zone. Below the zones of subduction and dipping toward the continents at an angle of about 45 degrees is a plane called the Benioff zone along which abundant earthquake foci are located. Modified from *Planet Earth* by John J. Renton. Copyright © 2002 by John J. Renton. Reprinted by permission of Kendall Hunt Publishing Company.

In general, zones of subduction form parallel to the continental margin and are associated with a chain of volcanoes called arc volcanoes. The arc volcanoes occur in two different scenarios. In one case, the zone of subduction is a considerable distance from the continental boundary and the associated chain of volcanoes, referred to as island arc volcanoes. These volcanoes form a chain of volcanic islands located between the zone of subduction and the mainland—an example being the volcanic island arc, Indonesia (**Figure 2.13**). In the second scenario, the zone of subduction is close to the continental margin and the volcanoes, referred to as continental arc volcanoes. These volcanoes form part of a mountain range along the margin of the continent—examples being the Andes Mountains of South America and the Cascade Mountains of our Pacific Northwest.

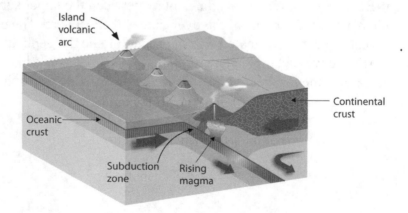

Figure 2.13 Volcanic Island Arcs. Volcanic arcs form when magma near a subduction zone rises and erupts. The magma accumulates until it breaks through the surface, forming a volcanic island. Sediments from the island arc and the continent accumulate in the back arc basin. Illustration © Kendall Hunt Publishing Company.

Hot Spots

While many of Earth's earthquakes and volcanoes have been explained by plate tectonics, there were other features and processes for which plate tectonics did not provide an explanation. Active volcanic activity far from the plate edges like the Hawaiian Islands is one such mystery. The Hawaiian Islands are older in the northwest and younger in the southwest. All of the Hawaiian Islands' active volcanoes are on the largest and southernmost island, Hawaii. The volcanoes that created the other Hawaiian islands are inactive. The source of their lava seemed to be from hot magma (molten rock that has not reached Earth's surface) rising from below. The age of the individual islands indicate that the hot spot is fixed and the plate is moving toward the northwest. These hot spots appear to have nothing to do with the processes responsible for plate tectonics. Hot spots are located at the top of a rising mantle plume that terminates at the top of the asthenosphere directly below the lithosphere where they provide the basaltic magma to form shield volcanoes. The Hawaiian Islands and the Emperor Seamounts were formed as the Pacific Plate passed over a stationary hot spot (**Figure 2.14** and **Figure 2.15**).

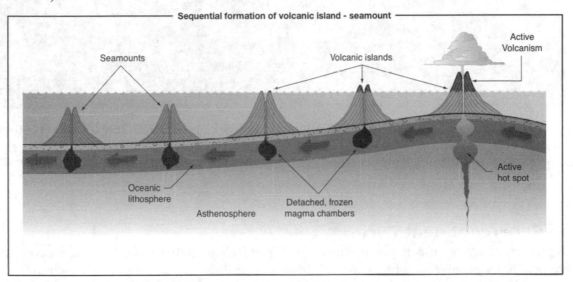

Figure 2.14 Volcanic Arcs. Volcanic arcs form when magma near a subduction zone rises and erupts. The magma accumulates until it breaks through the surface, forming a volcanic island. Sediments from the island arc and the continent accumulate in the back arc basin. Illustration © Kendall Hunt Publishing Company.

Figure 2.15 Hawaiian Islands. Example of a Volcanic Island Arc. Maui and the other Hawaiian Islands formed when hot, fluid magma erupted from a hot spot far from any convergent boundary. Volcanoes from this type of lava have long, gradual slopes.
Shutterstock #6393055, credit iofoto

The Supercontinent Cycle

Plate tectonics and its mechanisms supported Wegener's idea that all of the current continents were originally combined into a supercontinent called Pangaea, surrounded by a single superocean. Was Pangaea the only supercontinent to ever exist? The possibility that Pangaea was the only supercontinent to form during Earth's 4.5-billion-year history would essentially make its formation a unique event, an occurrence that would go against the concept of uniformitarianism.

The Wilson Cycle

J. Tuzo Wilson (1908–1993), a Canadian geologist who played a major role in defining plate tectonics, proposed the idea that super-continents were part of a natural cycle that has been going on since the onset of modern plate movements. In his honor, the cycle is called the Wilson cycle. According to Wilson, supercontinents form and, after existing for a period of time, break up to form a number of continents separated by newly formed oceans that widen at the expense of the once single superocean. Following the breakup, the cycle enters an opening phase during which the continents move apart and the ocean basins widen. After a period of about 250 million years, the opening phase of the cycle comes to an end as the cycle enters a closing phase as zones of subduction, form in the newly formed oceans, causing the continents to begin to converge. After another period of about 250 million years, all of the original newly formed oceans close again as the continents collide to form another supercontinent, completing the cycle. The cycle then repeats.

Lab Exercise

Lab Exercise: *Plate Tectonics*

In this lab exercise, you will make simple illustrations of three types of plate boundaries—convergent, divergent, and transform plate boundaries. You will draw arrows on each of your drawings indicating how the plate boundaries move. You will need to label each drawing and indicate what type of plate boundary you have illustrated. Remember that attention to detail is important when illustrating the concept of the three types of plate boundaries. Look at some of the figures in the laboratory manual and use them as a guide to assist you in illustrating the three types of plate boundaries. You need to label all plates, trenches, ridges, arcs, directions of stresses, lithosphere, and asthenosphere. Also you need to provide two examples of each type of plate boundary, labeling the specific continent or island name, ocean name, and so on.

Draw the three types of plate boundaries in the space provide below or on a separate piece of paper. Submit your work as directed by your instructor.

Plate Boundary #A—Divergent

Plate Boundary #B—Convergent

Plate Boundary #C—Transform

Online Activities

As per your instructor's directions, go to the online lesson for this lab and complete the activities assigned.

Quiz

Use Figure 2.16 to answer questions 1 through 5.

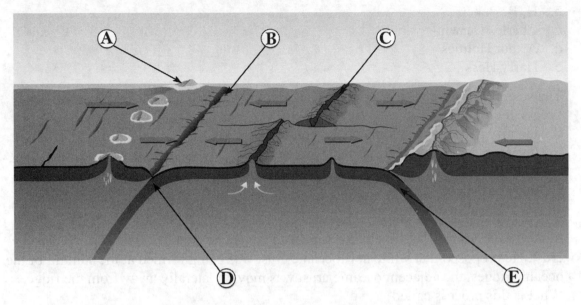

Figure 2.16 Plate Boundaries. Illustration by Don Vierstra

1. How is geologic structure that is labeled "A" formed?

2. What sort of plate boundary is at the point labeled "B"?

3. When an ocean plate converges with another plate, what is created on the seafloor at the line of convergence?

4. What type of plate boundary is being formed at the point labeled "C"?

5. What process is occurring at the points labeled "D" and "E"?

6. Do any of the continents appear to fit together? Explain.

7. Who proposed that all of the present continents were once joined together in a single supercontinent called Pangaea?
   a. Alfred Wegener
   b. H. B. Baker
   c. Charles Darwin
   d. Arthur Holmes
   e. Harry Hess

8. The scientific community rejected the theory of plate tectonics because Alfred Wegener could **NOT**
   a. identify a mechanism to move the continents.
   b. disprove competing theories that were not accepted by scientists.
   c. find geologic similarities on the different continents.
   d. none of the above.
   e. all of the above.

9. In the 1950s, Harry Hess interpreted this paleomagnetic data of newly formed oceanic crust. He proposed that while new oceanic crust was being formed at the summit of the oceanic ridges, the adjacent oceanic crust was moving laterally away from the ridge. What is this process called?
   a. deep-sea trench
   b. oceanic crust
   c. seafloor spreading
   d. hot spots
   e. none of the above

10. With the advent of plate tectonics, it was discovered that new oceanic lithosphere is being created at what location?
    a. seafloor spreading
    b. deep-sea trenches
    c. oceanic ridges
    d. continental crust
    e. lithosphere

Questions 11 through 16 are based on the online video, *Historical Development of Plate Tectonics Theory.* **You need to watch the entire segment in the online activity to answer all of the questions.**

11. A geologist by the name of Edward Suess not only noted that the continents fit together but also discovered a fossil that was identical in South America, Africa, and Australia. What type of fossil is it?
    a. palm
    b. fern
    c. redwood tree
    d. maple tree
    e. all of the above

12. In the early 1800s, geologist Edward Suess suggested that all the southern continents, including Antarctica, had once been joined into one large continent. What name did Suess call the one continent?
    a. Pangaea
    b. Megacontincnt
    c. Gondwanaland
    d. Laurasia
    e. none of the above

13. Alfred Wegener's own drawings show that all of the continents fit together in a jigsaw-like form. What two continents did Alfred Wegener proposed to "fit together" like a jigsaw puzzle?
    a. Africa and North America
    b. South America and North America
    c. Africa and Australia
    d. South America and Africa
    e. Eurasia and Africa

14. Wegener proposed that North America and Eurasia had also once been joined into one large continent called
    a. Pangaea.
    b. Megacontinent.
    c. Gondwanaland.
    d. Laurasia.
    e. Rodinia.

15. How many millions of years did Wegener propose that Pangaea had existed before it began to break up and drift across the oceans?
    a. 100 million years
    b. 150 million years
    c. 200 million years
    d. 250 million years
    c. 300 million years

16. In what century did we have new data provided by developing technologies to consider that continents could be on the move?
    a. the seventeenth century
    b. the eighteenth century
    c. the nineteenth century
    d. the twentieth century
    e. the twenty-first century

17. How do some rocks store information about Earth's magnetic field?

18. As liquid basalt cools, one of the minerals that forms is _____, a black magnetic mineral, found in igneous and metamorphic rocks as separate deposits.
    a. basalt
    b. magnetite
    c. cobalt
    d. silver
    e. aluminum

19. Which scientist's study of the magnetism of lava flows in Japan resulted in the discovery that Earth's magnetic field appears to have undergone reversals over time—that is, north and south magnetic poles have reversed their locations?
    a. Alfred Wegener
    b. Motonori Matuyama
    c. Charles Darwin
    d. Arthur Holmes
    e. Harry Hess

20. Since the original discovery of magnetic reversals, scientists have shown that these reversals have occurred over the past 10 million years at an average rate of 4 to 5 reversals per million years. The last such reversal occurred about how many years ago?
    a. 680,000 years
    b. 780,000 years
    c. 880,000 years
    d. 980,000 years
    e. 1,000,000 years

Questions 21 through 29 are based on the online video, *Evidence That Earth's Continents Move*. You need to watch the entire segment in the online activity to answer all of the questions.

21. What is the typical rate of seafloor spreading?
    a. 1–5 centimeters per year
    b. 6–10 centimeters per year
    c. 11–15 centimeters per year
    d. 16–20 centimeters per year
    e. 21–25 centimeters per year

22. If new crust is indeed being produced at the rifts, where does the additional older crust go?
    a. deep-sea trenches
    b. subduction
    c. oceanic crust
    d. continental crust
    e. seafloor spreading

23. Most of Earth's volcanoes are located in the _____ around the Pacific Rim just beyond the oceanic trenches, where magma, which is less dense than the surrounding rock, rises to the surface and erupts.
    a. Ring of Ice
    b. Ring of Water
    c. Ring of Fire
    d. Ring of Soil
    e. Ring of Steam

24. Tensional forces (pull-apart forces) generated in the lithosphere immediately above the rising portion of a convection cell results in rifting of the lithosphere and ultimate formation of what type of plate boundary?
   a. convergent
   b. transform
   c. divergent
   d. oceanic crust
   e. hot spot

25. Compression forces (forces colliding with each other) generated in the lithosphere above the adjacent down-going portion of the convection cell result in the formation of a deep-sea trench that eventually develops into what type of plate boundary?
   a. convergent
   b. transform
   c. divergent
   d. oceanic crust
   e. hot spot

26. Describe in two to three sentences what occurs at the Wadati-Benioff zone.

27. In a few sentences, explain the difference between island arc volcanoes and continental arc volcanoes.

28. Describe the geologic process of how volcanic hot spots are formed.

29.   Explain how the Wilson cycle works pertaining to modern-day continents.

ROCK DEFORMATION AND MOUNTAIN BUILDING

Lesson 3

AT A GLANCE

Purpose

Learning Objectives

Materials Needed

Overview

    Stress and Strain

    Orientation of Rock Strata

Lab Exercises

    Lab Exercise #1: *Fault Models*

    Lab Exercise #2: *Strata Folding*

Online Activities

Quiz

Purpose

This laboratory lesson will familiarize you with the enormous forces that deform the earth's crust and the various geological structures that result from such deformational forces. Understanding how these geological forces (i.e., compression, tension, and shear stress) can change or alter the land surface area will provide you insight about how earthquakes are generated, how tectonic movement of plates occurs, and how mountains and hills are created.

Learning Objectives

After completing this laboratory lesson, you will be able to:
- Characterize different types of rock deformation and geologic structures.
- Explain how surface features are caused and created by subsurface movements.
- Demonstrate and analyze fault movement and stress and strain of rock movement.
- Explain mountain building on Earth.

Materials Needed

- ❑ Pencil
- ❑ Eraser
- ❑ Scissors
- ❑ Clear plastic tape
- ❑ Ruler or protractor (in lab kit)
- ❑ Fault model from cardstock paper cut out (in lab kit)
- ❑ Three different colors of flexible foam (in lab kit)

Overview

Physical properties of the earth's rock must vary, depending on the geological environment in which the rock was deformed. In fact, deeply buried rock strata, if subjected to a deformational force, generally deform in a ductile manner (i.e., property of a substance that responds to stress by flowing or changing shape; also referred to as plastic), whereas rock strata at or near the earth's surface, if subjected to a deformational force, generally deform in a brittle manner (i.e., property of a substance that responds to stress by breaking or fracturing manner). This is because high temperature, high confining pressure, and the slow application of stress generally cause deeply buried rock strata to fold. Low temperature, low confining pressure, and the rapid application of stress generally cause near-surface rock strata to break.

Stress and Strain

Rock strata that have undergone a change in their original size or shape are said to be strained. The change in size and shape is generally caused by the enormous forces created during movements of the earth's tectonic plates over long periods of geological time. Such slowly applied but immense forces can build huge mountain ranges out of deformed rock strata. Geologists seek to unravel the history of rock deformation by studying the causes and effects of stress placed upon rock strata within the earth. Simply stated, stress is a directed force, externally applied, that tends to change the size and/or shape of rock strata.

The type of strain that results depends on the type of stress applied. There are three types of stress: tension, compression, and shear. The difference between them is the direction of the forces being applied.

Tension is a pulling apart or stretching force that can deform an object by making it longer and thinner (**Figure 3.1**). This is the same force involved in pulling apart dough or stretching a rubber band.

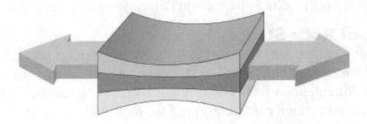

Figure 3.1 Tension The forces involved in tension operate directly opposite and away from each other. Anytime you pull on an object, you are applying tensional forces. Illustration by Don Vierstra

In compression, the forces act toward and directly opposite each other that shortens and widens an object (**Figure 3.2**). A trash compactor applies compression by pushing in on all sides, squashing trash into a compact block.

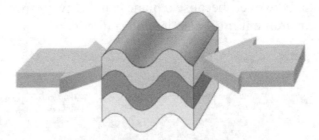

Figure 3.2 Compression The forces involved in compression act toward and directly opposite each other. Illustration by Don Vierstra

Shear stress is a tearing force in which one side of an object is pushed or pulled one way while the other side is pushed or pulled in the opposite direction (**Figure 3.3**). Shear is the force that tears paper and gives scissors their power to cut through things. In fact, scissors are often called shears after the type of stress they use to accomplish their mission.

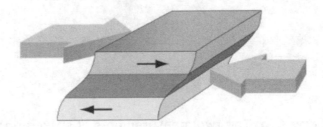

Figure 3.3 Shear Stress. The forces in shear also are directed toward each other, but are not directly opposed. Illustration by Don Vierstra

Any stress, no matter how small, produces some strain. For example, if a foam ball is squeezed in your hand, the bonds holding the ball's atoms together are compressed and the foam ball shortens slightly. But once the stress is removed, the atoms return to their original spacing and the foam ball rebounds to its original size. This type of strain is called elastic because the deformation is temporary and the specimen recovers fully. If the applied stress is great enough to break or rearrange the atomic bonds in a specimen, permanent strain may result. If bonds break, discrete failure surfaces may form, causing one part of a rock to move relative to another. This results in permanent deformation of a geologic fault plane.

Orientation of Rock Strata

Sedimentary layers, which are deposited in a horizontal position, can take on any orientation during deformation from slightly tilted to vertical to upside down. Further, deformed rock strata can change orientation quickly over relatively short distances. To understand the three-dimensional subsurface configuration of the rock strata, it is necessary to know the orientation of the rock layers.

Strike and Dip

Many geologic structures have planar components; folds have the planar surfaces of strata, while fault and joint surfaces are planar. Strike and dip are measurements that allow the spatial orientation of such features to be described in such a manner that anyone can visualize the orientation without actually seeing the feature. The strike of a planar feature is the direction of the line of intersection between the plane and the horizontal relative to true north (**Figure 3.4**). Dip is the angle between the plane and the horizontal measured perpendicular to strike. However, because a plane can dip away from a line in two possible directions, the dip measurement must also include a direction.

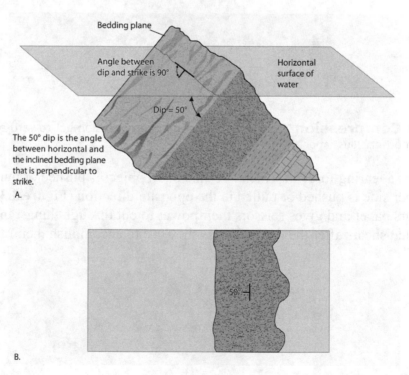

Figure 3.4 Strike and Dip. The two measurements of strike and dip allow a geologist to describe a planar surface in three-dimensional space. Note that the directions of strike and dip are always perpendicular to each other. Illustration by Don Vierstra

Strike and dip allow a geologist to describe a planar surface in three-dimensional space. Note that the directions of strike and dip are always perpendicular to each other (**Figure 3.5**).

Figure 3.5 Strike and Dip with Dip Angle. An example in the field of a strike and dip formation. Photograph by Joel Michaelsen

A good way to envision strike and dip is by means of a book and a table, using the table top as the imaginary horizontal plane. This can be done be designating the side of the table nearest you as south and the opposite side as north, the right side as east and the left side as west. Place the book vertically on its edge on the table so that it is aligned in a north-south direction. The book now has a north-south strike and a dip of 90 degrees. Next, tilt the book about 45 degrees to the right (to the east). Notice that that the book is inclined downward toward the left (to the west). The book still has a north-south strike, but the dip angle is now 45 degrees and the dip direction is to the west.

Types of Structures

Faults
Structural geologists must locate, observe, and interpret many structures, including various types of faults and folds. A fault is a break or rupture in the earth's crust, along which there has been movement. Therefore, faulting displaces the rock on one side of the break or fault plane, relative to the rock on the other side.

There are three types of faults: (1) normal faults, (2) reverse or thrust faults, and (3) strike-slip faults. Each is named by observing the sense of motion of the top block, or hanging wall, relative to the bottom block, or footwall. If the hanging wall moved downward relative to the footwall, then it is a normal fault **(Figure 3.6)**. This is generally caused by tension in the shallow reaches of the earth's crust.

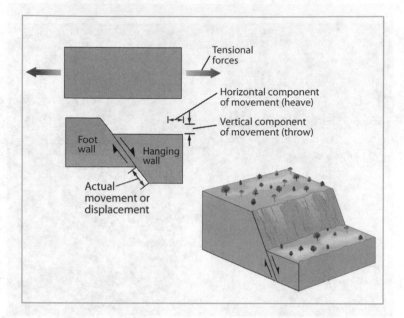

Figure 3.6 Normal Fault. Tensional stresses produce normal faults in which the hanging wall moves down relative to the footwall. From *Planet Earth* by John J. Renton. Copyright © 2002 by John J. Renton. Reprinted by permission of Kendall Hunt Publishing Company.

On the other hand, if the hanging wall moved upward relative to the footwall, then it is a reverse or thrust fault **(Figure 3.7)**, which is generally caused by compressive stress in the upper reaches of the earth's crust.

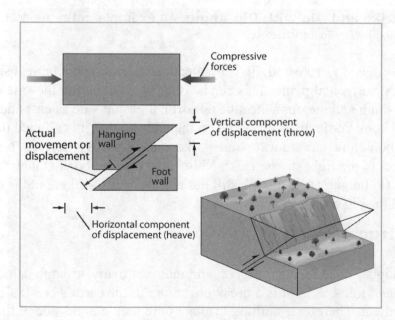

Figure 3.7 Reverse or Thrust Fault. Reverse or thrust faults form by the brittle failure of rocks under compression. As a result of the movement, the length of Earth's crust is shortened and the crust is locally thickened. From *Planet Earth* by John J. Renton. Copyright © 2002 by John J. Renton. Reprinted by permission of Kendall Hunt Publishing Company.

The difference between a reverse and thrust fault is the dip angle of the fault plane. If the dip angle is less than 45°, it is a thrust fault; if the angle is greater than 45°, it is called a reverse fault. In both thrust and reverse faults, the hanging wall has moved up relative to the footwall. The faults associated with zones of subduction are either thrust or reverse faults, depending on the angle of dip. If the thrust fault does not break or rupture the ground surface, it is called a blind thrust fault. Blind thrust faults are common in California and finding them before they generate a damaging earthquake can be quite difficult. In a blind thrust fault, sedimentary layers above the fault are not broken, but instead are folded because the fault did not have the energy needed to break the surface.

Strike-slip faults form from shear forces, where the plastic response of rocks to compressive stress takes place within the horizontal plane **(Figure 3.8)** because the fault plane is vertical or near-vertical with a horizontal displacement; there is no hanging or footwall. Strike-slip faults form under two scenarios, depending on the orientation of the shear forces. As one observes a strike-slip fault perpendicular to strike, if the rock on the opposite side of the fault has been moved to the right, the fault is referred to as a right-lateral strike-slip fault. If the rocks on the opposite side of the fault have been moved to the left, the fault is described as being a left-lateral strike-slip fault. The movement along the San Andreas Fault is a right-lateral movement (see **Figure 2.11**).

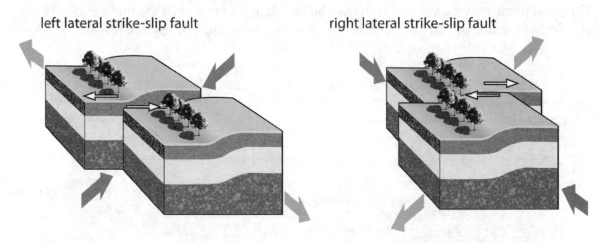

Figure 3.8 Left-Lateral and Right-Lateral Strike-Slip Faults. Illustration by Bob Dixon

Folds
Folds are bends in the rock strata and generally represent the ductile response of rock strata to compression within the earth's crust. Folds occur at all scales and range in size from small warps visible within individual outcrops to large-scale features that extend over many miles. Upfolded rock strata form arch like structures called anticlines, whereas downfolded rock strata form trough like structures called synclines. Rock strata on the flanks, or limbs, of an anticlinal fold dip outward in opposite directions, and older rock strata are found within the interior of these folded rock layers as a result of erosion. In contrast, rock strata in the limbs of a synclinal fold dip inward in opposite directions, and younger rock strata are found within the interior of these structures (see **Figure 3.9**).

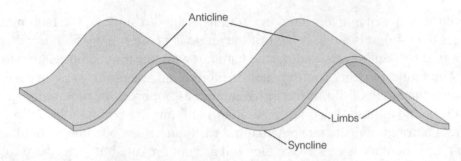

Figure 3.9 Anticline and Syncline Folds. The most commonly observed folds are anticlines and synclines. For simplicity, only one rock layer has been shown in the drawing. From *Planet Earth* by John J. Renton. Copyright © 2002 by John J. Renton. Reprinted by permission of Kendall Hunt Publishing Company.

Folds take many forms. Geologists describe a fold in terms of how its axial plane and limbs are positioned. An axial plane is an imaginary plane that runs through the center of the fold (**Figure 3.10**). If the axial plane divides the fold into two essentially equal and identical halves, the fold is said to be symmetric. If the two halves are different in area and/or shape, the fold is asymmetric.

The axial plane may be vertical or it may be inclined. The extent of the incline affects the position of the limbs, and also whether the fold is symmetrical or asymmetrical.

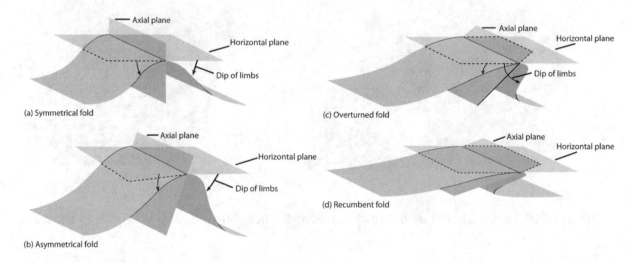

Figure 3.10 Types of Folds. Folds are described as being symmetric, asymmetric, overturned, and recumbent, depending on the relationship of the axial plane and the limbs relative to the horizontal. Illustration © Kendall Hunt Publishing Company

Figure 3.10 illustrates how the position of the axial plane forms four major types of folds. In a symmetrical fold (a), the axial plane is vertical, and the limbs are of equal lengths and have equal dip angles. An asymmetrical fold (b) has a slightly inclined axial plane, so the limbs are unequal and have different dip values. An overturned fold (c) is also asymmetric in that it does not have equal halves, but the difference between the halves is more radical. In an overturned fold, the axial plane is inclined far enough for the limbs to dip in the same direction. A recumbent fold (d) is the most extreme fold, with the axial plane and both limbs lying almost horizontal.

In general, symmetric folds form as the result of compression, whereas asymmetric folds form as the result of shear. The type of fold also indicates how much energy was present when the fold was created. The more energy, the more the axis of the fold inclines. Symmetric folds represent the least amount of energy, and recumbent folds form under the maximum amount of deformational energy.

The apparent motion of rocks that have faulted can be determined by the presence of slickensides, or drag folds. The apparent motion of rocks that have folded is determined by the direction in which the asymmetric folds incline. The same forces that produce folds and faults on a local scale have created mountains on a regional scale. These forces often occur at plate boundaries; the mountain building that occurs at plate boundaries is called orogeny.

Orogenic Styles

The term *orogeny* is defined as mountain building by compressional forces acting upon the layers of rock. The word "orogeny" comes from the Greek word "oros" for mountain and the word "genesis" means birth or origin, so the process of mountain building comes from forces or events that lead into severe structural deformation of the earth's crust by tectonic plate movement.

Ocean-Continent

The ocean-continent orogenic style originates when a denser oceanic plate moves underneath (subduction) a less-dense continental plate, an oceanic trench is produced on the ocean side and a mountain range on the continental side (see **Figure 3.11**). These rocks develop into a mountain range along the continental margin with the folded and faulted sedimentary component located inland. Examples of mountains created by the ocean-continent orogenic style are the Andes Mountains of South America and the Cascade Mountains of northern California, Oregon, and Washington State.

Ocean-Ocean

The initiation of the ocean-ocean orogenic style is illustrated in **Figure 3.12**. The mountain-building event begins with the formation of a chain of island arc volcanoes along a zone of subduction. Between the island arc and the continental margin, an oceanic depression forms, known as a back arc basin. Over time, sediments derived from both the continent and from the growing island arc are deposited into the back arc basin. While volume of sediments derived from the continent may decrease over time as the rocks of the continent are worn down, the island arc serves as a continuous source of sediment as new volcanoes continue to erupt and wash into the basin. With time, an igneous/metamorphic rock core develops under the chain of volcanic islands, converting the chain of islands into a major land mass (such as Japan) where the erosion of overlying volcanic rocks has exposed the igneous granitic core over about 10 percent of the land surface. As compression continues, the volcanic land mass is driven toward the continent, initiating the deformation of the sediments in the back arc basin.

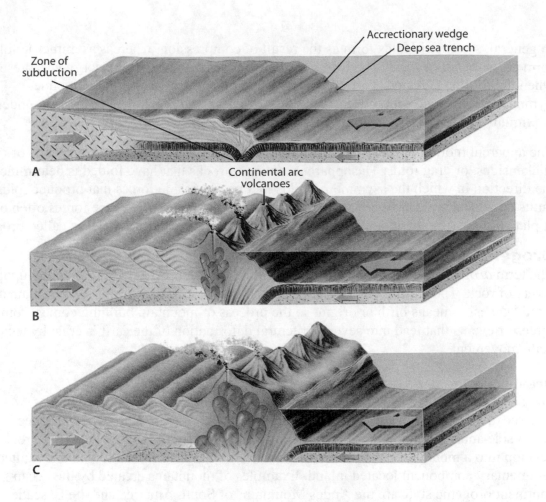

Figure 3.11 Ocean-Continent Orogeny. Ocean-continent orogeny begins when oceanic lithosphere subducts beneath continental lithosphere (A). The subduction results in rock melting to become magma, which rises to the surface and erupts (B). Over time, new igneous rock from the eruptions accumulates to form a string of volcanic mountains called a continental arc. From *Planet Earth* by John J. Renton. Copyright © 2002 by John J. Renton. Reprinted by permission of Kendall Hunt Publishing Company.

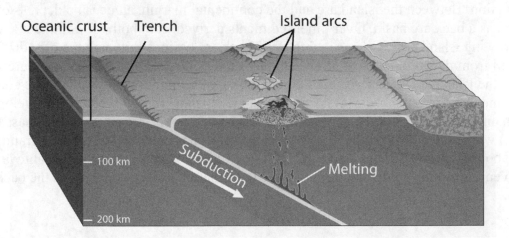

Figure 3.12 Ocean-Ocean Orogeny. Volcanic arcs form when magma near a subduction zone rises and erupts. The magma accumulates until it breaks through the surface, forming a volcanic island. Sediments from the island arc and the continent accumulate in the back arc basin. Illustration by Don Vierstra

Continent-Continent

The continent-continent orogenic style is illustrated in **Figure 3.13**, which involves the convergence and eventual collision of two continents as the oceanic lithosphere between the continents is consumed by a zone of subduction.

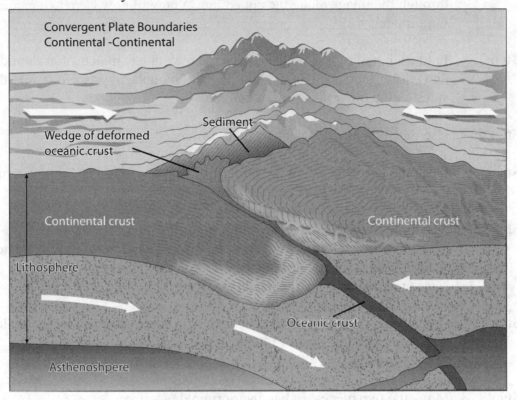

Figure 3.13 Continent-Continent Orogeny. Illustration by Don Vierstra

Lab Exercises

Lab Exercise #1: *Fault Models*

In this lab exercise, you will be creating and demonstrating the causes and effects of three different types of faults. Each fault will show some form of surface feature that provides clues to locating what type of fault is being expressed. Follow the steps below and record your observations in the space provided or on a separate piece of paper.

Reference **Figures 3.6**, **3.7**, and **3.8** (i.e., three different types of faults: normal, reverse, and strike-slip) as a guide to assist you in answering the questions pertaining to this exercise. *Note: The scale of the model is 1 millimeter (mm) = 1 meter (m).*

Make sure to save your results and observations. You will use the data to answer the questions at the end of this lesson.

Instructions and Observations

Step 1: Locate the fault model image (on white cardstock) found in your lab kit.

Step 2: Using a pair of scissors, cut along the outside borders of the image. Then, cut through the image along the dotted line. You will now have two pieces of the fault model.

Step 3: Fold each half of the model, so that the rock layers match. You should fold down three sides on one piece of the fault model and proceed to fold the three sides on the other piece of the fault model.

Step 4: Use transparent tape to connect the corners on each piece.

Step 5: Place the two pieces on a flat surface so that they stand up and are arranged side by side. Make sure that the rock layers match.

Step 6: Move the two pieces so that point S is next to point T. Use a ruler or protractor to determine how far the rock mass would move along a lateral fault if point S moved next to point T. Record the measurement.
Measured distance (on the model) = _____ mm

Step 7: Convert the measured distance to actual distance. (Remember the scale is 1 mm on the model equals 1 m of actual distance.)
Actual distance = _____ m

Step 8: Move the two pieces back to their original position.

Step 9: Move the two pieces so that point S is next to point R. Use a ruler or protractor to determine how far the rock mass would move along a lateral fault if point S moved from the initial position to point R. Record the measurement.
Measured distance (on the model) = _____ mm

Step 10: Convert the measured distance to actual distance. (Remember the scale is 1 mm on the model equals 1 m of actual distance.)
Actual distance = _____ m

Step 11: Observe the model. If point S moved to point R suddenly because of slippage along the fault, and if the stream flowed to the west, where would the stream flow relative to the landmarks in the area (railroad, power lines, tree, road, etc.)?

Step 12: Observe the model. Which type of fault would exist if point S moved near point R?
    a. a thrust fault
    b. a normal fault
    c. a reverse fault
    d. a right lateral strike-slip fault
    e. a left lateral strike-slip fault

Step 13: Hold the model in your hands, with one piece in each hand. Starting from the original position of the two pieces, slide one side down and the other side up so that point E and point F are aligned horizontally. Which type of fault does this demonstrate?
    a. a thrust fault
    b. a normal fault
    c. a right-lateral strike-slip fault
    d. a left-lateral strike-slip fault
    e. none of the above

Step 14: Starting from the original position of the two pieces, move one side down and the other side up so that point G and point H are aligned horizontally. Which type of fault does this demonstrate?
    a. a reverse fault
    b. a normal fault
    c. a right-lateral strike-slip fault
    d. a left-lateral strike-slip fault
    e. none of the above

Lab Exercise #2: *Strata Folding*

Some mountains are formed by folding and others are formed by fault movement. Deep within Earth's crust the layers of rock become extremely hot, thus becoming very pliable. Mountains ranges are formed when the colliding crust is compressed and pushed upward.

In this lab exercise, you will be creating and demonstrating two different kinds of folds. Each fold will demonstrate some form of surface feature that provides you a clue for identifying what type of fold is being expressed.

Make sure to save your observations. You will use the data to answer the questions at the end of this lesson.

Instructions and Observations

Step 1: Locate the three pieces of different colored flexible foam found in your lab kit.

Step 2: Stack the three pieces, one on top of the other. (Color order does not matter.) The different colored foam layers represent rock layers.

Step 3: Hold the left side of the foam stack with your left hand and hold the right side of the foam stack with your right hand.

Step 4: Hold up the layers of foam in the air with both hands. Move both hands toward each other (move your left hand toward the right and your right hand toward the left) to create an upward fold in the middle.

Step 5: Observe the fold from the side. What type of fold is created from the physical disruption of the rock layers?
   a. syncline
   b. anticline
   c. asymmetric fold
   d. recumbent fold
   e. none of the above

Step 6: Hold up the layers of foam in the air with both hands. Move both hands toward each other (move your left hand toward the right and your right hand toward the left) so as to create an downward fold or dip in the middle.

Step 7: Observe the fold from the side. What type of fold is created from the physical disruption of the rock layers?
   a. syncline
   b. anticline
   c. asymmetric fold
   d. recumbent fold
   d. none of the above

Online Activities

As per your instructor's direction, go to the online lesson for this lab and complete the activities assigned.

Quiz

Questions 1 through 9 are based on **Lab Exercise #1:** *Fault Models*

1. Record your answer from *Lab Exercise #1, step 6*.
   Measured distance = _____ mm

2. Record your answer from *Lab Exercise #1, step 7*.
   Actual distance = _____ m

3. Record your answer from *Lab Exercise #1, step 9*.
   Measured distance = _____ mm

4. Record your answer from *Lab Exercise #1, step 10*.
   Actual distance = _____ m

5. Record your answer from *Lab Exercise #1, step 11*.

6. Record your answer from *Lab Exercise #1, step 12*. Which type of fault would exist if point S moved near point R?
   a. a thrust fault
   b. a normal fault
   c. a reverse fault
   d. a right lateral strike-slip fault
   e. a left lateral strike-slip fault

7. Record your answer from *Lab Exercise #1, step 13*. Which type of fault would exist if point E moved near point F?
   a. a thrust fault
   b. a normal fault
   c. a right-lateral strike-slip fault
   d. a left-lateral strike-slip fault
   e. none of the above

8. Record your answer from *Lab Exercise #1, step 14*. Which type of fault would produce movement along the fault to place point G near point H?
   a. a reverse fault
   b. a normal fault
   c. a right-lateral strike-slip fault
   d. a left-lateral strike-slip fault
   e. none of the above

9. Why are faults generally associated with mountain ranges and folding of the rock layers?

For Questions 10 through 15, fill in the chart below with the stresses that cause movements along a fault.

Type of Fault	Cause of Fault Motion Stress: Which type of stress causes the faults to move? (Shear, Compression, or Tension)	Use arrows to describe the direction of the stress of the fault. Examples of rock stress: Tension ← → Compression → ← Shear → ←
Normal Fault	10.	13.
Thrust / Reverse Fault	11.	14.
Lateral Left or Right Strike Slip Fault	12.	15.

10. Normal Fault
    a. shear
    b. compression
    c. tension

11. Thrust / Reverse Fault
    a. shear
    b. compression
    c. tension

12. Lateral Left or Right Strike Slip Fault
    a. shear
    b. compression
    c. tension

13. Normal Fault
    a. → ←
    b. →
    c. ←

14. Thrust / Reverse Fault
    a. ← →
    b. → ←
    c. →
    d. ←

15. Lateral Left or Right Strike Slip Fault
    a. ← →
    b. → ←
    c. →
    d. ←

Questions 16 and 17 are based on **Lab Exercise #2:** *Strata Folding*

16. Record your answer from *Lab Exercise #2, step 5*. What type of fold is created from the physical disruption of the rock layers?
    a. syncline
    b. anticline
    c. asymmetric fold
    d. recumbent fold
    e. none of the above

17. Record your answer from *Lab Exercise #2, step 7*. What type of fold is created from the physical disruption of the rock layers?
    a. syncline
    b. anticline
    c. asymmetric fold
    d. recumbent fold
    e. none of the above

18. The best description of the sense of motion across the normal fault depicted in **Figure 3.6** is
    a. the hanging wall has moved down relative to the footwall.
    b. the footwall has moved down relative to the hanging wall.
    c. the hanging wall and footwall have moved horizontally in a right-lateral sense.
    d. the hanging wall and footwall have moved horizontally in a left-lateral sense.
    e. none of the above

19. The San Andreas Fault is a
    a. thrust fault.
    b. right-lateral strike-slip fault.
    c. left-lateral strike-slip fault.
    d. bilateral strike-slip fault.
    e. normal fault.

20. Faults associated with zones of subduction are _____ faults depending on the angle of the dip.
    a. normal
    b. reverse
    c. left lateral strike-slip
    d. right lateral strike-slip
    e. thrust or blind thrust

21. _____ are bends in the rock strata and generally represent the ductile response of rock strata to compression within the earth's crust.
    a. Axial surface
    b. Normal faults
    c. Folds
    d. Reverse faults
    e. Thrust

22. A continent-continent collision produces
    a. a trench.
    b. a spreading center.
    c. a mountain range.
    d. all of the above.
    e. blind thrust.

23. The Andes Mountains of South America and the Cascade Mountains of northern California, Oregon, and Washington State are examples of what type plate tectonic movement?
    a. ocean-ocean collision
    b. ocean-continent collision
    c. continent-continent collision
    d. normal fault
    e. a spreading center

24. When a denser oceanic plate moves underneath a less-dense continental plate, what two types of geologic structures are produced during this plate movement?
    a. oceanic trench and mountain range
    b. valley and hill
    c. hotspot and rift valley
    d. all of the above
    e. none of the above

Questions 25 through 30 are based on the online video, *The Rock Deformation Process*.

25. The Appalachian Mountains were created by what type of plate movement?
    a. ocean–ocean plate collision
    b. continent–continent plate collision
    c. ocean–continent plate collision
    d. normal fault
    e. reverse fault

26. What type of force was applied to a car's hood when it hit a tree or was applied by the drinking glass as it flattened the cookie dough?
    a. tensional
    b. compressive
    c. shear
    d. strain
    e. none of the above

27. Whether it is steel and aluminum, cookie dough, cheese, or paper, few substances stay the same when under stress; the response of a substance to stress is called
    a. tensional.
    b. compressive.
    c. shear.
    d. strain.
    e. none of the above.

28. Explain what happens to a substance once it is subjected to stress beyond its elastic limit. Give an example.

29. At some temperatures, the suddenness of the stress affects whether a substance will break or ooze. Silly Putty is an example of a substance that is brittle when cold but _____ at room temperature.
    a. strain
    b. ductile
    c. brittle
    d. strong
    e. inflexible

30. Rock has a response to stress similar to that of chocolate and Silly Putty. Crust that is close to the surface and cooler is more likely to be brittle and to break when stressed. Increase the pressure, however, and the crust will heat up, becoming ductile. Under heat and pressure, it will change its shape rather than break. Both brittle and ductile responses to stress are evident in
    a. subduction.
    b. mountain ranges.
    c. seafloor spreading.
    d. stream flow.
    e. none of the above.

EARTHQUAKES AND SEISMOLOGY

Lesson 4

Purpose

This laboratory lesson will familiarize you with geologic concepts pertaining to earthquakes and seismology.

Lesson Objectives

After completing this laboratory lesson, you will be able to:

- Identify various kinds of seismic waves.
- Measure the effect of rock strength on seismic wave velocity.
- Interpret the results from a seismograph and locate the epicenter of an earthquake.

Materials Needed

- ❑ Drafting compass (in lab kit)
- ❑ Ruler (in lab kit)
- ❑ Pencil and eraser
- ❑ Calculator

Overview

Earthquakes are ground vibrations caused by the release of energy from fault movements, asteroid impacts, volcanic eruptions, explosions, and movements of magma. This laboratory lesson will emphasize the characteristic behavior of energy releases from fault movements. Such releases of energy produce ground vibrations in the form of elastic waves, or seismic waves, that are propagated in all directions from the focus—the point of origin of the initial fault slip. The point on the earth's surface directly above the focus is known as the epicenter.

Seismic waves can be detected by an instrument called a seismograph, and the record produced by a seismograph is a seismogram. A worldwide network of seismic stations, or seismic observatories, provides records of the arrival times of seismic waves. Seismograms from at least three stations located around the focus of a given earthquake—but at some distance from it— provide the data needed to locate the epicenter.

Seismic Waves

Two general types of seismic waves are generated by an earthquake: body waves and surface waves. Body waves, which originate at the focus, travel through the earth—they penetrate the "body"—whereas surface waves travel along the earth's surface and do not play a role in the location of an earthquake's epicenter.

Body waves, which are used to locate earthquake epicenters, consist of primary waves and secondary waves. The primary wave is referred to as the P wave and the secondary wave is referred to as the S wave. The P wave is a compressional, or "push-pull," wave. It has the same wave form as a sound wave in that it vibrates parallel to its direction of propagation. The S wave, on the other hand, is a transverse or "side-to-side" wave. It vibrates at right angles to the direction of propagation. P and S waves are generated at the same time at the focus, but they travel at different velocities. The P wave travels faster than the S wave and, therefore, is the first wave to arrive at a seismic station. The S wave follows within seconds or minutes of the arrival of the P wave (see **Figure 4.1**).

Seismographs also detect and record surface waves, particularly L waves, also named Love waves, and R waves, also named Rayleigh waves. Love and Rayleigh waves travel at similar velocities through the earth. L and R waves are the last seismic waves to arrive at a seismic station because they do not take shortcuts through the earth, as do body waves.

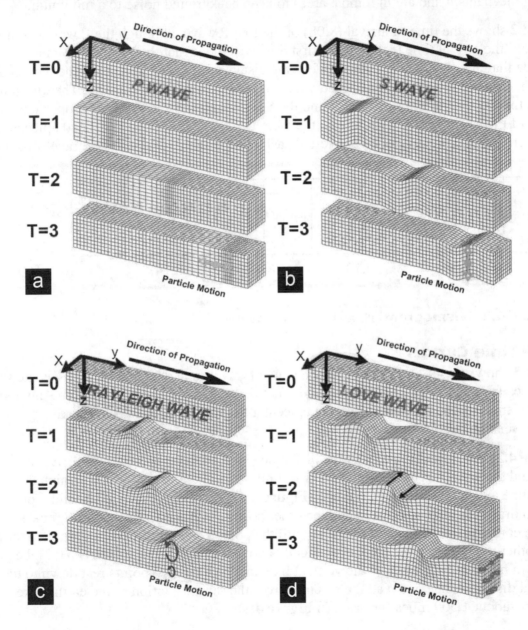

Figure 4.1 Seismic Waves. In P waves (a), particles oscillate back and forth along the direction of wave propagation. In S waves (b), particle motion is transverse, or side to side. In Rayleigh waves (c), the surface waves travel backward in vertical elliptical motion, and in Love waves (d), the surface waves travel in a transverse horizontal direction. Illustration by Larry Braile

Reading a Seismogram

A seismograph records the passing seismic waves as wiggly lines on time-scaled paper (the seismogram; refer to **Figure 4.2**) wrapped around a drum rotating at a fixed speed. Since the clocks at all seismic stations around the world are set at Greenwich Mean Time (GMT), all seismograms are based on a standardized clock. Background noise from vibrations caused by trucks, trains, heavy surf, construction equipment, and so forth, sometimes shows up on the seismogram as small irregular wiggles. For this reason, most modern seismographs contain a damping mechanism and are in remote areas to keep background noise to a minimum.

Figure 4.2 shows the time of arrival (8:08) of the first P wave, although the P waves continue to roll in until the arrival time (8:12) of the first S wave. Notice that the S wave has much larger amplitude than the P wave. The amplitude is the distance between the peak of the recorded wave and the line on the seismogram recorded when no seismic waves are arriving. The difference between the P-wave arrival time (8:08) and the S-wave arrival time (8:12) is proportional to the distance of the seismograph station from the vicinity of the earthquake focus and epicenter. The time difference, 6 minutes, can be converted easily into distance by means of travel-time curves.

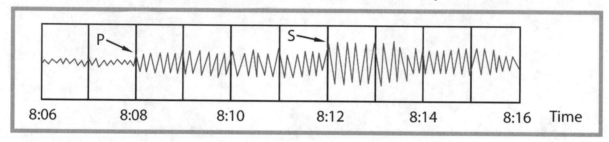

Figure 4.2 Seismogram. Illustration by Mark Worden

Travel-Time Curves

Figure 4.3 shows travel-time curves, which convert travel-time data recorded at seismic stations to distances from the epicenter, as measured on the earth's surface. The travel-time curves also convert seismic station distances from the epicenter to travel time, thus backtracking to the time the initial seismic energy was released.

In **Figure 4.2**, it was determined that the difference in travel time between the arrival of the first P wave and the arrival of the first S wave was 4 minutes. Therefore, scale off 4 minutes on the vertical time axis of the travel-time graph (**Figure 4.4**). This can be accomplished by placing one point of a drafting compass on zero and the other point on 4 minutes (**line a in Figure 4.4**). Then move the compass upward and to the right until the point formerly on zero lies on the P curve and the other point lies on the S curve vertically above it (**line b in Figure 4.4**). Hold the compass in place and then follow the vertical line on which the two points rest down to the horizontal distance scale and read the distance from the seismic station to the earthquake epicenter—about 1,500 miles (**arrow c in Figure 4.4**).

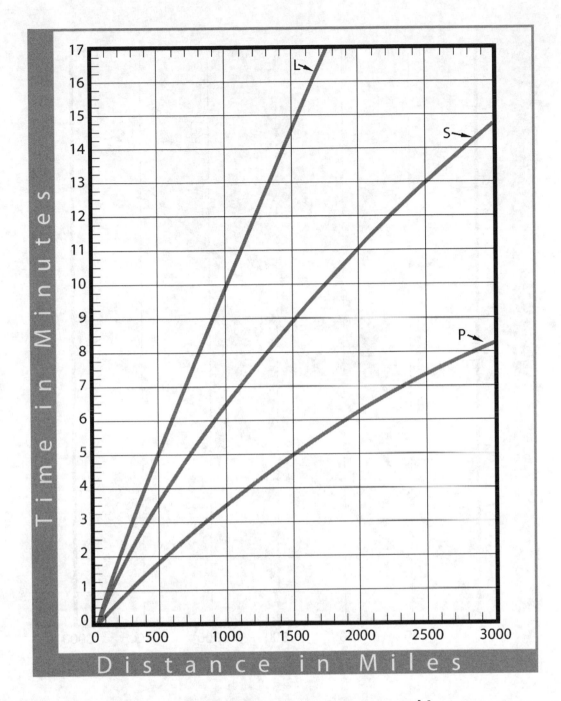

Figure 4.3 Travel-time curves for P waves, S waves, and L waves. Illustration by Don Vierstra

Now that the epicenter distance has been determined, one can also determine when the seismic waves started their journey of 1,500 miles to the seismic station. **Figure 4.4** shows that the intersection of the P-wave curve and the 1,500-mile mark corresponds to a horizontal projection of about 5 minutes. Therefore, it took the P wave 5 minutes to travel the 1,500-mile distance from the earthquake's epicenter to the seismic station. The time of origin of the earthquake can be determined by simply subtracting the 5-minute travel time for the P wave from the 8:08 arrival time for the P wave at the seismic station. So, the initial fault slip for this earthquake occurred at 8:03.

Lesson 4/Earthquakes and Seismology

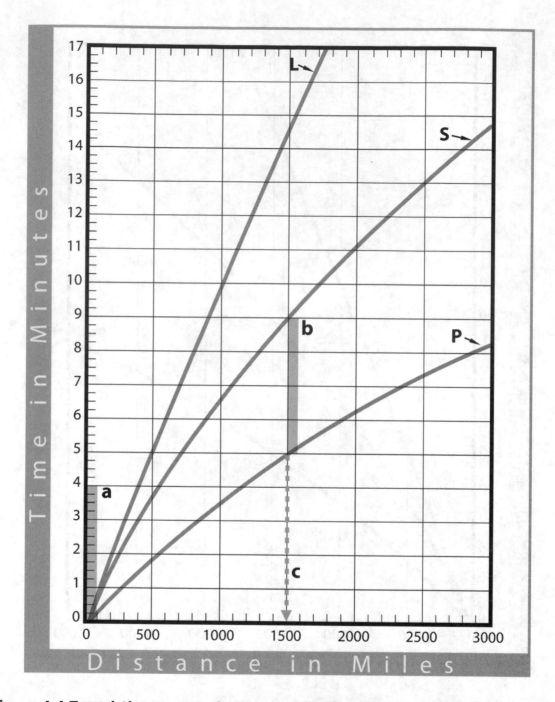

Figure 4.4 Travel-time curves for P waves, S waves, and L waves. Line **a** shows the distance from 0 to 4 minutes. Line **b** shows this same distance but from the P curve to the S curve. Arrow **c** indicates distance to the epicenter. Illustration by Don Vierstra

Figure 4.4 can also be used to determine the arrival time of the L wave at the seismic station. This can be done by scaling with your drafting compass the P-wave/L-wave travel-time difference for the 1,500-mile epicenter distance from the seismic station. To accomplish this, place one compass point on the P-curve intersection and one compass point on the L-curve intersection along a vertical projection from the epicenter distance of 1,500 miles. Move the compass down and to the left so that the distance between the two compass points can be read along the vertical time axis. The time difference of 9 minutes, 45 seconds, is added to the 8:08 P-wave arrival time, giving an arrival time of 8:17:45 for the L wave.

Locating the Epicenter

It takes at least three seismic stations to locate the epicenter of an earthquake. **Figure 4.5** shows the locations of seismic stations A, B, and C. The differences in P-wave/S-wave arrival times and the epicenter distances have been determined for each seismic station in the same manner as was done previously. The epicenter distances have been plotted on a map by drawing a circle around each seismic station using the map scale provided to determine the radius for each circle. One seismic station determines that the epicenter is somewhere on its epicenter circle. Two seismic stations narrow the location to the two points where the epicenter circles intersect. Three seismic stations narrow the location to one point where all three-epicenter circles intersect, designated "X" in **Figure 4.5**.

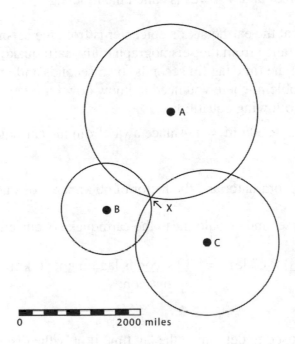

Figure 4.5 Locating the Epicenter. Three seismic circles narrow the location to one point where all the circles intersect. Illustration by Mark Worden

Lab Exercises

Lab Exercise #1: *Time Lag*

In this lab exercise, you will determine the distance to the epicenter of an earthquake. Make sure to save your results. You will use the data to answer the questions at the end of this lesson.

Locating the epicenter of an earthquake to pinpoint accuracy is not an easy task. However, a close estimate of epicenter location can be made with a few simple calculations. First of all, you need to know that there are two types of waves that produce an earthquake.

- P waves oscillate particles in the same direction as the wave is moving; and

- S waves oscillate particles at right angles to the direction of the wave.

P waves travel at about 6.0 km per second and S waves travel at about 4.0 km per second; therefore, P waves arrive at the seismographs first before the S waves do. The difference in arrival times between P waves and S waves is called the time lag.

Each kilometer (km) that the earthquake's epicenter is from the seismograph adds 5 seconds to the time lag. The distance from the seismograph to the earthquake's epicenter is determined by dividing the time lag (in seconds) by 5 seconds and multiplying by 60 km. Therefore for every problem where you need to know how far away the epicenter of an earthquake is, use the following equation:

$$\frac{\text{time lag (in seconds)}}{5 \text{ seconds}} \times 60 \text{ km} = \text{Distance away from the earthquake epicenter}$$

The 5 seconds in the denominator and the factor of 60 km are constants.

Example: A time lag of 30 seconds would mean the earthquake occurred 360 km away.

$$\frac{\text{time lag (in seconds)}}{5 \text{ seconds}} \times 60 \text{ km} = \frac{30 \text{ seconds lag time}}{5 \text{ seconds}} \times 60 \text{ km} = 360 \text{ km}$$

The same equation can be used to determine the lag time if only the distance is known.

$$\text{Time lag (in seconds)} = \text{Distance} \times \frac{5 \text{ seconds}}{60 \text{ km}}$$

Example: If the epicenter of an earthquake was 360 km away, the time lag is 30 seconds.

$$\text{Time lag (in seconds)} = \text{Distance} \times \frac{5 \text{ seconds}}{60 \text{ km}} = 360 \text{ km} \times \frac{5 \text{ seconds}}{60 \text{ km}} = 30 \text{ seconds}$$

Use the seismogram in **Figure 4.6** to determine the distance to the epicenter of an earthquake. Record your observations and calculations in the space provided or on a separate piece of paper.

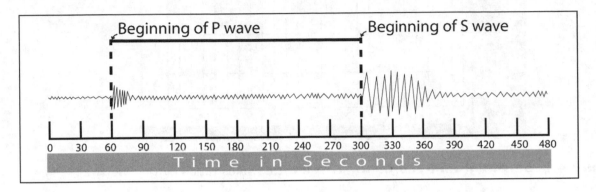

Figure 4.6 Seismogram. Illustration by Don Vierstra and Mark Worden

Instructions and Observations

Step 1: Use **Figure 4.6** to determine the time lag between the P and S wave.

Step 2: Use the Time Lag equation above to calculate the distance to the epicenter.

Step 3: Use the Time Lag equation above to calculate the time lag if the earthquake occurred 500 km away.

Lab Exercise #2: *Locating the Epicenter of an Earthquake*

In this lab exercise, you will locate the epicenter of an earthquake. A minimum of three seismic stations is necessary to locate an epicenter. This method of determining the epicenter of an earthquake is known as triangulation.

Below is a diagram (**Figure 4.7**), which shows seismogram records for an earthquake as recorded in three cities. The P wave is on the left and the S wave is on the right (Recall that P waves travel faster than S waves and therefore arrive at seismograph stations first.) The waves appear on the graph when the horizontal line becomes a sharp vertical line. A time scale is given below the seismogram so that the distance between the two arrival times can be read as seconds.

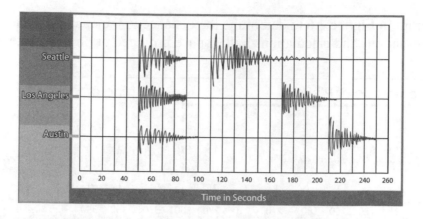

Figure 4.7 Seismogram Records for Three Cities. Illustration by Don Vierstra

Follow the instructions below to locate the epicenter of an earthquake. You will use **Figure 4.7** to determine time lag. Use the Time Lag formula to determine the distance from the epicenter of the earthquake to each of the cities. Then use the triangulation method to locate the epicenter. Submit your work as directed by your instructor.

Instructions and Observations

Step 1: Determine the time lag for Seattle, Washington.

Step 2: Calculate the distance from Seattle to the epicenter of the earthquake.

Step 3: Determine the time lag for Los Angeles, California.

Step 4: Calculate the distance from Los Angeles to the epicenter of the earthquake.

Step 5: Determine the time lag for Austin, Texas.

Step 6: Calculate the distance from Austin to the epicenter of the earthquake.

Use the information obtained above and the map below (**Figure 4.8**), to locate the epicenter.

Step 7: Using the scale on the map in **Figure 4.8**, put one point of your compass on 0 km and the other compass point on the distance calculated in step 2 above (for Seattle).

Step 8: Carefully lift the compass from the scale (so as not to move any of the compass points) and place one compass point on Seattle. Place the other compass point down and draw a complete circle.

Step 9: Continue on similar to steps 7 and 8 above and draw a circle around Los Angeles.

Step 10: Continue on similar to steps 7 and 8 above and draw a circle around Austin.

Step 11: Observe the point where the three circles intersect. Draw a small triangle at the point where the three circles intersect. This is the epicenter.

Step 12: What city is nearest to the epicenter?

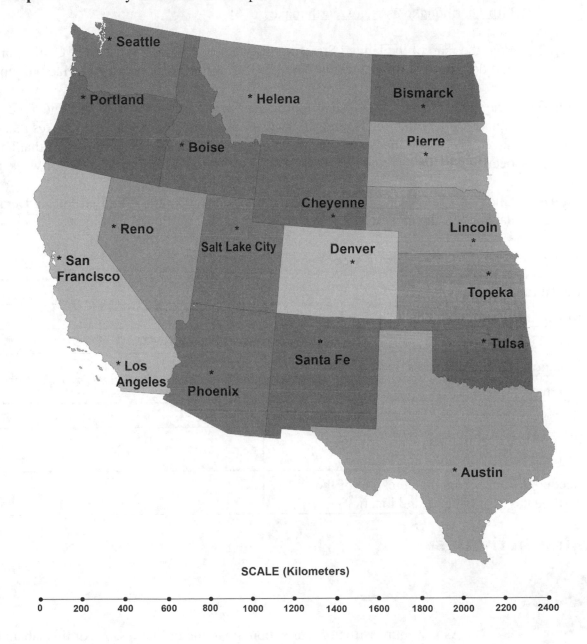

Figure 4.8 Western Part of the United States. Illustration by Marie Hulett

Lab Exercise #3: *USGS Earthquake Hazards Program*

In this lab exercise, you will go to the United States Geological Survey (USGS) website "Earthquake Hazard Program" where you will investigate how to look up current earthquake activity occurring in the continental United States.

Instructions and Observations

Step 1: Open an Internet browser and type in the web address http://earthquake.usgs.gov/earthquakes

Step 2: Find the map of the United States on the web page, locate the state of California, and double click on California. The USGS California-Nevada Fault Map will open.

Step 3: Drag your mouse (displayed as a little hand icon) across the map and find a red square. Notice that the legend shows that red squares represent earthquakes that have occurred in the last hour. (Note: If you can't locate any earthquakes that have occurred in the last hour, find one that has occurred within the last day or week.)

Step 4: Click on a red square until you see the Earthquake Details. The Earthquake Details data shows the most recent information about that particular earthquake.

Step 5: Use the table below to record your findings.

Earthquake Details	Results
Magnitude	
Date-Time	
Location (GPS coordinates)	
Depth of earthquake (below ground surface)	
Region	
First distance from the epicenter of the earthquake (list distance and location)	
Second distance from the epicenter of the earthquake (list distance and location)	

Online Activities

As per your instructor's direction, go to the online lesson for this lab and complete the activities assigned.

Quiz

Questions 1 and 2 are based on **Lab Exercise #1:** *Time Lag*

1. Record your answer from Lab Exercise #1, step 2.

2. Record your answer from Lab Exercise #1, step 3.

Questions 3 through 9 are based on **Lab Exercise #2:** *Locating the Epicenter of an Earthquake*

3. Record your answer from Lab Exercise #2, step 1.

4. Record your answer from Lab Exercise #2, step 2.

5. Record your answer from Lab Exercise #2, step 3.

6. Record your answer from Lab Excrcise #2, step 4.

7. Record your answer from Lab Exercise #2, step 5.

8. Record your answer from Lab Exercise #2, step 6.

9. Record your answer from Lab Exercise #2, step 12.

10. Record your answer from Lab Exercise #3, step 5, Magnitude

11. Record your answer from Lab Exercise #3, step 5, Date-Time

12. Record your answer from Lab Exercise #3, step 5, Location (GPS coordinates)

13. Record your answer from Lab Exercise #3, step 5, Depth of earthquake (below ground surface)

14. Record your answer from Lab Exercise #3, step 5, Region

15. Record your answer from Lab Exercise #3, step 5, First distance from the epicenter of the earthquake (list distance and location)

16. Record your answer from Lab Exercise #3, step 5, Second distance from the epicenter of the earthquake (list distance and location)

17. The focus of an earthquake is a point
    a. on the earth's surface where the initial release of seismic energy occurs.
    b. on the earth's surface where seismic waves are reflected downward.
    c. within the earth where seismic waves are reflected upward.
    d. within the earth where seismic waves are reflected downward.
    e. within the earth where the initial release of seismic energy occurs.

18. The epicenter of an earthquake is

    a. a point on the earth's surface directly above the initial release of seismic energy.
    b. a point within the earth directly beneath the initial release of seismic energy.
    c. a point on the earth's surface where the initial release of seismic energy occurs.
    d. a point within the earth where the initial release of seismic energy occurs.
    e. none of the above.

19. Which of the following seismic waves has the same wave form as a sound wave?

    a. surface wave
    b. P wave
    c. S wave
    d. L wave
    e. none of the above

20. Which of the following seismic waves is the first to arrive at a seismic station?

    a. surface wave
    b. P wave
    c. S wave
    d. L wave
    e. none of the above

21. Which of the following seismic waves is the last to arrive at a seismic station?

    a. L wave
    b. P wave
    c. S wave
    d. body wave
    c. none of the above

22. Which seismic wave vibrates side-to-side relative to its direction of propagation?

    a. surface wave
    b. P wave
    c. S wave
    d. L wave
    e. none of the above

23. The two kinds of body waves are

    a. surface waves and P waves.
    b. L waves and P waves.
    c. P waves and S waves.
    d. surface waves and S waves.
    e. L waves and S waves.

24. The following seismic waves are used to locate earthquake epicenters:

    a. surface waves and P waves.
    b. L waves and P waves.
    c. P waves and S waves.
    d. surface waves and S waves.
    e. L waves and S waves.

25. Which of the following statements is correct?

    a. P-wave amplitude is larger the S-wave amplitude.
    b. S-wave amplitude is larger than P-wave amplitude.
    c. P-wave amplitude and S-wave amplitude are about the same.
    d. P-wave amplitude is larger than all the other seismic waves recorded on a seismogram.
    e. S-wave amplitude is smaller than all the other seismic waves recorded on a seismogram.

26. Determining the distance along the earth's surface from a seismic station to the epicenter of an earthquake is based on

    a. the difference in arrival times between the first P wave and the first S wave.
    b. the difference in arrival times between the first P wave and the first L wave.
    c. the difference in arrival times between the first S wave and the first L wave.
    d. the difference in arrival times between all three seismic waves.
    e. none of the above.

27. To locate the epicenter of an earthquake, it takes

    a. one seismic station.
    b. at least two seismic stations.
    c. at least three seismic stations.
    d. at least four seismic stations.
    e. no seismic stations.

Questions 28 through 32 are based on the online video "Damage from Earthquake." You will need to watch the entire video segment to answer all of the questions.

28. A series of strong earthquakes occurred in the city of New Madrid in southeastern Missouri during 1811 through 1812 that could be felt as far away as what two cities?

29. What mighty river in the mid-west part of the United States was forever changed as a result of the earthquakes that occurred in New Madrid during 1811 through 1812?

30. Since the 1906 earthquake in San Francisco, California, what laws had become more stringent to protect public safety?

31. In Dr. Kate Hutton's interview, she describes the Los Angeles basin as filled with ancient sediments that have been washed off from the San Gabriel Mountains during the last few million years. What does Dr. Kate Hutton refer to the Los Angeles basin as?
    a. a bowl of cherries
    b. a bowl of Oreo cookies
    c. a bowl of chocolate chip ice cream
    d. a bowl of Jell-O
    e. a bowl of rice

32. Many of the structures that collapsed during the Loma Prieta earthquake in San Francisco Marina District were located on unconsolidated soils saturated with water. When seismic waves pass through the water-saturated soils, the shaking triggers what process to take place?

MINERALS

Lesson 5

AT A GLANCE

Purpose

Learning Objectives

Materials Needed

Overview

    Physical Properties of Minerals

    The Economic Importance and Practical Uses of Minerals

Lab Exercise

    Lab Exercise: *Mineral Identification*

Online Activities

Quiz

Purpose

This laboratory lesson will familiarize you with the physical properties of minerals, how the physical properties are used to identify minerals, and the economic importance and practical uses of minerals.

Learning Objectives

After completing this laboratory lesson, you will be able to:

- Describe the physical properties that identify and distinguish minerals.
- Identify minerals by means of distinguishing among their unique set of physical properties (hardness, fracture surfaces, streak, color, and so on).

Materials Needed

The Mineral Identification kit, which is part of your lab materials, is required for this exercise.

- ❏ Common household lemon juice, lime juice, or vinegar
- ❏ 10x-magnifying hand lens (in lab kit)
- ❏ Porcelain streak plate (in lab kit)
- ❏ Glass plate (in lab kit)
- ❏ Wire nail (in lab kit)
- ❏ Magnet (in lab kit)
- ❏ Ten mineral specimens (in lab kit)
- ❏ White sheet of paper

Overview

A mineral is defined as a naturally occurring, inorganic substance with a definite chemical composition, an orderly and predictable atomic structure, and definite physical properties. The chemical composition and crystalline structure determine the physical properties of a mineral—its color, hardness, shape, feel, and reflection or refraction of light. In fact, a well-formed mineral crystal is one of the most beautiful objects produced in nature. Minerals constitute the fundamental building blocks of the earth and are extremely important to humans in many different ways.

Although composed of even smaller units called atoms,—minerals are the smallest units that can be seen with the unaided eye or a low-magnification hand lens. The consistency in a mineral species' atomic arrangement from specimen to specimen, regardless of where the mineral crystallized, is one of nature's amazing phenomena. Geologists have identified more than 2,800 mineral species, of which only fifteen or twenty are considered common. This exercise will feature some of the common rock-forming minerals and a few others of economic importance.

Physical Properties of Minerals

The precise arrangement of atoms that extends throughout a mineral specimen controls its external shape and physical characteristics. Because the atomic structure of a mineral species is always the same, most of its physical properties are relatively constant and may be used for the mineral's identification. The more diagnostic physical properties of minerals are crystal form, cleavage, fracture surfaces, luster, color, streak, hardness, specific gravity, reaction to acid, and magnetism.

Crystal Form

If a mineral forms in an environment where its growth is unimpeded, it may develop smooth symmetrical faces that, together, outline a specific geometric shape. These symmetrical geometric forms are called crystals (**Figure 5.1**). The same mineral species always shows the same angular relations between crystal faces, a relationship called the constancy of interfacial angles. Perfect crystals in nature, however, are the exception rather than the rule and usually form under special conditions where there is open space for them to grow during crystallization. Examples of crystal forms include the minerals halite and fluorite, which crystallize as cubes; the mineral magnetite, which crystallizes as an octahedron; and the mineral quartz, which crystallizes as a six-sided prism that ends in a six-sided pyramid.

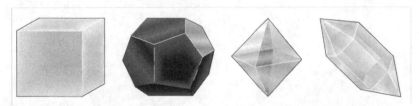

Figure 5.1 Common Crystal Forms. From *Planet Earth* by John J. Renton. Copyright © 2002 by John J. Renton. Reprinted by permission of Kendall Hunt Publishing Company.

Cleavage

Cleavage planes are flat surfaces along which some crystalline substances readily break or split because of weaknesses in the crystalline structure. They are surfaces of weak chemical bonding between layers of atoms that repeat as parallel sets. Therefore, each different set of cleavage planes has an orientation relative to the crystalline structure and is called a cleavage direction. In general, minerals can exhibit one, two, three, four, or six different cleavage directions (see **Figure 5.2**). For example, biotite has a single set of weak bonds. Cleaved fragments of biotite are bound by two parallel smooth surfaces. Such a mineral has one direction of cleavage (basal cleavage) because one set of parallel surfaces tends to form. The mineral pink microcline has two cleavage directions intersecting at right angles, hornblende has two cleavage directions intersecting at oblique angles, halite has three cleavage directions intersecting at right angles (cubic cleavage), calcite has three cleavage directions intersecting at oblique angles (rhombohedral cleavage), fluorite has four cleavage directions (octahedral cleavage), and sphalerite has six cleavage directions.

In assigning the number of cleavage directions to a specimen, do not refer to two parallel planes bounding the opposite sides of a specimen as two cleavage planes. In this case, the specimen has two cleavage surfaces but only one plane of cleavage, or one cleavage direction. Therefore, halite has cubic cleavage and six sides but only three planes of cleavage, because the six sides are made up of three parallel pairs of cleavage planes.

Fracture Surfaces

Fracture surfaces are uneven, irregular, nonparallel surfaces along which minerals break because of the absence of cleavage and the presence of a strong chemical bond. Quartz, for example, has no cleavage but instead breaks along smoothly curved surfaces called conchoidal fractures. "Splintery" (like wood) and "irregular" (like concrete) are other terms that describe the fracture appearance of particular minerals. Unlike cleavage surfaces, fracture surfaces reflect light in many different directions. A mineral with no cleavage simply fractures. An example is pink microcline, which has two directions of cleavage at right angles, plus a fracture direction.

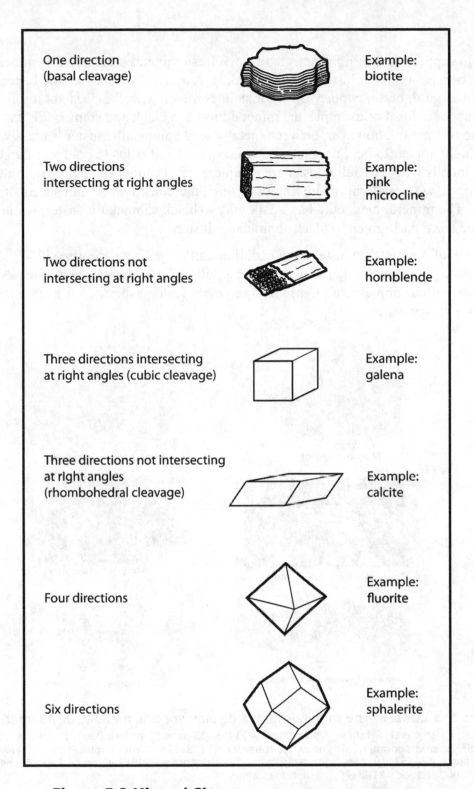

One direction
(basal cleavage)

Example:
biotite

Two directions
intersecting at right angles

Example:
pink
microcline

Two directions not
intersecting at right angles

Example:
hornblende

Three directions intersecting
at right angles (cubic cleavage)

Example:
galena

Three directions not intersecting
at right angles
(rhombohedral cleavage)

Example:
calcite

Four directions

Example:
fluorite

Six directions

Example:
sphalerite

Figure 5.2 Mineral Cleavage. Illustration by Don Vierstra

Luster

Luster is the appearance of light reflected from a fresh mineral surface. Most minerals have either a metallic or a nonmetallic luster (see **Figure 5.3**). A mineral with a metallic luster looks like a metal such as gold, brass, copper, silver, or stainless steel. Metallic does not imply "shininess" or anything about color. For example, the mineral biotite is black and shiny but it has a nonmetallic luster. The distinction, however, between metallic and nonmetallic luster is not always as clear-cut as it might appear to be. For some mineral specimens, it helps to hold them up to a light source; minerals with a metallic luster are opaque, so you cannot see light passing through even the thin edges, whereas light readily shows through the thin edges or thin sheets of the biotite specimen. The mineral magnetite has a dark gray to black submetallic luster, while the mineral hornblende has a dark-green to black nonmetallic luster.

Descriptions of nonmetallic luster include dull or earthy, resinous, pearly, silky, glossy, and glassy. Kaolinite and other clay minerals have a dull or earthy luster, sphalerite has a resinous luster (often called submetallic), gypsum has a pearly luster, asbestos has a silky luster, and quartz has a glassy luster.

Metallic (gold)

Vitreous (rose quartz)

Resinous (garnet crystals)

Waxy (chalcedony)

Pearly (muscovite mica)

Dull-earthy (barite)

Figure 5.3 Luster. The minerals above display specific metallic or nonmetallic lusters. Photo credits: Metallic, Shutterstock #51465025, credit Matthew Benoit; Vitreous, Shutterstock #58655551, credit optimarc; Resinous, Shutterstock #27787174, credit Nikolai Pozdeev; Waxy, Shutterstock #24152110, credit dmitriyd; Pearly, Shutterstock #56061226, credit Tyler Boyes; Dull-earthy, Shutterstock #2188460, credit Manamana

Color

Color is the most obvious physical characteristic of any mineral specimen. For some minerals, it provides a useful clue for identification. For other minerals, color can be misleading because some nonmetallic mineral species may occur in different colors as a result of small variations in chemical composition or small amounts of impurities within the mineral. For example, quartz may be colorless, white, rose, gray, yellow, or brown. However, some nonmetallic minerals have a common color that can be used as a clue to aid in mineral identification. Biotite is always black, or at least dark brown. Hornblende is always dark green-to-black, flint is always dark gray-to-black, and chert is always light gray.

Streak

The color of a mineral's powder is its streak. The streak is determined by rubbing the mineral specimen on a piece of unglazed porcelain, called a streak plate, and rubbing the streak with your finger. Some minerals have a streak that is the same color as the color of the hand specimen. Others have a streak that differs in color from the hand specimen. Unfortunately, because many light-colored minerals have white or pastel streaks, a streak test is not particularly useful in identifying nonmetallic minerals. Also, minerals that are harder than a streak plate will not be powdered during a streak test but instead will powder the streak plate. The streak of minerals with a metallic luster is especially diagnostic. A streak test would be very helpful in distinguishing between real gold, which has a yellow streak, and fool's gold (pyrite), which has a dark gray streak.

Hardness

Hardness describes a mineral's ability to resist scratching or abrasion. Hardness can be determined either by trying to scratch a mineral of unknown hardness with a substance of known hardness (such as a wire nail) or by using the unknown mineral to scratch a substance of known hardness (such as a glass plate). Hardness is measured on Mohs scale of hardness, which consists of ten common minerals in order of increasing hardness from No. 1 (talc) to No. 10 (diamond) (see **Figure 5.4**).

Mohs Scale of Hardness		Hardness of Some Common Objects	
Hardness	Mineral	Hardness	Object
10	Diamond		
9	Corundum		
8	Topaz		
7	Quartz		
6	Pink microcline		
		5.5	Glass plate, steel knife
5	Apatite	4.5	Wire, nail
4	Fluorite	3.5	Copper penny
3	Calcite	2.5	Fingernail
2	Gypsum		
1	Talc		

Figure 5.4 Mohs Scale of Hardness

Higher-numbered minerals will scratch lower-numbered minerals, but lower-numbered minerals cannot scratch higher-numbered minerals. All minerals of hardness 5.5 and higher will scratch the glass plate. In making hardness tests on a glass plate, however, do not hold the glass plate in your hands; keep the glass plate firmly on the table top before applying pressure with the mineral specimen. If you think that you have made a scratch on the glass, try to rub the scratch off. What appears to be a scratch may be only some of the mineral that has rubbed off on the glass. A steel knife blade, on the other hand, will scratch all minerals with a hardness of 5.5 or less, whereas a fingernail will scratch all minerals with a hardness of 2.5 or less. For example, you can scratch calcite (hardness 3) with a copper penny (hardness 3.5) but you cannot scratch the calcite with your fingernail (hardness 2.5). It is important to remember that each mineral on the hardness scale has an assigned number and the scale is relative not absolute. Therefore, although fluorite is a number 4 on the scale it is not twice as hard as gypsum (number 2), nor is it half as hard as topaz (number 8). Mohs hardness scale simply compares the hardness of one mineral to that of another.

Specific Gravity

The specific gravity of a mineral is a unit number that represents the ratio of the mineral's weight to the weight of an equal volume of water. For example, the mineral quartz (specific gravity 2.65) is 2.65 times heavier than an equal volume of water, whereas galena (specific gravity 7.4) is 7.4 times heavier than an equal volume of water. Gold (specific gravity 19) is 19 times heavier than an equal volume of water. Although accurate determination of specific gravity requires specialized equipment, "hefting" is an easy way to judge the specific gravity of one mineral relative to another. Hefting is done by lifting a piece of one mineral in one hand and lifting an equal-sized piece of another mineral in the other hand. The mineral specimen that feels heavier has the higher specific gravity. Most metallic minerals have higher specific gravities than nonmetallic minerals.

Reaction to Acid

Calcite will effervesce (fizz) when treated with dilute hydrochloric acid or common household lemon juice or lime juice (citric acid). Vinegar (acetic acid) may also cause a similar chemical reaction when applied to a freshly exposed calcite surface. The fizzing or bubbling action results from the liberation of gaseous carbon dioxide by the reaction of the acid with the calcium carbonate in the mineral.

Magnetism

Magnetism is exhibited by minerals such as magnetite. Magnetite can be either magnetic or nonmagnetic. Magnetic magnetite (lodestone) was used by ancient mariners to navigate and will attract steel paperclips or wire nails just like a magnet. Nonmagnetic magnetite will not attract these steel objects, but is attracted to a magnet because of its high iron content.

The Economic Importance and Practical Uses of Minerals

Humans have been mining minerals for thousands of years. Consumption of many of these minerals has increased exponentially over the past several decades. Our modern society focuses on the major minerals that are mined such as gold, silver, platinum, and diamond; however, our society relies upon other types of rocks and minerals for the infrastructure of our current civilization. For example, sheetrock and plaster come from a mineral called gypsum, which is calcium sulfate mineral. Sheetrock is used as wallboard for the interior walls in homes. Another example of industrial mineral is silica sand, which consists of quartz and it is used for making glass, ceramics, and microchips. Sodium chloride (NaCl) comes from a mineral called halite. Ancient seas or lakebeds dried up, leaving salt deposits; these salt deposits are mined for the mineral halite, which is used for human consumption and other industrial use. **Figure 5.5** lists some other commonly found minerals and their economic uses.

Mineral	Economic Uses
CALCITE ($CaCO_3$)	In the form of limestone, used as fertilizer, soil conditioner, in Portland cement, and as a source of lime; as ornamental stone in limestone, marble, travertine, and Mexican onyx
CHALCOPYRITE ($CuFeS_2$)	Ore of copper
PINK MICROCLINE (aluminosilicates of K, Na, Ca)	Major use in manufacturing of porcelain, glass, and ceramics; minor use as gemstones such as amazon stone, moonstone, and sunstone
GALENA (PbS)	Chief ore of lead; abrasive powder and sandpaper
GARNET (Ca, Fe, Al silicate)	Abrasive powder and sandpaper. Garnet is also a gemstone.
GRAPHITE (C)	Lubricant for machinery, heat-resistant material in foundries, pencil lead
GYPSUM ($CaSO_4 \cdot 2H_2O$)	Wallboard, plaster of Paris, drywall, sheetrock; some ornamental use in form called alabaster
HALITE (NaCl)	Used as table salt and as a source of sodium and chlorine chemicals; old salt mines used as storage sites
HEMATITE (Fe_2O_3)	Major ore of iron; minor use as a pigment (cave paintings were often done with hematite)
HORNBLENDE (Ca_2 [Mg,Fe]$_4$ Al(Si$_7$Al)O$_{22}$(OH,F)$_2$	Used in construction materials especially paving, and creation of ornamental bracelets
LIMONITE ($Fe_2O_3 \cdot nH_2O$)	Ore of iron; minor use as a pigment
MAGNETITE (Fe_3O_4)	Ore of iron
MUSCOVITE (complex silicate)	Used in sheets as an electrical insulating material, ground for use in wallpaper and paint, computer chip substrate
OLIVINE (Fe,Mg)$_2$SiO$_4$	Source of silicon for silicon chips in computers; gem variety, peridot
PYRITE (FeS_2) ("fool's gold")	Ore of sulfur used to make sulfuric acid; mined also for iron or associated gold or copper
QUARTZ (SiO_2)	Important gemstones, such as amethyst, tiger's eye, agate, and onyx.

Figure 5.5 Economic Uses of Minerals

Metallic Luster			
Hardness	**Streak**	**Color, etc.**	**Mineral**
6–6.5	greenish to black	brassy yellow, Specific Gravity (Sp. Gr.) = 4.2	Pyrite (iron sulfide, FeS_2)
6	dark gray	dark gray to black, submetallic luster, attracts magnet, Sp. Gr. = 5.18	Magnetite (iron oxide)
5–6.5	red to red-brown	silver to gray to brown, Sp. Gr. = 5.26	Hematite (iron oxide)
3.5–4	white to yellow-brown	brown to yellow, submetallic luster, 6 cleavage dir., Sp. Gr. = 4	Sphalerite (zinc sulfide)
2.5	gray to dark gray	steel gray, cubic cleavage, Sp. Gr. = 7.4	Galena (lead sulfide)
1	dark gray	gray to black, slippery feel, Sp. Gr. = 2.3	Graphite (carbon)

Nonmetallic Luster, Dark Color (with cleavage)			
Hardness	**Cleavage directions**	**Color, etc.**	**Mineral**
5–6	2 (intersecting at right angles)	green to black, Sp. Gr. = 3.2–3.4	Pyroxene (calcium ferromag. silicate)
5.5	2 (intersecting at 60° and 120°)	dark green to black, Sp. Gr. = 3.3	Hornblende (calcium ferromag. silicate)
2.5–3	1 (basal)	dark brown to black Sp. Gr. = 2.8–3.0	Biotite (ferromag. potassium hydrous aluminum silicate)
2	1 (basal)	dark green, Sp. Gr. = 2.6–3.0	Chlorite (ferromag. aluminum silicate)

Nonmetallic Luster, Dark Color (without cleavage)		
Hardness	**Color, etc.**	**Mineral**
7	dark gray to black, conchoidal fracture, Sp. Gr. = 2.65	Flint (silicon dioxide)
7	red, conchoidal fracture, Sp. Gr. = 2.65	Jasper (silicon dioxide)
7	olive green, sugary texture, Sp. Gr. = 3.2–3.5	Olivine (ferromag. silicate)
7	dark red, translucent, Sp. Gr. = 4	Garnet (complex silicate)
2–5	variable dark green and light green, Sp. Gr. = 2.2	Serpentine (hydrous magnesium silicate)

Figure 5.6 Mineral Identification Table

Nonmetallic Luster, Light Color (with cleavage)			
Hardness	**Cleavage**	**Color, etc.**	**Mineral**
6	1 (basal)	white to pink to salmon, Sp. Gr. = 2.5–2.6 Streak= white, luster= vitreous	Pink Microcline (potassium aluminum silicate)
4	4 (octahedral)	yellow to colorless to blue to green, Sp. Gr. = 3.2	Fluorite (calcium fluoride)
3	3 (rhombohedral)	white to yellow to colorless to gray; effervesces, Sp. Gr. = 2.7	Calcite (calcium carbonate)
2.5	1 (basal)	colorless to yellow to light brown, Sp. Gr. = 2.8–3.0	Muscovite mica (potassium hydrous aluminum silicate)
2.5	3 (cubic)	colorless to yellow to white to gray, Sp. Gr. = 2.16	Halite (sodium chloride)

Nonmetallic Luster, Light Color (without cleavage)		
Hardness	**Color, etc.**	**Mineral**
7	colorless to white to gray, glassy luster, conchoidal fracture, Sp. Gr. = 2.65	Quartz (silicon dioxide)
7	light gray, opaque, Sp. Gr. = 2.65	Chert (silicon dioxide)
5	white to yellow to brown, six-sided crystals, Sp. Gr. = 2.3–2.4	Apatite (calcium fluorophosphate)
2	colorless to white, luster is vitreous to silky, pearly, or waxy; white streak Sp. Gr. = 2.31–2.33	Gypsum (calcium sulfate)
1	white to gray to yellow to light green, soapy feel, Sp. Gr. = 2.7–2.8	Talc (hydrous magnesium silicate)

Figure 5.6 Mineral Identification Table (continued)

Lab Exercise

Lab Exercise: *Mineral Identification*

In this laboratory exercise, you will identify some minerals. The ability to identify minerals is one of the most fundamental geological skills. It is an essential skill in identifying rocks, for one must first identify the minerals within a rock before the rock itself can be identified. Only after minerals and rocks have been identified can their origin, classification, and alteration be adequately understood. The ability for a geologist to identify minerals by using the simplest tools is often a necessity, particularly when working in the field.

Instructions and Observations

Retrieve the bag labeled **Lab #5** Mineral Identification Samples from your lab kit. Use the steps below to identify the ten minerals labeled A through J. To get you started, a few hints will be provided for Mineral Specimen A:

1. This mineral does not have a metallic luster.
2. This mineral is not considered to be a dark-colored mineral.
3. This mineral has two cleavage directions intersecting at right angles.
4. This mineral will scratch a glass plate but it will not scratch quartz.

Step 1: After placing the specimens on a white sheet of paper, separate the minerals with metallic luster from those with nonmetallic luster. Use the table below to record your findings. List each specimen in the appropriate column).

Metallic luster	Nonmetallic luster
Specimen(s):	Specimen(s): Specimen A

Step 2: List as many of the physical properties of each metallic mineral as you can determine, using the available tools and your senses. Then identify each metallic mineral in the mineral identification table provided (see **Figure 5.6**). Use the table below to record your findings.

Specimen	Color, cleavage, etc.	Streak	Hardness	Mineral

After you have identified the metallic minerals, continue with the steps below to identify the nonmetallic minerals.

Step 3: Separate the dark-colored nonmetallic minerals from the light-colored nonmetallic minerals. Use the table below to record your findings.

Dark-colored nonmetallic minerals	Light-colored nonmetallic minerals
	Specimen A

Step 4: Separate those minerals with cleavage from those minerals without cleavage. Use the table below to record your findings.

Dark-colored nonmetallic minerals with cleavage	Dark-colored nonmetallic minerals without cleavage	Light-colored nonmetallic minerals with cleavage	Light-colored nonmetallic minerals without cleavage
		Specimen A: two directions intersecting at right angles	

Step 5: List the physical properties of each mineral and make your identification from **Figure 5.6** as you did with the metallic minerals.

Specimen	Color, cleavage, etc.	Streak	Hardness	Mineral
Specimen A			Scratch glass plate, does not scratch quartz	

Online Activities

As per your instructor's direction, go to the online lesson for this lab and complete the activities assigned.

Quiz

Questions 1 through 20 are based on the Lab Exercise: *Mineral Identification*.

1. What mineral is specimen A?

   a. fluorite
   b. gypsum
   c. calcite
   d. quartz
   e. pink microcline

2. Specimen B has

   a. a dull or earthy luster.
   b. a silky luster.
   c. a metallic luster.
   d. a glassy luster.
   e. a pearly luster.

3. The hardness of Specimen B is

   a. 2.
   b. 3.
   c. 5.
   d. 6.
   e. 7.

4. Specimen B is

   a. fluorite.
   b. gypsum.
   c. calcite.
   d. quartz.
   e. pink microcline.

5. Specimen C has

   a. basal cleavage.
   b. cubic cleavage.
   c. rhombohedral cleavage.
   d. octahedral cleavage.
   e. conchoidal fracture.

6. Specimen C is

    a. hornblende.
    b. magnetite.
    c. chalcopyrite.
    d. galena.
    e. biotite.

7. Specimen D has

    a. basal cleavage.
    b. cubic cleavage.
    c. rhombohedral cleavage.
    d. octahedral cleavage.
    e. conchoidal fracture.

8. Specimen D

    a. effervesces.
    b. attracts a magnet.
    c. has crystal faccs.
    d. feels greasy.
    e. has a very high specific gravity.

9. Specimen D is

    a. fluorite.
    b. gypsum.
    c. calcite.
    d. quartz.
    e. pink microcline.

10. The hardness of Specimen E is

    a. 1.
    b. 2.
    c. 3.
    d. 4.
    e. 5.

11. Specimen E is

    a. fluorite.
    b. gypsum.
    c. calcite.
    d. quartz.
    e. pink microcline.

12. Specimen F has a cleavage of

    a. 1 (basal).
    b. 4 (octahedral).
    c. 3 (rhombohedral).
    d. 3 (cubic).
    e. none of the above.

13. Specimen F is
    a. hornblende.
    b. magnetite.
    c. fluorite.
    d. halite.
    e. biotite.

14. Specimen G
    a. effervesces.
    b. attracts a magnet.
    c. has six cleavage directions.
    d. feels greasy.
    e. has a very low specific gravity.

15. Specimen G is
    a. hornblende.
    b. magnetite.
    c. pyrite.
    d. galena.
    e. biotite.

16. Specimen H has
    a. basal cleavage.
    b. cubic cleavage.
    c. rhombohedral cleavage.
    d. octahedral cleavage.
    e. conchoidal fracture.

17. Specimen H is
    a. hornblende.
    b. magnetite.
    c. muscovite.
    d. halite.
    e. biotite.

18. Examine the cleavage of specimen I. As you have probably have noticed, specimen I has cleavage going in two directions that are not at right angles to each other. Specimen I is
    a. hornblende.
    b. magnetite.
    c. fluorite.
    d. halite.
    e. biotite.

19. Specimen J has
    a. basal cleavage.
    b. cubic cleavage.
    c. rhombohedral cleavage.
    d. octahedral cleavage.
    e. conchoidal fracture.

20. Specimen J is
    a. hornblende.
    b. magnetite.
    c. biotite.
    d. muscovite.
    e. pyrite.

21. Explain how to determine the hardness of a mineral?

Questions 22 through 29 are based on the online video, *Mineral Classification*.

22. What is the name of the National Monument located in New Mexico that contains large deposits of gypsum?
    a. Bandelier National Monument
    b. Capulin Volcano National Monument
    c. El Malpais National Monument
    d. Gila Cliff Dwellings National Monument
    e. White Sands National Monument

23. Halite is an example of a simple crystalline structure. What does sodium lose when it combines with chlorine to form sodium chloride (NaCl)?
    a. neutron
    b. proton
    c. electron
    d. orbital
    e. none of the above

24. When a mineral breaks, it often does so along its plane or planes, which is known as
    a. luster.
    b. streak.
    c. hardness.
    d. cleavage.
    e. color.

25. Most common minerals are made up of the most abundant elements in the earth's crust. What are some of those elements?
    a. osmium, magnesium, and oxygen
    b. calcium, silicon, and strontium
    c. potassium, carbon, and nitrogen
    d. chlorine, sulfur, and zirconium
    e. oxygen, californium, and aluminum

26. What percentage of the mineral group silicates is contained within the earth's crust?

    a. 50%
    b. 60%
    c. 70%
    d. 80%
    e. 90%

27. An example of a mineral composed of isolated tetrahedra is the gemstone peridot. Peridot is a member of the _____ group, the largest group of minerals with isolated tetrahedron structure.

    a. amphibole
    b. mica
    c. olivine
    d. pyroxene
    e. silicates

28. The mineral structures composed of isolated tetrahedral have no planes of weakness, which means minerals such as garnet have no

    a. cleavage.
    b. luster.
    c. streak.
    d. color.
    e. specific gravity.

29. In the pyroxene group (single-chain silicates), each tetrahedron shares two of its oxygen atoms with a neighboring tetrahedral to form a chain. What is the ratio of oxygen to silicon atoms to form a single-chain silicate?

    a. 1 oxygen: 1 silicon
    b. 2 oxygen: 1 silicon
    c. 3 oxygen: 1 silicon
    d. 4 oxygen: 1 silicon
    e. none of the above

IGNEOUS ROCKS AND VOLCANISM

Lesson 6

AT A GLANCE

Purpose

Learning Objectives

Materials Needed

Overview

> **Types of Volcanoes**
>
> **Volcanic Deposits**
>
> **Distribution of Volcanoes**
>
> **Volcanic Temperatures**
>
> **Volcanic Gases**
>
> **Igneous Rock Textures**
>
> **Igneous Rock Composition**
>
> **Crystallization of Magmas**

Lab Exercises

> **Lab Exercise #1:** *Identification of Igneous Rocks*
>
> **Lab Exercise #2:** *Volcanism*

Online Activities

Quiz

Purpose

In this laboratory lesson, you will be identifying different types of igneous rocks by learning the origins of how these different types of igneous rocks formed through volcanic activity. Nearly 80 percent of Earth's surface, both above and below sea level, contains the remnants of igneous rocks that were formed by volcanism.

Learning Objectives

After completing this laboratory lesson, you will be able to

- Understand volcanic processes and the factors that determine the eruptive style.
- Identify different types of volcanoes and global distribution of volcanoes.
- Understand the processes and origins of igneous rocks formation.
- Classify different types of igneous rocks by their composition (i.e., color, mineralogy, and so forth) and interpret textural features of igneous rocks.

Materials Needed

- ❑ 10x-magnifying hand lens (in lab kit)
- ❑ Ten igneous rock specimens (in lab kit)
- ❑ Pencil
- ❑ Eraser
- ❑ Metric ruler (in lab kit)
- ❑ White sheet of paper

Overview

A rock is any natural aggregate of minerals, glass, or organic particles. Some examples of igneous rock types can be found below.

- Granite is a rock composed of several minerals.
- Rock salt is composed of the mineral halite.
- Obsidian is composed of volcanic glass.
- Coal is composed of organic particles, chiefly carbonized plant remains.

Three major rock types have been recognized. They are *igneous*, rocks that formed by the cooling and crystallization of molten material within the earth, at the earth's surface or on the seafloor; *sedimentary*, rocks that formed from sediment derived from preexisting rocks, by precipitation from saturated solutions, or by the accumulation of organic materials; and *metamorphic*, rocks that have been changed from preexisting rocks into new rocks with different textures and mineralogy because of the effects of heat, pressure, and/or chemical reactions.

Igneous processes provide some of the most spectacular geologic activity at the earth's surface. Igneous rocks also form deep within the earth and therefore provide important clues regarding the earth's antiquity, the internal composition of the earth, and the earth's geologic history. Thus, understanding igneous rocks and igneous rock processes is vitally important to understanding the earth itself.

Magma is molten rock beneath the earth's surface created by intense heat generate within the planet. If magma flows onto the earth's surface or onto the seafloor, it is referred to as lava. Igneous rocks are formed underground from the cooling and crystallization of magma or on the earth's surface or seafloor from the cooling and crystallization of lava. Igneous rocks that were created from magma inside the earth are *intrusive* igneous rocks, whereas those created at the earth's surface are *extrusive* igneous rocks.

More than 500 active volcanoes and thousands of extinct volcanoes exist on Earth today. In fact, more than 80 percent of the earth's surface, both above and below sea level, is volcanic in origin. Furthermore, if it were not for the gaseous emissions of volcanoes, there would be no atmosphere nor oceans. Well-known examples of active volcanoes (those that have erupted during historic time) include Mauna Loa and Kilauea on the island of Hawaii, Mount Etna on Sicily, Mount Fujiyama in Japan, and Mount Saint Helens in the state of Washington.

Volcanism has also played an important role in other parts of the solar system, particularly during the formation and early history of the four inner terrestrial planets as well as a large number of moons. Olympus Mons, a huge volcanic structure on the planet Mars about the size of the state of Missouri, is the largest known volcanic mountain in the solar system. Spacecraft images of the surface of Venus have revealed an abundance of volcanic features on that planet, and active volcanism has been observed on the Jovian moon Io and possibly on the Neptune moon Triton.

Types of Volcanoes

Volcanoes form where magma and its associated gases from deep within the earth break through the earth's surface in the form of lava, pyroclastic debris (a volcanic eruption where hot fragments of ejected material are thrown into the atmosphere), or a combination of the two. Over time, these deposits build an array of volcanic topographic features, which are classified primarily by their topographic form.

Shield Volcanoes

A typical shield volcano eruption usually starts out with lava fountains, spurts of basaltic lava flung into the air as gas rapidly escapes. A string of lava fountains sometimes erupts from a fissure, producing a "curtain of fire." Once most of the dissolved gases are released, the eruption is usually characterized by a reduced outpouring of nonviscous or highly fluid basaltic lava. These lava flows may extrude from a central vent and/or fissures that open along the volcano's flanks. The results are very wide and short in the creation of a shield volcano, which inevitably is created by thousands of individual lava flows. The very fluid nature of basaltic lava allows it to flow for great distances as thin sheets, thus preventing it from supporting steep slopes.

The island of Hawaii consists of five huge shield volcanoes, two of which, Kilauea and Mauna Loa, are active much of the time. These Hawaiian volcanoes are the largest volcanoes on the planet. Mauna Loa is nearly 100 kilometers wide at the base and rises nearly 10 kilometers above the surrounding seafloor. Its volume is estimated to be about 50,000 cubic kilometers. By contrast, the largest volcano in the continental United States, Mount Shasta in Northern California, has a volume of 205 cubic kilometers.

Lava Plateaus

Mafic magma, breaking through oceanic crust as a point source of basaltic lava creates Hawaiian-type shield volcanoes on the seafloor. However, when mafic magma breaks through continental crust along faults or fractures as a linear source of basaltic lava (also known as a fissure eruption), lava plateaus are created instead. These volcanic features are related to shield volcanoes in that they are vast areas covered by basalt. The Columbia River Plateau in Washington and Oregon, and the Snake River Plain in Idaho are examples. Lava plateaus are created when basaltic lava pours from long fissures for an extended period of time, ultimately burying the surrounding countryside. The Columbia River Plateau, for example, is more than one mile thick and contains individual flows that cover huge areas, in one case more than 40,000 square kilometers.

Cinder Cones

If the magma reaching the earth's surface is highly charged with dissolved gases, an explosive eruption of pyroclastic debris may result. Most of the pyroclastic debris explosively ejected during a volcanic eruption falls near the magma conduit. If a volcano has a prolonged eruptive history, layer upon layer of pyroclastic debris will accumulate to form a cinder cone, but such cones of pyroclastic debris rarely exceed 400 meters in height.

A central crater, or saucer-shaped depression, is usually maintained during cone construction because of the continual expulsion of pyroclastic debris at the summit. Wizard Island in Crater Lake, Oregon, is an example of a cinder cone, as is the volcano Paricutin, which constructed its cone in the middle of a cornfield in Mexico sometime between February, 1943, and 1952.

Cinder cones erode easily because they are constructed of unconsolidated pyroclastic debris. In contrast, rocks formed by the crystallization of magma within the volcanic conduits are resistant to erosion. They often remain as isolated and steep topographic pillars or volcanic necks after the cinder cones have been eroded away.

Composite Volcanoes

Some volcanoes are characterized by eruptive cycles that start out with the explosive ejection of pyroclastic debris and finish with less violent extrusion of lava flows. If this cycle is repeated often during the eruptive life of a volcano, the alternating pyroclastic layers and lava flows accumulate around the central vent to create a composite volcano (also known as a stratovolcano), which is often symmetrical. These volcanoes typically have concave upward profiles with slopes at their summits reaching as much as 30 degrees and slopes toward their bases decreasing to less than 5 degrees.

Composite volcanoes often erupt violently because the gases in the viscous magma build to very high pressure before the stiff magma finally breaks through the surface. Volcanic ash produced by large explosive eruptions may be carried around the world. The violent eruption of Mount Saint Helens (part of Cascade Mountain Range) in Washington State in 1980, gave geologists an unprecedented opportunity to study the eruptive stages of a typical composite volcano. Major eruptions of composite volcanoes are usually preceded by small bursts of steam or ash as small pockets of gas escape. Subsequently, the lava and overlying material violently explode into pyroclastic fragments of all sizes. The expelled debris is either thrown vertically into the air or cascades down the flanks of the volcano in clouds of red-hot gas and pyroclastic debris.

In some cases, the magma chamber feeding a volcano may be emptied in a single eruption. The unsupported roof at the summit might then collapse into the evacuated chamber, leaving a large, steep-walled depression called a caldera on the summit surface. Crater Lake in Oregon is really a caldera that formed when Mount Mazama, an ancient composite volcano, blew its top about 6,600 years ago. Calderas may form at the summit of any volcano, but they form most often in composite volcanoes. A volcanic crater technically becomes a caldera when its diameter exceeds one kilometer.

Composite volcanoes are the typical large textbook volcanoes of the continents and the island arcs. Familiar examples include Mount Fujiyama in Japan, Mount Vesuvius in Italy, and many of the volcanic peaks in the Cascade Range such as Mount Saint Helens (Washington State in the Pacific Northwest) and Mount Shasta (Northern California).

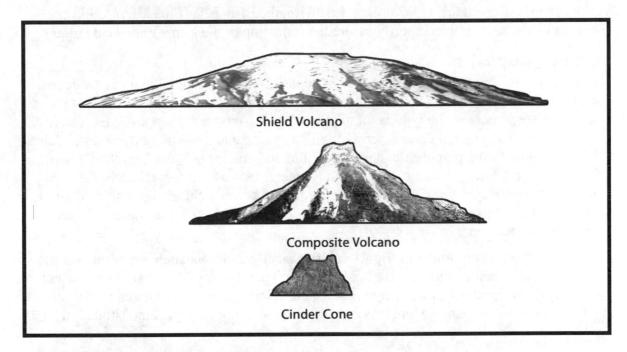

Figure 6.1 Types of Volcanoes. The three examples are not drawn to scale, but they illustrate the visual geologic structural differences between each of the three types of volcanoes. Illustration by Bob Dixon

Lava Domes

If the magma reaching the earth's surface is highly viscous or pasty, it may form a relatively small but steep-sided and bulbous extrusion known as a lava dome. These are generally composed of felsic lavas, although some are intermediate in composition. They commonly form in the craters or on the flanks of large composite volcanoes and expand from within. As molten lava works its way into the dome, it causes the dome to expand, releasing cooled and solidified fragments from its outer shell. A rhyolite lava dome occupies the crater floor of Mount Saint Helens. A lava dome that formed in the Santa Maria volcano in Guatemala in 1922 took two years to grow to 500 meters in height and 1,200 meters wide.

Pyroclastic Sheets

Felsic volcanic rocks a few meters to hundreds of meters thick cover vast areas on the earth's surface. Based on observations of historic pyroclastic flows involving lateral expulsions of hot gases and hot felsic ash, these ancient deposits probably originated as rhyolitic ash flows, not as rhyolitic lava flows or rhyolitic ash falls. They cover far greater areas than any observed during historic time, however, and apparently erupted from long fissures rather than from a central vent. In fact, the pyroclastic material within many of these flows was so hot when it settled to the ground that the ash particles fused to form a highly consolidated ash deposit known as welded tuff.

Geologists believe that major pyroclastic flows initiate from fissures created during the formation of calderas over felsic magma chambers. For example, it appears that the Yellowstone Tuff erupted during the formation of a large caldera in what is now Yellowstone National Park in Wyoming. Likewise, the Bishop Tuff in eastern California appears to have been erupted shortly before the formation of the Long Valley caldera.

Volcanic Deposits

Volcanic activity creates two main classes of deposits—lava flows and pyroclastic debris. Lava flows are the most abundant deposits produced by mafic volcanoes and, in fact, account for 99 percent of the volume of the Hawaiian Islands above sea level. Explosive volcanism creates tephra, a general term for airborne volcanic material or pyroclastic debris. Geologists classify the pyroclastic debris according to particle size: ash (less than 2 mm), lapilli (2 mm to 64 mm), blocks (ejected solids greater than 64 mm), and bombs (ejected molten material greater than 64 mm). When a volcanic bomb is flung high into cold air, it often spins and falls back to Earth as a solidified football shape, whereas the blocks are usually equidimensional in shape.

Explosive volcanic eruptions can trigger mudflows and debris avalanches as well. Mudflows generally result when a volcanic eruption is accompanied by a rapid meltdown of ice and snow. Debris avalanches spawned by volcanism or related seismic activity can result in a great deal of property damage and loss of life, as Mount Saint Helens demonstrated in 1980.

Distribution of Volcanoes

Active volcanoes are widely distributed over the earth's surface, but their specific locations are controlled by geological conditions that exist within the earth's crust and mantle. Composite volcanoes are concentrated along the certain types of convergent plate boundaries margins of, whereas shield volcanoes are at intraplate positions over hot spots, or mantle plumes, which create zones of intense heat, that remain fixed in space for millions of years. When tectonic plates converge—as is the case along the Ring of Fire or the circum-Pacific belt, which nearly encircles the margins of the Pacific Ocean—intense volcanic and earthquake activity results. In fact, 60 percent of all active volcanoes are located along the circum-Pacific belt. Mount Saint Helens is one of the many composite volcanoes on the North American segment of this belt.

About 20 percent of all active volcanoes are in the Mediterranean belt, including famous Italian volcanoes such as Mount Etna, Stromboli, and Mount Vesuvius. Most of the volcanoes in this belt are composite volcanoes. The remaining active volcanoes, for the most part, are at or near the mid-oceanic ridges.

Volcanic Temperatures

No direct measurements of magma temperatures below the earth's surface have been made. Extruded basaltic lavas, on the other hand, usually have temperatures that range between 1,000°C and 1,200°C, whereas temperatures of 1,350°C have been recorded above lava lakes in Hawaii where volcanic gases react with the atmosphere.

Little is known about the temperature of rhyolitic lavas because eruptions of such lavas are rare and generally explosive. The temperatures of some lava domes, as measured remotely by an instrument known as an optical pyrometer, indicate surface temperatures of these domes as high as 900°C, although the surface of a lava dome would be expected to be much cooler than its interior.

Volcanic Gases

Samples of gases from present-day volcanoes indicate that as much as 80 percent of all volcanic gases are water vapor. Volcanoes also commonly emit minor amounts of carbon dioxide, free nitrogen gas, sulfur dioxide, hydrogen sulfide, and very small amounts of carbon monoxide, free hydrogen gas, and free chlorine gas. Although the amount of gases dissolved in magmas is variable, it is rarely more than a few percent by weight. However, it is not possible to determine how much of these gases are of magmatic origin and how much of it results from reactions between the ascending magma and the intruded bedrock and associated groundwater.

Igneous Rock Textures

The size of the mineral grains in an igneous rock generally indicates the rate at which the magma or lava cooled and crystallized. For example, mineral grains that form in a slowly cooling magma within the earth's crust (intrusive igneous rocks) become large since they have a long time to grow. Mineral grains that form in a rapidly cooling lava on the earth's surface (extrusive igneous rocks) will be much smaller since they have little time to grow. However, if lava is suddenly cooled, or quenched, then there is no time for mineral grains to grow, and an amorphous volcanic glass called obsidian forms instead. The following are textures of igneous rocks:

Pegmatitic texture (very coarse-grained)

If certain conditions related to magma viscosity and water content exist, very large mineral grains may result (generally larger than 1 cm). Examples are granite-pegmatite, diorite-pegmatite, and gabbro-pegmatite.

Phaneritic texture (coarse-grained)

An intrusive igneous rock that has macroscopic (large) mineral grains can be seen without magnification, but not coarse enough to be considered pegmatite. The dimensions of the individual mineral grains range from about 1 mm to about 10 mm (1 cm). An example is diorite.

Aphanitic texture (fine-grained)

An extrusive igneous rock composed of mineral grains that are microscopic—they cannot be discerned with the unaided eye. Examples are basalt, rhyolite tuff, and andesite.

Porphyritic texture (mixed texture)

An igneous rock has two sizes of mineral grains. A porphyritic igneous rock forms when magma remains at depth before it is placed either on or near the surface. This two-stage cooling history is revealed by the presence of large mineral grains called phenocrysts embedded in a finer-grained matrix. The matrix may be either phaneritic or aphanitic. An example of the former is granite porphyry; the latter is rhyolite porphyry.

Vesicular texture

Vesicular texture is characterized by the presence of vesicles, or gas bubbles, which become frozen in extrusive igneous rocks as they cool and solidify. There are two major types of vesicular igneous rocks: pumice and scoria. Pumice is a light-colored, frothy glass with so many tiny vesicles and such a low density that it floats on water. Scoria is porous, dark, igneous rock that contains so many vesicles that it resembles a sponge.

Glassy texture

Glassy texture resembles glass. The resulting extrusive igneous rock is obsidian, a natural volcanic glass.

Pyroclastic texture

Pyroclastic texture is fragmented volcanic debris (tephra) that has explosively expelled into the air during violent volcanic eruptions and falls in various shapes and sizes. Such pyroclastic materials include fragments of volcanic ash (particle size less than 2 mm), lapilli or cinders (2 mm to 64 mm), and volcanic bombs and blocks (64 mm and larger). Igneous rocks composed of pyroclasts include tuff (composed of volcanic ash) and volcanic breccia (composed chiefly of cinders, volcanic bombs, and volcanic blocks).

Composition / Texture	Felsic (Light)	Intermediate	Mafic (Dark)	Ultramafic
	Abundant quartz Abundant K-feldspar Minor Na-plagioclase Minor ferromagnesian minerals	Minor quartz Abundant plagioclase Variable ferromagnesian minerals Minor K-feldspar	Abundant ferromagnesian minerals Abundant Ca-plagioclase	Abundant ferromagnesian minerals
Pegmatitic	GRANITE-PEGMATITE	DIORITE-PEGMATITE	GABBRO-PEGMATITE	
Phaneritic	GRANITE (SYENITE[1])	DIORITE	GABBRO	PERIDOTITE
Aphanitic	RHYOLITE TUFF[2]	ANDESITE	BASALT	
Glassy	OBSIDIAN			
Vesicular	PUMICE		SCORIA	
Pyroclastic	VOLCANIC TUFF (fragments less than 2 mm)			
	VOLCANIC BRECCIA (fragments greater than 2 mm)			

1. Name applied to felsic rocks resembling granite but containing no quartz.

2. Name applied to felsic rocks resembling rhyolite but containing no quartz.

Figure 6.2 Igneous Rock Classification Chart

Igneous Rock Composition

Refer to the Igneous Rock Classification Chart depicted in **Figure 6.2** above. The mineralogical content of an igneous rock is controlled by the chemical composition of its parent magma. Although there are varieties of magma compositions, most range between two extremes: felsic and mafic.

Felsic magmas are rich in aluminum, silicon, sodium, and potassium. They crystallize to form generally light-colored igneous rock composed primarily of the light-colored minerals K-feldspar, sodium-plagioclase, and quartz. These often have lesser quantities of biotite, muscovite, and/or hornblende, referred to as accessory minerals because of their low abundance. If felsic magmas cool and crystallize slowly, they form an intrusive phaneritic igneous rock called granite. The extrusive aphanitic equivalent is rhyolite. Two rare felsic igneous rocks are intrusive syenite, which is similar to granite but contains no quartz, and trachyte, which is similar to rhyolite but contains no quartz.

Mafic magmas contain abundant iron, magnesium, and calcium. These magmas also contain silicon and aluminum but in proportionally smaller amounts than felsic magmas. When mafic magmas cool and crystallize, they form dark-colored igneous rocks composed primarily of dark-colored ferromagnesian minerals olivine and/or pyroxene and dark-colored calcium-plagioclase. If mafic magmas cool and crystallize slowly, they form an intrusive phaneritic igneous rock called gabbro. The extrusive aphanitic equivalent is basalt.

Magmas with compositions between those of the felsic and mafic varieties are intermediate magmas. These magmas cool and crystallize to form igneous rock containing abundant plagioclase along with hornblende and/or biotite. Quartz, K-feldspar, and/or pyroxene are common accessory minerals. If intermediate magmas cool and crystallize slowly, they form an intrusive phaneritic igneous rock called diorite. The extrusive aphanitic equivalent is andesite.

A less common type of magma contains an unusually large amount of ferromagnesian elements and crystallizes to form ultramafic igneous rocks. They usually have phaneritic textures and therefore are mostly intrusive. Because of their extremely high temperatures of crystallization, extrusive aphanitic ultramafic igneous rocks are rare, since most ultramafic magmas solidify before reaching the earth's surface. The most common type of ultramafic igneous rock is peridotite, which is composed of olivine, pyroxene, and/or calcium-plagioclase.

Crystallization of Magmas

A liquid magma cools and solidifies to igneous rock through the crystallization and growth of minerals. Crystallization begins when magma cools, but not all minerals begin to crystallize simultaneously. The order in which mineral species begin to crystallize within silicate magmas has been determined by detailed textural studies of igneous rocks and laboratory experiments, which simulate cooling magma. The sequence of crystallization (*Bowen's Reaction Series*) is depicted in **Figure 6.3,** and provides insight into the formation of the various types of igneous rocks. An examination of **Figure 6.3** indicates that the first minerals to crystallize tend to be low in silica.

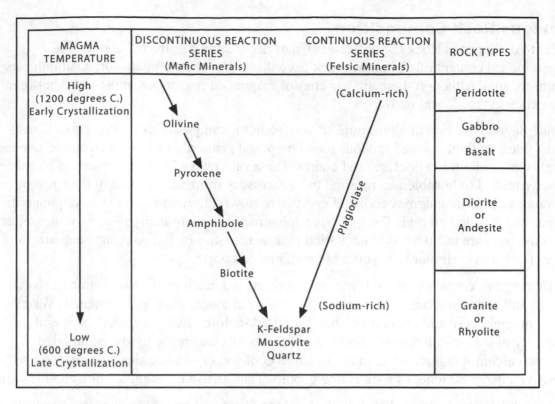

Figure 6.3 Bowen's Reaction Series. Illustration by Mark Worden

The right side, or plagioclase side, of the diagram, is the continuous reaction series. In this reaction, the first mineral to crystallize, calcium-rich-plagioclase, continues to react with the remaining melt as the magma cools. The result is the progressive substitution of sodium for calcium in the plagioclase without a change in the crystal structure. As cooling continues, the composition of the plagioclase becomes progressively enriched in sodium and silica.

The discontinuous reaction series on the left side of the diagram involves the common ferromagnesian minerals found in igneous rocks. In this series, the first mineral to crystallize is olivine. As magma continues to cool, the olivine crystals react with the remaining cooling magma and convert to pyroxene. During further cooling, the pyroxene reacts with the remaining melt and converts to hornblende. Finally, the hornblende reacts with the remaining melt and converts to biotite.

The discontinuous and continuous reactions terminate with the formation of biotite and sodium-plagioclase. However, cooling of a mafic magma is rarely slow enough to allow completion of all discontinuous and continuous reactions. During the final stage of magma cooling, small amounts of K-feldspar, muscovite, and quartz may crystallize independently. Therefore, if the original magma is low in silica and high in iron and magnesium, the melt may solidify before the complete series of reactions has occurred, resulting in a mafic igneous rock such as gabbro. Conversely, if the original magma is high in silica and low in iron and magnesium, the melt may reach the final stages of the reaction series, resulting in a felsic igneous rock such as granite.

On the other hand, changes in the composition of the original melt may also take place through fractional crystallization, in which early formed mineral crystals separate from the melt by gravity settling or filtration; by assimilation, in which the ascending magma incorporates and melts chunks of the surrounding rock; or by mixing of two magmas of different composition.

Just as *Bowen's Reaction Series* can be used to predict the order of crystallization, it can also be used to predict the melting order for mineral grains in a rock that is heating. Minerals that crystallize at low temperatures, such as K-feldspar, muscovite, and quartz, will also melt at low temperatures. Minerals that crystallize at high temperatures, such as olivine and calcium-plagioclase, will also melt at high temperatures. Selective melting, also known as partial melting, is another process by which magmas of more than one composition can evolve. Therefore, as rocks undergo partial melting, the early formed (low-temperature) magmas may ascend or otherwise separate from the solid portion of the rock to produce felsic magma. As the temperature increases, however, the remaining portions of the rocks may melt to produce higher temperature magma of intermediate or even mafic composition.

Lab Exercises

Lab Exercise #1: *Identification of Igneous Rocks*

The identification and classification of igneous rocks is based on texture and mineralogical composition. Color is also useful because it is a reflection of the mineralogical composition.

Instructions and Observations

Step 1: Retrieve the bag labeled **Lab #6** Igneous Rock Samples from your lab kit and place the specimens on a white sheet of paper. To identify the ten igneous rocks (specimens #1 through #10), the best approach is to separate the rock specimens into felsic, intermediate, and mafic categories.

Step 2: Separate each of the igneous rocks from their compositional category into the textural categories described in this lesson. Also note any diagnostic properties such as phenocrysts or vesicles. For the phaneritic (coarse-grained) igneous rock-specimens, identify as best as you can the minerals present in each specimen, using the 10-power magnifying hand lens from your lab kit.

Using **Figure 6.2**, identify and name each igneous rock specimen in your collection by filling in the Igneous Rock Lab Chart with the igneous rock samples. Use the word bank below of igneous rock samples to write the rock names in the Igneous Rock Lab Chart. Submit your work as directed by your instructor.

Igneous Rock Word Bank:

Red Granite	Rhyolite	Basalt	Gabbro
Gray Granite	Obsidian	Diorite	
Rhyolite Tuff	Pumice	Andesite	

Igneous Rock Lab Chart

Composition and Texture	*Light-Colored (Felsic)* Colors—white, tan, gray, pink, red Minerals—abundant quartz, abundant K-feldspar, minor Na-plagioclase, minor ferromagnesian	*Medium-Colored (Intermediate)* Colors—gray, green Minerals—minor quartz, abundant plagioclase, variable ferromagnesian minerals, minor K-feldspar	*Dark-Colored (Mafic)* Colors—dark green, dark gray, black Minerals—abundant ferromagnesian minerals, abundant Ca-plagioclase
Pegmatitic (very large coarse mineral grained)			
Phaneritic (coarse grained–individual mineral grains range 1 mm to about 10 mm)			
Aphanitic (fine grained)			
Glassy (cooled quickly at surface–resembles glass)			
Vesicular (frothy, bubbly porous–resembles a sponge), cooled very quickly and released gases			

Lab Exercise #2: *Volcanism*

In this lab exercise, you will go to the United States Geological Survey (USGS) website, "Volcano Hazards Program," where you will investigate how to look up current volcanic activity.

Instructions and Observations

Step 1:   Open an Internet browser and type in the web address http://volcanoes.usgs.gov/

Step 2:   Look on the USGS Volcano Hazards Program webpage and locate the latest U.S. Volcano alert.

Step 3:   Look at the headings across the top of the webpage and click on the "Activity" link. You will be taken to the Volcano Status Map of the Pacific Rim.

Step 4:   What do the various colored triangle-shaped icons mean?

Step 5:   Find a volcano along the Pacific Rim that has a Ground-based Volcano Alert Level on it (you may need to zoom in or out). Click on the triangle to see a pop-up screen of information pertaining to the activity of the volcano.

    a.   What is the volcano alert level of the volcano you chose within the Pacific Rim?

    b.   What is the aviation color code for the volcano you chose?

Step 6:   Look at the Menu bar of the left-hand side of the screen underneath the word "Activity." Click on the *About Alerts* link to find out additional information about USGS Volcanic Activity Alert Notification System.

Step 7:   Look at the Menu bar again on the left-hand side of the screen underneath the word "Activity" and click on *Alert Creation*. Using your own words, summarize the three-step process for alerting the public regarding a volcanic activity?

Online Activities

As per your instructor's direction, go to the online lesson for this lab and complete the activities assigned.

Quiz

1. Which of the following are the largest volcanoes in the world?

    a. the volcanoes in the Cascade Mountains

    b. the Hawaiian volcanoes

    c. the volcanoes in the Aleutian Islands

    d. the volcanoes in the Andes Mountains

    e. the Italian volcanoes

2. When mafic magma breaks through continental crust along extensive faults or fracture systems, which of the following often results?

    a. shield volcanoes

    b. lava plateaus

    c. composite volcanoes

    d. lava domes

    e. pyroclastic sheets

3. Wizard Island in Crater Lake, Oregon, is an example of a

    a. cinder cone.

    b. volcanic neck.

    c. lava dome.

    d. composite volcano.

    e. spreading-ridge pillow basalt.

4. The volcanism associated with what is now Yellowstone National Park could best be described as a

    a. shield volcano.

    b. lava plateau.

    c. pyroclastic sheet.

    d. spreading-ridge pillow basalt.

    e. rift-valley basalt flow.

5. Volcanic activity creates two main classes of deposits. What are those deposits called?

6. Geologists classify the pyroclastic debris according to four different particle sizes. List the four classifications and their sizes.

7. Why is there so much volcanic activity around the Pacific Rim?

8. What percentage of water vapor is emitted into the atmosphere by volcanic eruption?
   a. 50%
   b. 60%
   c. 70%
   d. 80%
   e. 90%

9. Why are geologists unable to determine the amount of minor gases that are emitted by volcanoes when they erupt?

10. If oceanic crust is rich in ferromagnesian minerals, what type of rock would you expect to be on the ocean floor?

11. Continental crust is primarily granitic rock. What will be its mineral composition?

12. According to Bowen's Reaction Series, minerals do not crystallize from magma in random order, but instead crystallize based on temperature. Mafic minerals that form early at high temperatures are rich in iron and magnesium, while late forming, low temperature, felsic minerals contain sodium-rich minerals and are light in color. According to Bowen's Reaction Series (**Figure 6.3**) and using your igneous rock grid, is basalt an early forming or late forming rock?

13. Specimen #2 has a
    a. pegmatitic texture.
    b. phaneritic texture.
    c. aphanitic texture.
    d. porphyritic texture.
    e. glassy texture.

14. Specimen #2 crystallized from
    a. a felsic magma.
    b. an intermediate magma.
    c. a mafic magma.
    d. an ultramafic magma.
    e. none of the above

15. Specimen #2 is
    a. gabbro.
    b. diorite.
    c. syenite.
    d. gray granite.
    e. red granite.

16. Specimen #5 is
    a. rhyolite.
    b. andesite.
    c. basalt.
    d. pumice.
    e. obsidian.

17. Specimen #6 is
    a. rhyolite.
    b. andesite.
    c. basalt.
    d. pumice.
    e. obsidian.

18. Specimen #7 has
    a. a pegmatitic texture.
    b. a phaneritic texture.
    c. an aphanitic texture.
    d. a porphyritic texture.
    e. a glassy texture.

19. Specimen #7 crystallized from
    a. a felsic magma.
    b. an intermediate magma.
    c. a mafic magma.
    d. an ultramafic magma.
    e. none of the above.

20. Specimen #7 is
    a. gabbro.
    b. diorite.
    c. syenite.
    d. gray granite.
    e. red granite.

21. Specimen #8 is
    a. an ultramafic igneous rock.
    b. a mafic igneous rock.
    c. an intermediate igneous rock.
    d. a felsic igneous rock.
    e. none of the above.

22. Specimen #8 is
    a. rhyolite.
    b. andesite.
    c. basalt.
    d. pumice.
    c. obsidian.

23. Specimen #9 crystallized from
    a. a felsic magma.
    b. an intermediate magma.
    c. a mafic magma.
    d. an ultramafic map.
    e. none of the above

24. Specimen #9 is
    a. gabbro.
    b. diorite.
    c. syenite.
    d. gray granite.
    e. red granite.

25. Specimen #10 is
    a. rhyolite.
    b. andesite.
    c. basalt.
    d. pumice.
    e. obsidian.

26. Specimen #1 is
    a. rhyolite tuff.
    b. basalt.
    c. pumice.
    d. red granite.
    e. obsidian.

27. Specimen #3 is
    a. rhyolite tuff.
    b. basalt.
    c. andesite.
    d. red granite.
    e. obsidian.

28. Specimen #4 is
    a. gabbro.
    b. basalt.
    c. pumice.
    d. rhyolite.
    e. obsidian.

Questions 29 through 31 are based on **Lab Exercise #2:** *Volcanism*

29. Record your answer from *Lab Exercise #2, step 4.*

30. Record your answer from *Lab Exercise #2, step 5 a & b.*

31. Record your answer from *Lab Exercise #2, step 7.*

SEDIMENTARY ROCKS

Lesson 7

AT A GLANCE

Purpose

Learning Objectives

Materials Needed

Overview

> **Sediment**
>
> **Sedimentary Structures**
>
> **Environments of Deposition**
>
> **Origin of Sedimentary Rocks**
>
> **Ancient Environments of Deposition of Sediments**

Lab Exercises

> **Lab Exercise #1:** *Grain Analysis*
>
> **Lab Exercise #2:** *Identification of Sedimentary Rocks*

Online Activities

Quiz

Purpose

The activities in this lesson will lay the foundation for the understanding the process of formation and use of sedimentary rocks. Sedimentary rocks cover more than half of the land surface area of Earth and understanding the characteristics of sedimentary rocks is extremely important for many reasons economically and environmentally.

Learning Objectives

After completing this laboratory exercise you will be able to:
- Describe how to identify textural features of sediment.
- Explain the process of sedimentary rock formation.
- Explain how to classify sedimentary rocks.
- Express how the deposition of sediments created ancient environments.

Materials Needed

- ❏ 10-power magnifying hand lens (in lab kit)
- ❏ Seven sedimentary rock specimens (in lab kit)
- ❏ Five bags of sedimentary grains labeled Bag A, Bag B, Bag C, Bag D, and Bag E (in lab kit)
- ❏ Common household lemon juice or lime juice
- ❏ White sheet of paper

Overview

Sedimentary rocks form at or near the surface of Earth; therefore, the sedimentary rock provides us with a record of the history of Earth's surface. The location of ancient beaches, rivers, deserts, glaciers, and oceans can be determined by analyzing sedimentary rocks. In addition, the vast majority of all fossils are found in sedimentary rocks, and much of our understanding of the history of life is based upon the diversity and changes in the fossil record. If it were not for sedimentary rocks, there would be no *fossils* and no *fossil fuels*. Without fossils, there would be no clue as to the abundance, diversity, and evolution of the life forms that preceded us. Fossils also provide information regarding the environments in which they lived. Without fossil fuels, there would be no coal, no oil, and no natural gas to power our society. Sedimentary rocks provide most of our iron and aluminum and much of our construction materials, such as Portland cement and gypsum wallboard. Without sedimentary rocks, modern society would have a very different look than it does today.

Sediment

Sediment is any loose or fragmental debris, such as sand, mud, leaf litter, broken sea shells, and so forth. All sediment has a source, or place of origin, where it was formed by the mechanical disintegration of rocks, by the chemical decomposition of rocks, or by the life cycles of plants and animals. After sediment is created at the source, it is generally eroded and transported by water, ice, or wind to another location.

The transportation process often separates sediment particles according to their densities and grain sizes—a process known as sorting. A well-sorted sediment is composed of grains that are similar sizes and/or densities, whereas a poorly sorted sediment is composed of grains that vary widely in size and/or density

Since well-sorted sediments have generally been transported over long distances and have been subjected to considerable abrasion, they are usually composed of well-rounded grains. A good example is beach sand. Conversely, since poorly sorted sediments have generally been transported over short distances and have been subjected to relatively little abrasion, they are usually composed of angular grains. A good example is mudflow debris.

Sediment-particle size or grain size, is expressed in terms of the Wentworth grain size scale:

Gravel (very coarse-grained): grains larger than 2 mm in diameter (granules, pebbles, cobbles, boulders)

Sand (coarse-grained): grains from 1/16 mm to 2 mm in diameter

Silt (fine-grained): grains from 1/256 mm to 1/16 mm in diameter

Clay (fine-grained): grains less than 1/256 mm in diameter

Sedimentary Rocks: Textural Features

Figure 7.1 Sedimentary Rocks: Textural Features. Illustration by Marie Hulett

Sedimentary Structures

Sediments are frequently deposited in layers called beds, which, in turn, are separated by bedding planes or layered surfaces. Beds are parallel, nearly planar units of sediment that mark successive depositional episodes. They are characterized by changes in grain size or composition at the time of sedimentation. Bedding in layers thinner than 1 cm is known as lamination.

Figure 7.2 Sedimentary Beds. From *Planet Earth* by John J. Renton. Copyright © 2002 by John J. Renton. Reprinted by permission of Kendall Hunt Publishing Company

Graded bedding can develop if the grain size varies within a bed. In a graded bed, the sediment fines upward—the grain size decreases from coarse at the bottom to fine at the top. This is generally the result of the larger grains reaching the bottom of the bed first because of their greater settling velocities.

Cross-bedding is another example of sedimentary structures. This results when loose sediment is transported by water currents or by the wind along the floor of the depositional environment (any environment in which sediments accumulate). Sedimentary particles transported in one direction create asymmetrical ripples or dunes (i.e., faces of the slope are steep down current and they are gentle slopes facing up current), whereas sedimentary particles sloshed back and forth by waves create symmetrical ripples (i.e., oscillation ripple marks will form in any body of water where gentle waves are touching the bottom). All of these sedimentary features form on the bedding surface but have internal structures composed of laminae that dip at angles to the bedding surface, hence the name "cross-bedding."

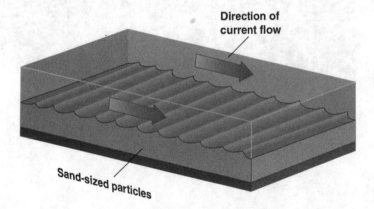

Figure 7.3 Cross-bedding with Asymmetrical Ripple Marks. From *Planet Earth* by John J. Renton. Copyright © 2002 by John J. Renton. Reprinted by permission of Kendall Hunt Publishing Company

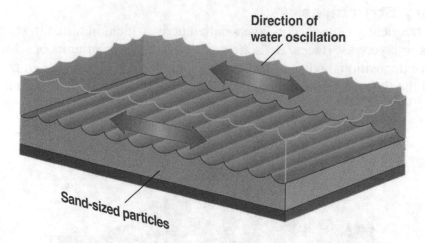

Direction of water oscillation

Sand-sized particles

Figure 7.4 Cross-bedding with Oscillation (Symmetrical) Ripple Marks.
From *Planet Earth* by John J. Renton. Copyright © 2002 by John J. Renton. Reprinted by permission of Kendall Hunt Publishing Company

Everyone has seen the polygonal, curling plates of semiconsolidated mud in the bottom of a dried mud puddle. If such plates are covered by the influx of additional sediment and preserved, they may appear in the geologic record as mudcracks (**Figure 7.6**). Mudcracks are interpreted as having formed in a warm, dry region adjoining the ocean or an inland lake that was periodically flooded and subjected to evaporation and drying of the sediment surface. Mudcrack environments are located in tidal mudflats or land areas, which are exposed to rain.

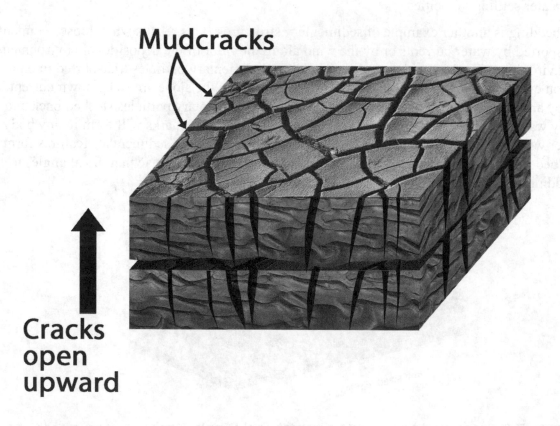

Mudcracks

Cracks open upward

Figure 7.5 Mudcracks. Illustration by Bob Dixon.

Although sedimentary structures are often observed in the field and are useful in identifying depositional environments, they are rarely discernible in small hand specimens of sedimentary rock.

Environments of Deposition

Sediments are deposited in many environments. Some environments are very energetic, involving strong currents and appreciable hydraulic force, such as a river channel. Other environments are not very energetic, involving relatively weak currents and low levels of hydraulic force, such as the bottom of a lake or the deep seafloor. More energetic sedimentary environments generally result in the transportation and deposition of coarse- to very coarse-grained sediments such as sand and gravel. Less energetic sedimentary environments generally result in the transportation and deposition of fine-grained sediments such as silt and clay. Structural features, such as bedding, and textural features, such as grain size, grain sorting, and grain roundness, all produce clues to the environment of deposition.

Below are some of the common depositional environments along with the typical sediments found in these environments and the relative amount of energy characteristic of each environment (**Figure 7.6**).

Environment	Sediment	Relative Energy
Glacial—mountain valleys and polar regions	All sizes, unsorted	High
Eolian (wind-driven)—deserts and coastal dunes	Sand, cross-bedding	High
Fluvial (channel)—stream and river channels	Gravel and sand, some sorting	High
Lacustrine (lake bottom)—freshwater basins	Clay and silt	Low
Evaporite—coastal bays or inland seas in arid climates	Chemical precipitation	Low
Deltaic (river delta)—coastal deposition at river mouths	Clay, silt, and sand; cross-bedding	Low-to-moderate
Beach—long shore drift	Sand; cross-bedding	Moderate-to-high
Organic reef (equatorial)—coastal coral and algal reefs	Limey mud and debris	Low-to-high
Deep seafloor—often oxygen-starved	Organic-rich clay and silt; lamination	Low

Figure 7.6 Common Environments of Deposition

Origin of Sedimentary Rocks

Sedimentary rocks are created when sediments are lithified or consolidated from loose debris into solid rock. The transformation of unconsolidated sediment into solid rock takes place by compaction, the compression of buried sediments and accompanying loss of intergranular pore space; by cementation, the binding together of sediment particles by means of cementing agents, such as silica, calcium carbonate, or iron oxide; and by crystallization, the direct precipitation of sedimentary minerals from oversaturated water solutions. Each of the above lithification processes can occur independently or together, and they can take place as sediments are deposited, shortly after the deposition of the sediments, or long after the sediments have been deposited.

Fine-grained sedimentary rocks such as shale and siltstone are created when weight compacts water-saturated mud until much of the intergranular water is driven out, causing the clay and silt particles to tenaciously bond to each other. Grains of quartz sand, on the other hand, can be cemented together by quartz overgrowths or by other cementing agents, such as calcium carbonate or iron oxide. These agents are precipitated by groundwater passing through the intergranular pore spaces, resulting in well-cemented sandstone. Cementing agents can be identified fairly easily. If sandstone has been stained red, the cementing agent is iron oxide. If the cementing agent reacts with acid by fizzing (effervescing), then the sand grains are bonded together with calcium carbonate. If there is no acid reaction, then the cementing agent is silica. The crystallization or direct precipitation of mineral matter from oversaturated water solutions in a salt lake or a highly saline body of marine water can result in the creation of evaporites, such as rock salt or rock gypsum (gyprock).

Because of the different origins of sediments, geologists have divided sedimentary rocks into two groups: clastic sedimentary rocks, composed of weathered, eroded, and mechanically transported solid fragments of preexisting rocks; and chemical sedimentary rocks, formed from soluble materials resulting from the chemical decomposition of preexisting rocks. Chemical sedimentary rocks are further divided into two subgroups—those precipitated in a biological or organic manner and those precipitated in a nonbiological or inorganic manner.

Detrital Sedimentary Rocks

Clastic rocks are considered fragmented and terrigenous (meaning earthborn), so detrital (refers to materials eroded, transported, and deposited at a location remote from the point of origin) sedimentary rocks are both clastic and terrigenous which are identified by the size of their grains. A clast is any individual grain or rock fragment that is physically broken from a larger rock material. Clastic sediment, therefore, is composed chiefly of clasts that have been transported to, and deposited at, a resting place. Since some sedimentary rocks are composed mainly of clastic sediment, geologists refer to them as clastic sedimentary rocks. Clastic sedimentary rocks are classified according to their texture (grain size) and mineralogical composition. **Figure 7.7** depicts one commonly used scheme based on both clast size and clast composition.

Chemical and Biological (Organic) Classification of Sedimentary Rocks

Chemical sedimentary rocks generally result from the precipitation of a solid from a solution containing one or more chemical substances. The precipitation of solid material can be either an organic process, as in the case of marine organisms building their shells or skeletons out of calcium carbonate or silica, or an inorganic process, as in the case of the evaporation of seawater and the precipitation of rock salt and gyprock from the residual oversaturated solution.

Organic precipitation involves the extraction of dissolved chemicals from seawater or freshwater and the shells secrete calcium carbonate. For example, some types of microscopic, single-celled plankton such as foraminifera and coccoliths secrete calcium carbonate, whereas other types of microscopic, single-celled plankton such as radiolaria and diatoms secrete silica. When these plankton die, their microscopic hard parts collect on the seafloor or lake bed, often in thick layers, resulting in fine-grained, organic-chemical sedimentary rocks such as chalk (composed of fossil coccoliths) and diatomite (composed of fossil diatoms). An example of a coarse-grained, organic-chemical sedimentary rock is coquina, which is composed of broken and cemented seashell fragments. Fossiliferous limestone (a sedimentary rock consisting of more than 50 percent calcium carbonate, $CaCO_3$, primarily in the form of the mineral calcite) results when fine-grained, organic-chemical sedimentary detritus is mixed with macroscopic (invertebrate) fossil debris, such as the remains of clams and sea snails.

Another common rock formation in the organic-chemical sedimentary rock category is bituminous coal (soft coal). It is composed of compressed and carbonized plant remains that originated in some freshwater swamp or salt marsh. Coal can provide information about the chemistry of an ancient depositional environment. The bituminous coal stage is reached after passing through two intermediate stages: peat and lignite.

Inorganic precipitation, such as that which occurs during the evaporation of water, results in residual evaporite deposits. For example, if a shallow marine embayment were to become isolated and the seawater were to gradually evaporate, the concentration of dissolved substances would progressively increase to the point where the water would become oversaturated with respect to certain dissolved substances, and mineral precipitation would occur. Generally, the first mineral to precipitate in this case is calcite (limestone), then gypsum (gyprock), and finally halite (rock salt). Inorganic precipitation of calcite can result in the creation of coarse-textured crystalline limestone or a fine-textured variety known as micrite, both of which react vigorously when tested with acid. Micrite is believed to have an organic origin, as well.

The rock formation chert, which is composed of microscopic particles of silica and is interlayered with limestone or chalk, may also have either an inorganic or organic origin.

The rock formation dolostone, which is also in the inorganic-chemical sedimentary rock category, is composed of the mineral dolomite rather than calcite. Most dolomite forms as magnesium-rich groundwater reacts with previously deposited $CaCO_3$. No organisms secrete shells of dolomite directly, but they may have altered preexisting calcite-rich rocks.

Figure 7.7 displays a classification of common detrital, biological (organic), and chemical sedimentary rocks arranged according to texture and composition.

Detrital Sedimentary Rocks		
Size	**Composition and Texture**	**Name**
Gravel (larger than 2 mm)	Gravel (larger than 2 mm)	Gravel (larger than 2 mm)
	Angular fragments of any lithology, similar to conglomerate	Breccia
Sand (1/16 mm to 2 mm)	Quartz with some accessory minerals, usually cemented by silica, calcium carbonate, or iron oxide	Sandstone
	Quartz and feldspar mixed, usually cemented by silica, iron oxide, or calcium carbonate	Arkose
Silt (1/256 mm to 1/16 mm)	Mixture of quartz particles and clay minerals, with massive, unlayered structure	Siltstone (massive)
Clay (smaller than 1/256 mm)	Mostly clay minerals, compacted into clumps or blocks	Claystone (massive)
	Mixture of quartz particles and clay minerals; finely laminated into thin layers; smooth to slightly gritty; grains are very hard to detect with unaided eye; fissile (i.e., breaks into sheets); slick when wet	Shale (fissile)

Chemical Sedimentary Rocks		
Texture	**Composition**	**Name**
Coarse-grained, crystalline	Grains of crystalline calcite (calcium carbonate); effervesces freely	Crystalline limestone
Fine-grained	Clay-sized calcite (calcium carbonate); effervesces freely	Micrite
Coarse-grained	Mainly halite (sodium chloride); may contain fine-grained impurities in bands or layers (with K and Mg salts)	Rock salt
Coarse- to fine-grained	Mainly gypsum (hydrated calcium sulfate)	Gyprock
Fine-grained, may be amorphous	Various forms of silica such as jasper, opal, flint, chalcedony; often occurs in layers, lenses, or nodules	Chert
Coarse-grained	Mainly dolomite (calcium magnesium carbonate); usually forms through the alteration of limestone by Mg-rich groundwater solutions; fizzes weakly when powdered	Dolostone

Figure 7.7 Sedimentary Rock Classification

Biological (Organic) Sedimentary Rocks		
Texture	**Composition**	**Name**
Fine- to coarse-grained	Macroscopic invertebrate fossils in a fine-grained calcium-carbonate matrix; effervesces freely	Fossilifereous limestone
Fine-grained	Clay-sized calcium carbonate; effervesces freely	Micrite
Coarse-grained	Abundant macroscopic invertebrate fossils, loosely cemented shell fragments of calcium carbonate; effervesces freely	Coquina
Fine-grained	Abundant microfossils, cemented skeletal fragments composed of calcium carbonate; effervesces freely	Chalk
Fine-grained, may be amorphous	Formed from cementation of microscopic marine skeletons composed of silica; conchoidal fracture; usually gray, brown, black or mixture of colors; hard rock—can scratch glass	Chert
Fine-grained	Loosely cemented microfossil (phytoplankton) skeletons composed of silica	Diatomite
Fine- to coarse-grained	Brown, partially carbonized plant fibers	Peat
	Brown to black carbonized plant remains	Lignite
	Black carbonized plant remains; conchoidal fracture	Bituminous coal

Figure 7.7 Sedimentary Rock Classification (continued)

Ancient Environments of Deposition of Sediments

Layers of sedimentary rock provide a historical record of past environments through the deposition of and relative abundance of minerals, sedimentary features, sedimentary bed patterns, and the remains of plants and animals. Geologists use the present to unlock the mysteries of the past by deciphering the history contained within sedimentary rocks. Fossils within sedimentary rock provide geologists with abundance of information regarding what type of habitats existed within these ancient environments. By studying the habitats of modern plants and animals and comparing them to the ancient organisms, we can use the fossil to interpret the ancient depositional setting of the environment. For instance, in modern marine environments the shape of animal shells determines the level of water agitation. Organisms such as clams that live in agitated aqueous environments usually have round, short, and thicker shell structure as compared to clams that live in quieter aqueous environments. Geologist observing the fossil remains of these shells can determine the appropriate depositional setting to the layer of rock in which these aquatic organisms were found.

Lab Exercises

Lab Exercise #1: *Grain Analysis*

In this laboratory exercise, you will identify some sedimentary rocks. The identification and classification of sedimentary rocks is based on texture and composition.

Use the table below to identify the contents of the bags in your lab kit. Record your results in the space provided or on a separate piece of paper. Make sure to save your results. You will use the data to answer the questions at the end of this lesson.

Instructions

Step 1: Retrieve Bag A, Bag B, Bag C, Bag D, and Bag E from your lab kit. The individual bags contain different types of sedimentary grains.

Step 2: Place a white sheet of paper on a flat surface.

Step 3: Spread out the contents of Bag A on the white sheet of paper.

Step 4: Analyze the sediment sample for the three very distinct textural features: grain size, grain shape, and grain arrangement. Use your hand lens and refer to **Figure 7.1 Sedimentary Rocks: Textural Features**. Record your observations.

Step 5: Repeat the process for Bag B, Bag C, Bag D, and then Bag E. Record your observations in the chart below.

Sediment Grain Sample	Grain Arrangement (well sorted, moderately sorted, or poorly sorted)	Grain Size (Grains visible—larger than sand, grains visible from 1/16 mm to 2 mm diameter, grains barely visible—feels gritty, or grains not visible—feels smooth)	Grain Shapes (well rounded, rounded, or angular)	Identify and write down in the space provided what sample you have identified
Bag A				
Bag B				
Bag C				
Bag D				
Bag E				

Lab Exercise #2: *Identification of Sedimentary Rocks*

In this laboratory exercise, you will identify some sedimentary rocks. The identification and classification of sedimentary rocks is based on texture and composition.

Use the steps below to identify the ten minerals in your lab kit. Record your results in the space provided or on a separate piece of paper. Make sure to save your results. You will use the data to answer the questions at the end of this lesson.

Instructions:

Step 1: Retrieve the bag labeled **Lab #7** Sedimentary Rocks Samples from your lab kit. The bag contains rock specimens #11 through #17.

Step 2: After placing them on a white sheet of paper, separate the rock specimens into detrital (clastic) sedimentary rocks, chemical rocks, and biological (organic) sedimentary rocks. Use the chart below to record the specimen numbers in the correct column.

Detrital (clastic) rocks Specimen #	Chemical rocks Specimen #	Biological (organic) rocks Specimen #

Step 3: Estimate the grain size and shape for each of the sedimentary rock specimens. Use the 10-power magnifying hand lens from your lab kit to determine the major constituents (i.e., quartz grains, rock fragments, and so on). Also note diagnostic features such as shale lamination (fissility), and brightly colored cementing agents, such as iron oxide. Use **Figure 7.7** to identify and name each specimen in this group.

Detrital (clastic) rocks Specimen #	Major constituents and diagnostic features	Rock Name

Step 4: Place a drop of lemon juice or lime juice on each of the specimens in the biological sedimentary rock group. If there is a reaction, look for other diagnostic features such as possible fossil remains. Identify and name each specimen in this group. For the remaining biological rock specimens, determine the diagnostic features of each specimen and determine the rock name (see **Figure 7.7**).

Biological rocks Specimen #	Reaction to lemon/lime juice and diagnostic features	Rock Name

To get you started, a couple of hints are provided for Specimen #11.

A. It is a clastic sedimentary rock

B. The clasts are more than 1/16 mm in diameter but not more than 2 mm in diameter (coarse-grained or coarse-textured)

Online Activities

As per your instructor's direction, go to the online lesson for this lab and complete the activities assigned.

Quiz

Questions 1 through 5 are based on **Lab Exercise #1:** *Grain Analysis*

1. Bag A is _____

2. Bag B is _____

3. Bag C is _____

4. Bag D is _____

5. Bag E is_____

Questions 6 through 20 are based on **Lab Exercise #2:** *Identification of Sedimentary Rocks*

6. The mineral grains (with no cleavage) in Specimen #11 are
    a. biotite mica.
    b. feldspar.
    c. quartz.
    d. calcite.
    e. hornblende.

7. Specimen #11 is
    a. quartz chert.
    b. shale.
    c. limestone (micrite).
    d. conglomerate.
    e. gray sandstone.

8. Specimen #12 has black carbonized plant remains. What is specimen #12?
    a. shale
    b. fossiliferous limestone
    c. bituminous coal
    d. calcite
    e. hornblende

9. The depositional environment for Specimen #13 is
    a. the deep seafloor.
    b. the bottom of a lake.
    c. a lake bottom.
    d. a river channel.
    e. none of the above.

10. The largest grain-size dimension for Specimen #13 is
    a. greater than 2 mm in diameter.
    b. between 1/16 mm and 2 mm in diameter.
    c. between 1/256 m and 1/16 mm in diameter.
    d. less than 1/256 m in diameter.
    e. none of the above.

11. Specimen #13 is
    a. quartz chert.
    b. shale.
    c. limestone (micrite).
    d. conglomerate.
    e. gray sandstone.

12. Specimen #14 contains obvious
    a. reptilian fossils.
    b. mammalian fossils.
    c. invertebrate fossils.
    d. microfossils.
    e. coprolite.

13. Specimen #14 is
    a. gray sandstone.
    b. conglomerate.
    c. fossiliferous limestone.
    d. gyprock.
    e. none of the above.

14. Specimen #15 is
    a. a clastic sedimentary rock.
    b. an (organic) biological sedimentary rock.
    c. an (inorganic) chemical sedimentary rock.
    d. capable of being either b or c.
    e. none of the above.

15. Specimen #15 is
    a. quartz chert.
    b. shale.
    c. limestone (micrite).
    d. conglomerate.
    e. gray sandstone.

16. Which of the following is a diagnostic feature of Specimen #17?
    a. It effervesces when tested with acid.
    b. It is a very coarse-grained sedimentary rock.
    c. It is a fissile sedimentary rock.
    d. It is obviously the product of a high-energy depositional environment.
    e. none of the above

17. Specimen #17 is
    a. conglomerate.
    b. limestone (micrite).
    c. gyprock.
    d. quartz chert.
    e. shale.

18. Specimen #16 is composed of
    a. silica.
    b. calcium carbonate.
    c. calcium magnesium carbonate.
    d. gypsum.
    e. clay and silt.

19. Which of the following is a diagnostic feature of Specimen #16?
    a. It effervesces when tested with acid.
    b. It is a very coarse-grained sedimentary rock.
    c. It is a fine-grained sedimentary rock.
    d. It is formed from cementation of microscopic marine skeletons composed of silica.
    e. It is obviously the product of a high-energy depositional environment.

20. Specimen #16 is
    a. conglomerate.
    b. limestone (micrite).
    c. bituminous coal.
    d. quartz chert.
    e. shale.

Questions 21 through 25 are based on the online video, *The Historical Significance of Sedimentary Rocks*.

21. When rocks weather into particles, most of the rocks don't stay in place. Name three ways that weathered rock particles are carried away.

    a. _____

    b. _____

    c. _____

22. Geologists classify sedimentary rock particles based upon their grain size. List the four types of particles in order from smallest to largest.

    a. _____

    b. _____

    c. _____

    d. _____

23. Name the two processes by which sedimentary rocks are formed and provide a definition for each process.

24. Many of the brightly colored layers of rock in the Grand Canyon are what type of sedimentary rock?
    a. limestone (micrite)
    b. sandstone
    c. bituminous coal
    d. chert
    e. shale

25. The most common chemical sedimentary rocks are largely composed of what type of chemical compound?
    a. calcite (calcium carbonate)
    b. silica
    c. gypsum
    d. kaolinite
    e. quartz

METAMORPHISM AND METAMORPHIC ROCKS

Lesson 8

AT A GLANCE

Purpose

Learning Objectives

Materials Needed

Overview

Lab Exercise

Online Activities

Quiz

Purpose

The activities in this lesson will lay the foundation for understanding how metamorphism plays an important role in the creation of metamorphic rocks as a result of high levels of heat and pressure within the interior of the earth. Furthermore, metamorphic rocks are of great economic importance such as slate, a metamorphic rock, is generally an excellent material to build the foundation of your home, and marble, another example of a metamorphic rock, is used for many kitchen and bathroom tiling and countertops.

Learning Objectives

After completing this laboratory lesson, you will be able to:
- Explain the origin of metamorphic rocks.
- Describe the process of how metamorphic rocks are created.
- Characterize the different textural features of metamorphic rocks.
- Express how the mineralogical composition of metamorphic rocks works.

Materials Needed

- ❑ Common household lemon juice or lime juice
- ❑ 10x-magnifying hand lens (in lab kit)
- ❑ Metamorphic rock specimens (in lab kit)
- ❑ White sheet of paper

Overview

Although it is not uncommon for rocks to be subjected to temperatures and pressures that are high enough to melt them, some rocks undergo changes in texture and mineralogical composition while still in the solid state below their melting points. Metamorphic rocks form in the solid state at varying depths within the earth's crust. Preexisting rocks change physically or chemically under conditions of elevated temperature, elevated pressure, or both. These changes can occur as a result of recrystallization of existing minerals, the growth of new minerals, or both. The resulting metamorphic rock is a product of many variables, including the original composition, temperature and pressure, presence of chemically active fluids, and the presence or absence of deforming stresses. Because of these variables, this group of rocks is generally regarded as the most difficult to understand. The process of metamorphism affects all rocks—igneous, sedimentary, or preexisting metamorphic.

Considerable information, however, can be extracted from metamorphic rocks in spite of their variable and sometimes complex origin. Because minerals that form during metamorphism are sensitive to temperature and pressure, metamorphic rocks often serve as historical thermometers and barometers for Earth's crust. Also, metamorphic rocks form in a wide variety of geologic settings. They form the central cores of Earth's mountain ranges, are often associated with igneous intrusions, and occupy the vast and ancient interiors of the continents. Therefore, metamorphic rocks hold secrets related to the creation and evolution of the continents—a process spanning at least 4 billion years.

Types of Metamorphism

Metamorphism takes place when a rock is subjected to a change in environmental conditions that produces mineral instability, such as changes in temperature and/or pressure. There are two main types of metamorphism: contact and regional.

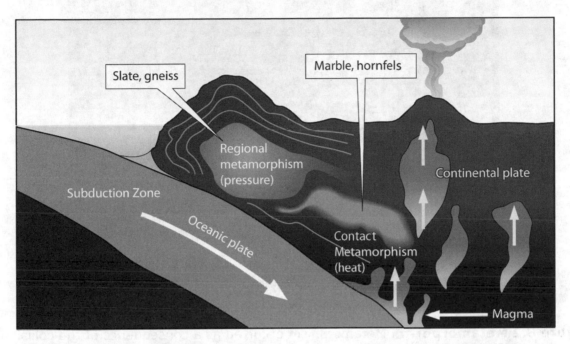

Figure 8.1 Contact and Regional Metamorphism. This geologic cross section demonstrates how contact and regional metamorphisms are created when two plates collide. Illustration by Don Vierstra.

Figure 8.1 shows how contact metamorphism has been produced by heat of magma, which is rising from the partial melting of the descending Nazca Plate (see **Figure 8.2**). Regional metamorphism is the result of folding, thus creating the Andes Mountain range.

Figure 8.2 Metamorphism. Metamorphism occurred as a consequence of the collision of the Nazca and South American plates. Illustration by Marie Hulett.

Contact Metamorphism

The metamorphism associated with small-scale intrusions of magma into the host rock, called the country rock, results in high-temperature contact metamorphism. The magmatic heat from the intrusion produces significant mineralogical changes in the country rock. The metamorphic effects are greatest at or near the contact zone between the invading magma and the country rock. These metamorphic effects progressively diminish away from the zone of contact, creating a contact metamorphic aureole or halo of alteration surrounding the magma chamber. The aureole is characterized by high-temperature minerals close to the contact zone and progressively lower-temperature minerals radiating from the contact zone. Chemical constituents originating within the magma may migrate into the surrounding country rock, bringing about mineralogical changes by a metamorphic process called metasomatism.

The extent of the aureole depends upon the temperature and amount of the invading magma, the mineralogical composition of the country rock, and the presence or absence of fluids. The thickness of the aureole, therefore, may vary from a few millimeters to hundreds of meters. Some rock types, such as limestone, are very reactive and can undergo major changes during contact metamorphism, especially if fluids are actively involved in the transfer of heat and chemical constituents. Such contact metamorphic activity can convert large volumes of limestone into ore-bearing rock called skarn.

Regional Metamorphism

The largest volume of metamorphic rock is produced by large-scale processes associated with regional metamorphism, which is caused by tectonic or mountain-building events. During periods of mountain building, large segments of the earth's crust are deformed as a result of high pressure and high-temperature effects. These deformed areas often occur in belts thousands of kilometers long and hundreds of kilometers wide, as in the case of the Appalachian Mountain belt. Crustal rocks in these deformed belts have been subjected to enormous compressive stress, or directed stress, as well as high geothermal temperatures, to produce major physical and mineralogical changes in the rock. In fact, deeply buried rocks undergoing regional metamorphism often are deformed in such a manner that the rock bends, which can result in metamorphic rocks with distinctive directional properties.

The regional metamorphism effects generally cause a preexisting rock such as shale to metamorphose into slate, whereas sandstone is metamorphosed into quartzite, limestone is metamorphosed into marble, and bituminous coal is metamorphosed into anthracite coal. The metamorphism of shale, a common sedimentary rock, provides a simple way of illustrating metamorphic intensity. The sequence of increasing metamorphic intensity shows the gradual change from shale to slate to phyllite to schist to gneiss. Slate represents low-grade metamorphism, phyllite represents low- to intermediate-grade metamorphism, schist represents intermediate- to high-grade metamorphism, and gneiss represents high-grade metamorphism. As metamorphic intensity increases, there are corresponding mineralogical and textural changes that occur within the rocks.

Tectonics of Metamorphism

Seafloor spreading and plate tectonics play a major role in the creation of metamorphic rocks. Ascending magma beneath divergent spreading zones, such as the Mid-Atlantic Ridge and the East Pacific Rise, can cut through the oceanic crust as tabular intrusions, or dikes, producing contact metamorphic aureoles. Seawater penetrating deep fractures in the newly created but still hot oceanic crust can become a chemically charged fluid that metamorphoses parts of the new seafloor by metasomatism. Oceanic crust and marine sediment may be dragged down, or subducted, at convergent plate boundaries along continental margins, only to be regurgitated within the overriding continental crust as massive intrusions. These, in turn, subject the country rock to repeated and extensive waves of metamorphism. Directed stress, or compression, in these convergent regions results in lateral compaction and crustal thickening on a regional scale, accompanied by regional metamorphic effects.

Metamorphic Reactions

Each mineral is stable or in equilibrium with its environment over a range of temperature and pressure known as the mineral's stability field. However, if a mineral is subjected to temperature/pressure conditions outside of its stability field, the mineral is no longer stable or in equilibrium with its environment and must undergo change or convert to a stable configuration. For example, the quartz, calcite, and clay minerals that are found in common sedimentary rocks are stable or in equilibrium with their environment at or near the earth's surface. But these minerals become unstable when they are subjected to the high-temperature and high-pressure environment associated with metamorphism. Consequently, the previously stable minerals seek to restore the equilibrium that formerly existed by evolving into a form that is stable within the new environment. Generally, this is done by simple recrystallization of existing minerals or the growth of entirely new stable minerals.

The most common mineralogical change is recrystallization, or the slow conversion of small crystals of one mineral into larger crystals of the same mineral. For example, microscopic muscovite crystals in slate can progressively grow or recrystallized while being subjected to progressively greater degrees of metamorphism. They can become larger muscovite crystals in phyllite and even larger crystals in schist.

If the original rock, or precursor, is chemically complex, metamorphism can convert preexisting minerals into new minerals by the recombination of the same chemical elements. For example, shale generally contains a lot of clay minerals, but clay minerals vary widely in chemical composition. Therefore, they provide a large reservoir of silicon, potassium, sodium, iron, magnesium, and calcium that can be recombined into many different minerals. During regional metamorphism, there is little change in the bulk composition of the rock. This often makes it possible to identify the precursor of a given metamorphic rock by its overall chemical composition.

Metasomatism may also change mineralogy through the addition or subtraction of elements by migrating hydrothermal fluids, resulting in the growth of a new crop of unusual minerals. For example, skarn is a metamorphic rock derived from limestone, but because of metasomatic transfers, skarn also contains many unusual silicate, carbonate, and sulfide minerals. Metasomatism takes place only in open systems where chemically charged hydrothermal fluids are free to come and go, and where elements can readily be gained or lost. By contrast, the other metamorphic reactions occur only in closed systems, where essentially no elements are gained or lost.

Metamorphic Grade

Contact and regional metamorphism produce varying degrees of change in the preexisting rocks. As discussed previously, the aureole associated with contact metamorphism is defined by a decrease in the degree of metamorphism as the distance from the magmatic intrusion increases. The same is true of regional metamorphism, since rocks on the outer margins of a deformed mountain belt may be only slightly metamorphosed, whereas the rocks in the core of the deformed mountain belt may be intensely metamorphosed.

The tendency for minerals to achieve equilibrium with their surroundings leaves a record of the intensity of metamorphism, or metamorphic grade. The record consists of stable minerals that represent the levels of temperature and pressure encountered during metamorphism. Low-grade (low temperature/low pressure) metamorphism is characterized by minerals that cannot exist during high-grade (high-temperature/high-pressure) metamorphism and vice versa. Consequently, certain minerals found in metamorphic rocks serve as thermometers and barometers, recording the environmental conditions that prevailed during metamorphism. For example, tracing a layer of shale into a regionally metamorphosed region would mark the boundary between metamorphosed and unmetamorphosed rock where the mineral chlorite made its first appearance. Chlorite, therefore, is an index mineral for low-grade metamorphism. The chlorite zone would eventually give way to the biotite zone at the first appearance of the mineral biotite, even though chlorite might still be present. A line on a map separating the chlorite zone from the biotite zone is called an isograd and represents a line of equal metamorphic intensity. The biotite zone would be sequentially followed by the garnet zone, the staurolite zone, the kyanite zone, and the sillimanite zone (see **Figure 8.3**). The chlorite zone would mark a segment of the shale that was subjected to low-grade metamorphism, whereas the sillimanite zone would mark a segment of the shale that was subjected to high-grade metamorphism.

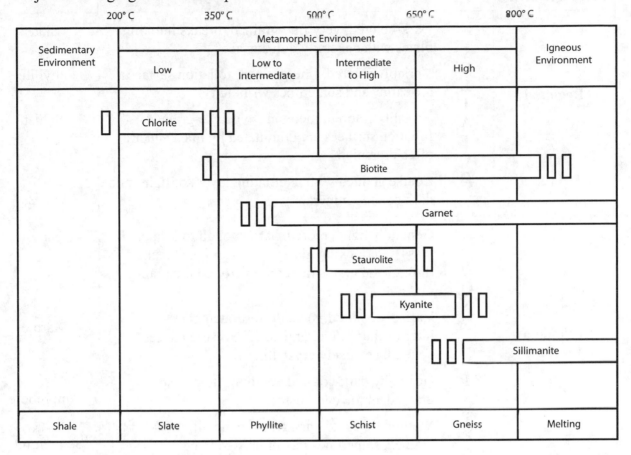

Figure 8.3 Stability of Mineral Species in Different Metamorphic Environments.
Illustration by Mark Worden.

Classification of Metamorphic Rocks

The classification of metamorphic rocks is difficult because of the high degree of compositional variability among the many precursors and the varied environmental conditions in which metamorphic rocks have formed. The presence or absence of foliation, which are directional properties, serves as the primary basis for classification of foliation. Therefore, metamorphic rocks are divided into two groups: foliated and nonfoliated (see **Figure 8.4**).

Foliated Metamorphic Rocks

Foliated metamorphic rocks have distinctive directional properties, usually expressed as a well-defined parallel alignment of constituent minerals, especially platy minerals. They are subdivided into four rock types on the basis of metamorphic grade: slate, phyllite, schist, and gneiss.

Slate is a dark-colored, fine-grained, low-grade metamorphic rock. The mineral constituents consist mostly of microscopic flakes of mica, which generally have recrystallized from the clay minerals of a fine-grained sedimentary-rock precursor such as shale. Because of the abundance and parallel alignment of platy minerals, slate tends to split into thin plates that have a dull appearance.

Type of Metamorphism		Comments	Rock Name
Regional	**F O L I A T E D**	Dark-colored, very fine-grained, breaks into thin plates with generally dull surfaces	Slate
		Variably colored, fine-grained, foliation surfaces are satiny and sometimes wrinkled	Phyllite
		Variably colored, medium- to coarse-grained, foliation surfaces are dominated by mica and are often crumpled	Schist
		Coarse grained with alternating layers of light- and dark colored minerals	Gneiss
Regional or Contact	**N O N F O L I A T E D**	Generally light colored, hard enough to scratch glass, interlocking glassy quartz grains, breaks through the grains rather than around the grains, massive	Quartzite
		Variably colored, too soft to scratch glass, interlocking calcite grains, effervesces (fizzes), generally coarsely crystalline	Marble
		Generally dark-colored, medium- to coarse-grained, mafic composition	Amphibole
		Mottled light and dark green, generally fine-grained, sometimes moderately foliated	Serpentinite
		Shiny black, fine-grained, hard, often breaks along glossy conchoidal fracture surfaces	Anthracite coal
Contact		Dark-colored, fine-grained, massive, dense	Hornfels

Figure 8.4 Classification and Identification of Metamorphic Rocks

Phyllite is a variably colored, fine-grained, low- to intermediate-grade metamorphic rock. Its mineral constituents tend to be slightly larger than those in slates, but most are still difficult to see with the unaided eye. The platy minerals are strongly aligned, resulting in breakage surfaces that have a lustrous or silvery sheen because of light reflection off oriented flakes of mica. Phyllite surfaces may be slightly contorted or wrinkled.

Schist is a variably colored, medium- to coarse-grained, intermediate- to high-grade metamorphic rock. Its individual mineral constituents may be observed with the unaided eye, and its foliation surfaces, which are dominated by mica, are frequently crumpled and contorted. Common mineral constituents include muscovite, biotite, amphibole, quartz, sodium-plagioclase, and K-feldspar.

Gneiss is typically a coarse-grained, high-grade metamorphic rock. Its mineral constituents may be observed with the unaided eye and consist of alternating compositional layers of light and dark minerals, referred to as gneissic banding. Common mineral constituents include amphibole, quartz, K-feldspar, and plagioclase. Gneiss with the mineralogical composition of granite is called granite gneiss.

Nonfoliated Metamorphic Rocks
Nonfoliated metamorphic rocks do not have directional properties. Instead, they are massive and break into pieces that are usually equidimensional rather than tabular because of equidimensional mineral grains. Six rock types are common: quartzite, marble, amphibolite, hornfels, serpentinite, and anthracite coal.

Quartzite is a hard, generally light-colored, metamorphic rock composed of recrystallized quartz grains that have been solidly fused together, primarily by quartz overgrowths. Quartzite, unlike its sandstone precursor, breaks through rather than around the quartz grains when fractured. Quartzite, like quartz, has a hardness of 7 and, therefore, can readily scratch a glass plate. (Recall from Lesson 5 that a glass plate is 5.5 on Mohs scale of hardness.)

Marble is a medium- to coarse-grained, variably-colored, metamorphic rock composed of tightly-interlocking grains of recrystallized calcite. Marble, like its limestone precursor, effervesces when tested with acid. Like calcite, it also has a hardness of 3 and, therefore, cannot scratch a glass plate.

Amphibolite is a medium- to coarse-grained, generally dark-colored, metamorphic rock with a mafic composition. Most are composed largely of amphibole and plagioclase like their mafic igneous-rock precursors.

Hornfels is a dense, fine-grained, dark-colored, metamorphic rock. It results from either the contact metamorphism of a mafic igneous rock precursor or the contact metamorphism of a fine-grained sedimentary rock precursor such as shale or siltstone. Its mineralogical composition varies depending upon that of its precursor.

Serpentinite is a generally fine-grained, mottled dark and light green, metamorphic rock composed chiefly of the mineral serpentine. Its precursor is the ultramafic igneous rock peridotite, and it is sometimes moderately foliated.

Anthracite coal is a hard, fine-grained, shiny-black metamorphic rock, also called hard coal. Like its bituminous-coal precursor, it is composed of carbonized plant remains, but unlike its precursor, it cannot be easily broken apart. Anthracite coal has a homogeneous texture and often breaks along glossy, conchoidal fractures.

A general outline for the classification of metamorphic rocks is depicted in **Figure 8.4**. However, the classifications of metamorphic rocks are based on the presence or absence of foliation. For example, schist is a foliated metamorphic rock because its precursor had a mineralogical composition that allowed the formation of abundant platy minerals. Marble, on the other hand, is a nonfoliated metamorphic rock because its precursor had a mineralogical composition that did not allow the growth of abundant platy minerals. Therefore, both schist and marble may be found side by side in the field and can form under identical environmental conditions.

Lab Exercise

Lab Exercise: *Identification of Metamorphic Rocks*

In this laboratory exercise, you will identify some metamorphic rocks. The identification and classification of metamorphic rocks is based on texture and composition.

Retrieve the bag labeled **Lab #8** Metamorphic Rock Specimens from your lab kit and place the specimens on a white sheet of paper. Use the steps below to identify the eight metamorphic rocks (specimens #18 through #25). Record your results in the space provided or on a separate piece of paper. Make sure to save your results. You will use the data to answer the questions at the end of this lesson.

To get you started, two hints are provided below for identifying specimen #18:

A.   The mineral constituents in this specimen are primarily K-feldspar, quartz, and biotite.

B.   Although it is not readily recognizable in a small hand specimen, this metamorphic rock is characterized by alternating layers of light-colored and dark-colored minerals.

Instructions and Observations

Step 1:   Separate the eight metamorphic rock specimens (found in your lab kit) into foliated and nonfoliated categories.

Foliated Specimen #	Nonfoliated Specimen #

Step 2: Arrange the foliated specimens in sequence from very fine grained to coarse grained. Use the 10-power magnifying hand lens from your lab kit to assist you.

Foliated	Specimen #
Very fine grained	
Coarse grained	

Step 3: Use the information in **Figure 8.4** to identify and name the foliated specimens.

Foliated Specimen #	Rock Name

Step 4: Write the specimen numbers of the nonfoliated specimens in the table below. Use the information in **Figure 8.4** to identify and name the nonfoliated specimens. Use the 10-power magnifying hand lens from your lab kit to assist in the identification of the mineral constituents in the coarse-grained specimens.

Keep in mind the following characteristics:

- Marble is softer than glass and will effervesce when treated with acid.
- Quartzite is rich in silica and, therefore, is harder than glass and will not effervesce when treated with acid.

Nonfoliated Specimen #	Rock Name

Online Activities

Go to the online lesson for this lab and complete the activities as assigned by your instructor.

Quiz

1. What is metamorphism?

2. How is foliation different than sedimentary layering?

3. What properties of slate make it good roofing material?

4. Can metamorphism caused solely by elevated temperature occur without the presence of magma? Why or why not?

5. What is a metamorphic grade? Provide an example of a metamorphic grade.

Questions 6 through 25 are based on the Lab Exercise: *Identification of Metamorphic Rocks.* **Refer to your results from the lab exercise and Figure 8.3 to assist you in answering the questions.**

6. Specimen #18 formed at which of the following temperatures?
   a. temperatures less than 350°C
   b. temperatures from 350°C to 500°C
   c. temperatures from 500°C to 650°C
   d. temperatures greater than 650°C
   e. none of the above

7. Which of the following index minerals might one **NOT** expect to find in specimen #18?
   a. sillimanite
   b. kyanite
   c. garnet
   d. biotite
   e. chlorite

8. Specimen #18 is
   a. gneiss.
   b. mica schist.
   c. phyllite.
   d. slate.
   e. none of the above.

9. Specimen #19 formed at which of the following temperatures?
   a. temperatures less than 350°C
   b. temperatures from 350°C to 500°C
   c. temperatures from 500°C to 650°C
   d. temperatures greater than 650°C
   e. none of the above

10. Specimen #19 is
    a. gneiss.
    b. mica schist.
    c. phyllite.
    d. slate.
    e. none of the above.

11. Specimen #20 formed at which of the following temperatures?
    a. temperatures less than 350°C
    b. temperatures from 350°C to 500°C
    c. temperatures from 500°C to 650°C
    d. temperatures greater than 650°C
    e. none of the above

12. Specimen #20 is
    a. gneiss.
    b. mica schist.
    c. phyllite.
    d. slate.
    c. none of the above.

13. Specimen #21 is
    a. a low-grade metamorphic rock.
    b. a low- to intermediate-grade metamorphic rock.
    c. an intermediate- to high-grade metamorphic rock.
    d. a high-grade metamorphic rock.
    e. none of the above.

14. Which of the following index minerals might one expect to find in specimen #21?
    a. chlorite
    b. garnet
    c. staurolite
    d. kyanite
    e. sillimanite

15. Specimen #21 is
    a. gneiss.
    b. mica schist.
    c. phyllite.
    d. slate.
    e. none of the above.

16. The precursor for specimen #22 might have been
    a. rock salt.
    b. gyprock.
    c. sandstone.
    d. shale.
    e. limestone.

17. Specimen #22 is
    a. marble.
    b. quartzite.
    c. hornfels.
    d. anthracite coal.
    e. none of the above.

18. The precursor for specimen #23 might have been
    a. rock salt.
    b. gyprock.
    c. sandstone.
    d. shale.
    e. limestone.

19. Specimen #23
    a. is harder than glass.
    b. effervesces when treated with acid.
    c. is composed mostly of mica.
    d. has a dull luster.
    e. involves none of the above.

20. Specimen #23 is
    a. marble.
    b. quartzite.
    c. hornfels.
    d. anthracite coal.
    e. none of the above.

21. The precursor for specimen #24 might have been
    a. gabbro, basalt, or shale.
    b. diorite, andesite, or sandstone.
    c. granite, rhyolite, or limestone.
    d. peridotite, pegmatite, or volcanic tuff.
    e. none of the above.

22. Specimen #24
    a. is a product of contact metamorphism.
    b. effervesces when treated with acid.
    c. is composed mostly of mica.
    d. has a coarse-grained texture.
    e. involves none of the above.

23. Specimen #24 is
    a. marble.
    b. quartzite.
    c. hornfels.
    d. anthracite coal.
    e. none of the above.

24. The precursor for specimen #25 might have been
    a. shale.
    b. limestone.
    c. basalt.
    d. volcanic glass.
    e. bituminous coal.

25. Specimen #25 is
    a. marble.
    b. quartzite.
    c. hornfels.
    d. anthracite coal.
    e. none of the above.

GEOLOGIC TIME

Lesson 9

AT A GLANCE

Purpose

Learning Objectives

Materials Needed

Overview

> **Catastrophism**
>
> **Components of Geologic Time**
>
> **Fossil Records**
>
> **Radiometric Dating**

Lab Exercise

> Lab Exercise: *How to Calculate a Half-Life of a Radioactive Isotope*

Online Activities

Quiz

Purpose

The activities in this lesson will lay the foundation for understanding and applying techniques in interpreting the dating of rocks. For example, if you were drilling deep water well into Earth's crust on your property, you would encounter the geologic record of your property, which are layers of sedimentary rock stacked on top of each other like pages in a book. Each layer of rock can tell you a story about how it got there and where it has come from through a geologic record of the area.

Learning Objectives

After completing this laboratory lesson, you will be able to:
- Describe how scientists come to explain the origins of Earth through geologic time.
- Demonstrate techniques for relative and absolute dating of rocks.
- Explain geologic history and how it applies to relative dating and absolute dating.
- Calculate the half-life of a radioactive isotope.

Materials Needed

The activities will be performed using the following materials. Be sure you have all listed materials before starting the activity.
- ❑ Pencil
- ❑ Eraser
- ❑ Calculator

Overview

Questions concerning the age of Earth go back to antiquity. It is interesting to note that some of the oldest known estimates considered Earth to be very old. The Greek philosopher Xenophanes (c. 570–470 B.C.) correctly concluded that areas where fossiliferous rocks were exposed had not only once been covered by the sea, but that significant amounts of time had passed since that land had been part of the sea. In 450 B.C., the Greek historian Herodotus (c. 484–425 B.C.) watched the Nile River delta slowly add sediment with each yearly flood and he realized that it must have required an enormous amount of time to build the entire structure.

The first real attempt at establishing the age of Earth was made in 1644 by John Lightfoot (1602–1675), who was the Vice-Chancellor of Cambridge University. Lightfoot claimed that Earth was created at 9:00 A.M. on October 26 in 3926 B.C In 1658, James Usher (1581–1656), the Archbishop of Armagh, Ireland, claimed a date of October 23 in 4004 B.C. Both of these men, being scholars of theology, determined the age of Earth by using the Old Testament Book of Numbers to calculate how long it would take to form all of the tribes of Israel beginning with Adam and Eve. While many today would scoff at such an approach, one must understand that both men were simply using what they considered to be the most reliable source of information available, which to them was the Bible. Usher's calculated date was entered as a footnote into the Great Edition of the English Bible in 1701 by Bishop Lloyd. For nearly a hundred years afterward, to deny the 4004 B.C. date for the creation of Earth was tantamount to heresy, a charge that few thinkers of the day welcomed.

Catastrophism

Catastrophism was based on the theory that Earth's age was about 6,000 years old. The emergence study of earth science was forced to employ extraordinary means to explain the formation of all of Earth's rocks and landscapes. Mountains were described as having been created by violent, convulsive eruptions that lifted huge masses of rock out of the ocean. Features such as the Grand Canyon would have been explained as the result of a cataclysmic wrenching and tearing of Earth's crust. It would never have been considered that mountains formed slowly over very long periods of time by the convergence of lithospheric plates or that the Grand Canyon was the result of millions of years of slow stream erosion following slow uplift of what is now called the Colorado Plateau. The answer was the theory of catastrophism and taught that the present configuration of Earth's crust is the result of sudden, violent, short-lived, worldwide events. The theory of catastrophism would dominate earth science until the appearance of James Hutton.

James Hutton (1726–1797) is considered the father of modern geology. Although educated in medicine, Hutton never practiced medicine. It was largely his interest in the soil, and the free time he had as a rich landowner, that allowed him to roam the hills of his beloved Scotland where he observed many geologic processes. He saw outcrops of granite, which had decomposed into small grains. He sampled the bed loads of the streams and found these same grains. He then concluded that the streams carried the grains to the ocean where they were deposited. Hutton observed the first steps in the formation of sedimentary rocks from these sedimentary grains.

Hutton also understood the relative ages of rocks when he observed granitic rocks penetrating overlying schist. In addition, based on the relationship between the two rock types, he was convinced that the granite had once been molten and did not precipitate in water as was being taught at the time. One of the most important and famous of his observations was the one he made at Siccar Point (**Figure 9.1**).

Figure 9.1 Siccar Point is a promontory along the east coast of Scotland where vertically oriented sedimentary rocks cut across each other by less steep layers of sedimentary rock. From *Planet Earth* by John J. Renton. Copyright © 2002 by John J. Renton. Reprinted by permission of Kendall Hunt Publishing Company.

It was the exposure at Siccar Point, along the North Sea coast of Scotland, that convinced James Hutton of the great age of Earth. The Devonian Old Red Sandstone resting on the upturned edges of folded Silurian sedimentary rocks indicated that they were deposited at very different times. The exposure is a classic example of what geologists call an angular unconformity. An unconformity is essentially a break in the recorded history of Earth in that the ages of the rocks on opposite sides of the surface of unconformity are significantly different. In the case of the outcrop at Siccar Point, the upper layers of sedimentary rocks are about 345 million years old while the lower layers of sedimentary rocks are about 425 million years old; a difference of 80 million years. An angular unconformity results when a sequence of rocks becomes eroded and uplifted during a mountain building episode.

While exposed as land, weathering and erosion eroded the deformed older rocks down to a relatively flat surface after which the entire rock section was re-submerged below sea level. Over time, land-derived sediments such as those Hutton observed being transported by streams draining the Scottish Highlands were deposited into the ocean on top of the original rock section. The younger sediments ultimately underwent lithification and the entire rock section emerged again from the water. The rocks exposed at Siccar Point formed in exactly this way.

Components of Geologic Time

Geologists base time on relative and absolute dating techniques. Relative age dating is the process of determining when something happened or formed in its order of occurrence within the framework of geologic time. For example, based upon the physical appearance of two individuals, one could conclude with a degree of certainty that the average high school student is younger than the average retiree. Absolute (or chronologic) age dating of these two individuals would entail determining how many years have passed since each was born. The availability of other information, such as the number of months, weeks, days, hours, and minutes that have passed, would allow the absolute age to be determined with increasing precision.

Geologists interpret Earth's history from observing rock outcrops and geologic cross sections by mapping rock layers (i.e., sedimentary, igneous and metamorphic rocks), geologic structures, and evaluating the age of those rock layers and structures. The geologic time scale provides a series of chronological measurements relating rock layers to time (i.e., relative and absolute age dating) and it describes the relationship between time and events that have occurred during the history of Earth.

Principle of Relative Age Determining Relative Age

Geologists apply a variety of physical laws for determining the relative age of rocks based on their physical appearances. You will need to become familiar with the principles of relative age determination, which are listed below.

I. **Principle of Original Horizontality**—Sedimentary layers of rock or lava flows accumulate as horizontal layers like sheets of paper in a book (see **Figure 9.2**).

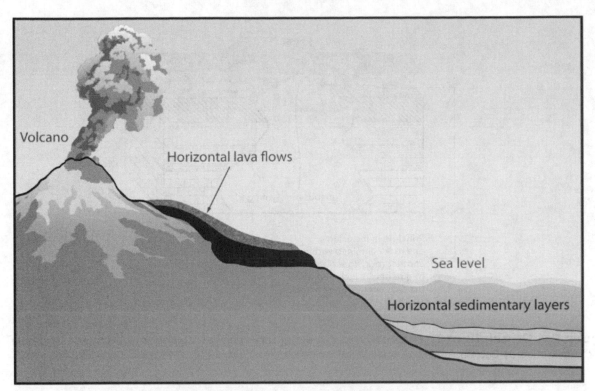

Figure 9.2 Principle of Original Horizontality Sedimentary deposits and lava flows generally settle out in horizontal layers. Illustration by Don Vierstra

II. **Principle of Superposition**—The principle that in a sequence of sedimentary rocks, unless overturned, the oldest beds are at the bottom and the youngest beds are at the top (**Figure 9.3**).

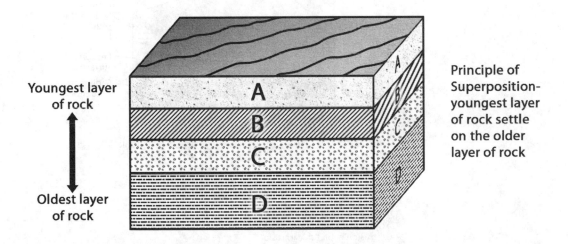

Figure 9.3 Principle of Superposition. Youngest layer of rock settles on the older layer of rock. Illustration by Bob Dixon

III. **Principle of Inclusion**—Any piece of rock that has been included into another rock or sedimentary layer must be older than the rock or sediment into which it was placed (**Figure 9.4**).

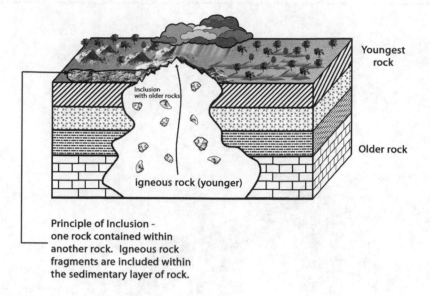

Figure 9.4 Principle of Inclusion. Older sedimentary rock is included in the younger igneous rock. Illustration by Bob Dixon

III. **Principle of Cross-Cutting Relationships**—Geologic features that cut across other geologic features are younger than the bodies they cut through; for example, the magma body is younger than the surrounding rock. Cross-cutting rock features include fractures or cracks in rocks, faults, or masses of magma that cut across an older layer of rock before the magma cooled.

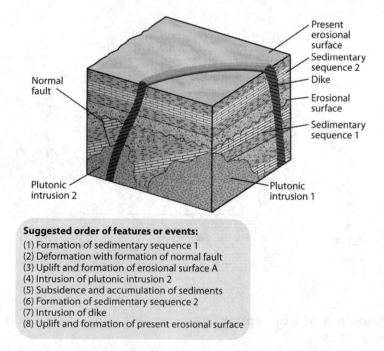

Suggested order of features or events:
(1) Formation of sedimentary sequence 1
(2) Deformation with formation of normal fault
(3) Uplift and formation of erosional surface A
(4) Intrusion of plutonic intrusion 2
(5) Subsidence and accumulation of sediments
(6) Formation of sedimentary sequence 2
(7) Intrusion of dike
(8) Uplift and formation of present erosional surface

Figure 9.5 Principles of Cross-Cutting Relationships. A geologic feature or rock is younger than any geologic feature or rock that it cuts across. Illustration by Don Vierstra

IV. **Law of Unconformities**—An unconformity is a break in the geologic record that has formed where layers of rock were not deposited for a time or else the layers were removed by erosion (i.e., the wearing away of any part of Earth's surface by natural processes). Unconformities appear to be "'lines'" in a cross section that represent periods of erosion or nondeposition. Three kinds of unconformities exist: (1) angular unconformity, (2) disconformity, and (3) nonconformity.

Angular unconformity is where the rocks are tilted and are overlain by flat-lying rock. This forms when new horizontal layers of rock cover up older layers that are folded by mountain building processes and eroded down to the surface (**Figure 9.6a**). Disconformity is where rock strata (layers) or lava flows are parallel with each other (**Figure 9.6b**). The last of the unconformities is nonconformity where younger sedimentary rock is above and metamorphic or igneous rock is found below or adjacent to each other. It forms when sedimentary layers of rock or lava flows are deposited on metamorphic or igneous rock formations (**Figure 9.6c**).

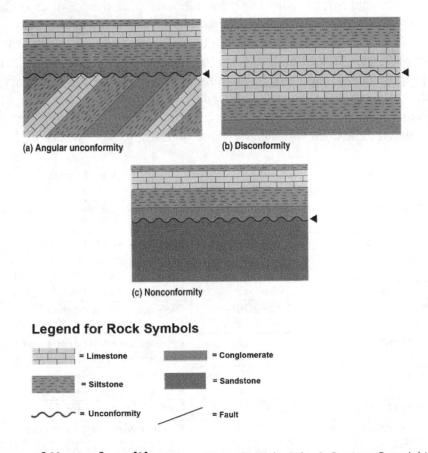

(a) Angular unconformity   (b) Disconformity

(c) Nonconformity

Legend for Rock Symbols

= Limestone   = Conglomerate

= Siltstone   = Sandstone

= Unconformity   = Fault

Figure 9.6 Types of Unconformities. From *Planet Earth* by John J. Renton. Copyright © 2002 by John J. Renton. Reprinted by permission of Kendall Hunt Publishing Company.

Fossil Records

William Smith (1769–1839) was one of the leaders in the development of the geologic subscience of stratigraphy, which matched up separate rock layers in the field. Using this knowledge of the layered rock's order he was able to predict the sequence of rocks that would be found at depth at any site based on the rock layer at the surface and predict what the rock sequence would be at some distant, yet unexcavated site. As his work continued, Smith began to become familiar with the fossil content of the rocks and soon became able to identify a particular rock strata based on the fossil content. A fossil is evidence of past life through the remains or traces of prehistoric life of a plant or animal organism in strata. Although fossils had been collected for centuries, collectors were rarely versed in earth science and never noted the particular strata from which the fossils came. Smith was soon able to demonstrate that although a particular layer might change in lithology (composition) over a long distance, it could still be identified by its characteristic fossil assemblage, the very correlation that James Hutton (the father of modern geology) was never able to do.

Principle of Faunal Succession

Smith never understood the cause of the variations he observed in the fossil content of sedimentary rocks. That explanation would not come for more than a half-century, when, in 1859, Charles Darwin (1809–1882) published *On the Origin of Species*. As our understanding of plant and animal evolution developed in the years that followed, Smith's work eventually was formulated into the Principle of Faunal Succession. The principle states that the fossil assemblage found in sedimentary rocks that accumulated during any particular period of geologic time is unique to that time interval and is fundamentally different from the fossil assemblages found in rocks that accumulated earlier or later. An index fossil is a fossil of an organism that was common and had widespread geographic distribution during a limited time period in Earth's history (refer to **Figure 9.7** for the relative age of index fossils). More than any other single tool at the disposal of a geologist, fossils are used to correlate rocks of similar rock types and to establish the relative age equivalence of isolated exposures of rock anywhere on Earth.

Era	Period	Time (in millions of years)	Key Events
Cenozoic	Quaternary	1.8–present	Glaciations; mammals increased; humans
	Tertiary	65–1.8	Mammals diversified; grasses
Mesozoic	Cretaceous	145–65	Aquatic reptiles diversified; flowering plants; mass extinction
	Jurassic	208–145	Dinosaurs diversified; birds
	Triassic	245–208	Dinosaurs; small mammals; cone-bearing plants
Paleozoic	Permian	290–245	Reptiles diversified; seed plants; mass extinction
	Pensylvanian	323–290	Reptiles; winged insects diversified; coal swamps
	Mississippian	354–323	Primitive amphibians
	Devonian	410–354	Fishes diversified; land vertebrates
	Silurian	440–410	Land plants; land animals (arthropods)
	Ordovician	505–440	Aquatic arthropods; mollusks; vertebrates (jawless fishes)
	Cambrian	544–505	Marine invertebrates diversified; most animal phyla evolved
Precambrian Time	-	4550–544	Anaerobic, then photosynthetic prokaryotes; eukaryotes, then multicellular life

Figure 9.7 Index Fossils Relative Age to Geologic Time Scale

Radiometric Dating

Isotopes

Atoms consist of protons, neutrons, and electrons. An amu, *atomic mass unit*, is the unit of mass equal to that of a proton or neutron. The protons and neutrons of an atom are located at the central nucleus of the atom. The electrons reside in shells outside of the nucleus. The atomic number of an element is equal to the number of protons in the nucleus and determines the identity of the element. The atomic mass of an element is equal to the sum of the number of protons and neutrons in the nucleus and is measured in amus. Isotopes are elements that have the same atomic number but different atomic masses. The atomic number of carbon is 6, $_6C$, meaning that all atoms of carbon have 6 protons in the nucleus. Carbon has three different isotopes, $_6C^{12}$, $_6C^{13}$, and $_6C^{14}$, which have respectively 6, 7, and 8 neutrons in the nucleus. For example, 98.89 percent of all natural carbon atoms are C^{12} with the remaining 1.11 percent being mostly C^{13} and trace amounts of C^{14}. The radioactive isotope C^{14} (carbon-14) is used to date the age of human remains and artifacts.

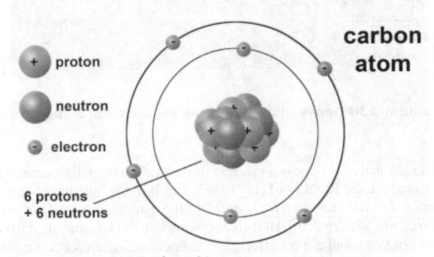

Figure 9.8 Carbon Atom. Illustration by Marie Hulett

Parent-Daughter Isotopes

During the decay series, the original radioactive isotope called the parent isotope or parent atom decomposes. The original parent atom decomposes into smaller radioactive nuclei, called the daughter isotopes or daughter atoms. The decay series continues until the radioactive isotopes decay to an atom whose nucleus is stable (nonradioactive), at which point the decay series comes to an end. During radioactive decay, parts of the unstable nuclei are released as atomic particles along with the emission of gamma radiation. Two types of particles are released: (1) the beta particle, and (2) the alpha particle along with gamma radiation. The entire decay series beginning with the radioactive isotope of uranium, U^{238}, to the stable end product of the decay series, lead^{206}, is illustrated in **Figure 9.9**. As beta particles, alpha particles, and gamma radiation move through the surrounding material, some of the energy is converted to heat—one source of heat within Earth's crust.

Radiometric dating involves dating techniques that use the ratio of parent and daughter isotopes of radioactivity elements to obtain the absolute age of rocks and minerals. The procedure is primarily used to date igneous rocks. The calculation of the age of geologic materials in years is performed by measuring the concentration of short-life radioactive elements such as carbon-14 or by measuring the concentration of long-life radioactive elements such as uranium-238 plus its decay product, lead-206 (see **Figure 9.9**).

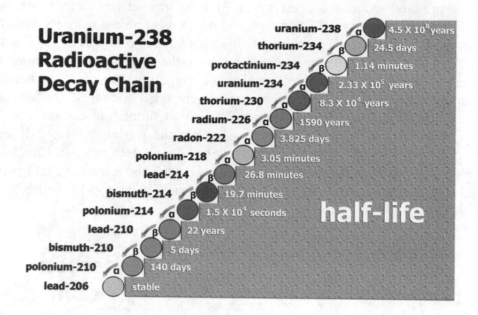

Figure 9.9 Uranium-238 Decay Chain to Stable Product Lead-206. Illustration by Marie Hulett

Half-Life

The half-life of a radioactive isotope is a measure of the rate at which the parent isotope decays to the daughter isotope. Lord Rutherford (1871–1937) defined the half-life of a radioactive isotope as the amount of time required for one-half of the parent atoms to disintegrate into the daughter atoms (refer to **Figure 9.10**). Half-lives of radioactive isotopes range from fractions of seconds to billions of years and are not affected by temperature, chemical composition or any other conditions. Of the many existing radioactive elements, those listed in **Figure 9.11** are the most useful in the radiometric dating of geologic materials.

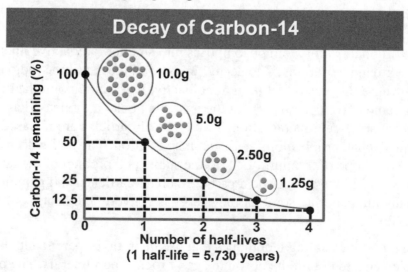

Figure 9.10 Half-Life The half-life of a radioactive isotope is the amount of time required for one half of the parent atoms to disintegrate into the daughter atoms. Illustration by Marie Hulett

Parent Element	Daughter Element	Half-Life in Years
Carbon-14	Nitrogen-14	5,730
Uranium-235	Lead-207	704 million
Potassium-40	Argon-40	1.251 billion
Uranium-238	Lead-206	4.468 billion
Rubidium-87	Strontium-87	48.8 billion

Figure 9.11 Useful Elements for Radiometric Dating

Lab Exercise

Lab Exercise: *How to Calculate a Half-Life of a Radioactive Isotope*

Example 1: Carbon-14 has a half-life of 5,730 years. If the sample contains 80 grams (g) originally, determine how much is left after 17,190 years.

Half-life = 5,730 years
Mass of sample = 80 grams
Total time of decay = 17,190 years

Step 1: Calculate how many half-lives have passed during the decay of the 80 g sample.

This is calculated by the total time of decay divided by the half-life in years for the parent element.

$$\frac{\text{Total time of decay}}{\text{Half-life}} = \frac{17,190 \text{ years}}{5,730 \text{ years}} = \textbf{3 half-lives}$$

Step 2: Next calculate how much of the sample will remain after 3 half-lives.

This is done by first taking the amount of the sample and dividing by two. Then repeat the process for as many times as the number of half-lives computed in Step 1. In this example, 3 half-lives passed during the decay so the amount of the sample will be divided by two, three times.

80 g ÷ 2 = 40 g [after 1 half-life of carbon-14]
40 g ÷ 2 = 20 g [after 2 half-lives of carbon-14]
20 g ÷ 2 = 10 g [after 3 half-lives of carbon-14]

The final mass of an 80 gram sample of carbon-14 after 17,190 years is **10 grams**.

Example 2: If 80 g of carbon-14 decays until only 20 g of carbon is left after 11,460 years, determine the half-life of carbon-14.

Mass of sample = 80 g
Final mass of sample = 20 g
Total time of decay = 11,460 years
Number of half-lives = ___ half-lives
Half-life = _____ years

Step 1: Calculate how many half-lives have passed during the decay of the 80 g sample.

This is determined by first dividing the amount of the sample by two. Then repeat the process until you get the desired amount that remains.

80 g ÷ 2 = 40 g   [after 1 half-life of carbon-14]
40 g ÷ 2 = 20 g   [after 2 half-lives of carbon-14]

Two half-lives have passed.

Step 2: Determine the half-life. This is calculated by the total time of decay divided by the number of half-lives from Step 1.

$$\frac{\text{Total time of decay}}{\text{Number of half-lives}} = \frac{11{,}460 \text{ years}}{2 \text{ half-lives}} = \textbf{5{,}730 years}$$

The half-life of carbon-14 is 5,730 years.

Online Activities

Go to the online lesson for this lab and complete the activities as assigned by your instructor.

Quiz

1. Which of these individuals is regarded as the founder of modern geology?
   a. James Usher
   b. James Hutton
   c. John Lightfoot
   d. James Playfair
   e. William Smith

2. The theory of rock and landscape evolution that was a direct result of early belief in a 6,000-year-old Earth is called _____.

3. Which of the following principles is not usually used in the determining the relative age of rocks?
   a. Principle of Cross-Cutting Relationships
   b. Principle of Original Horizontality
   c. Principle of Superposition
   d. Principle of Faunal Succession
   e. Principle of Uniformitarianism

4. The outcrop made famous by James Hutton at Siccar Point, Scotland, is an excellent example of a(n) _____.

List each of the rock units shown in the geologic cross section below (**Figure 9.12**) from youngest (5) to oldest (10).

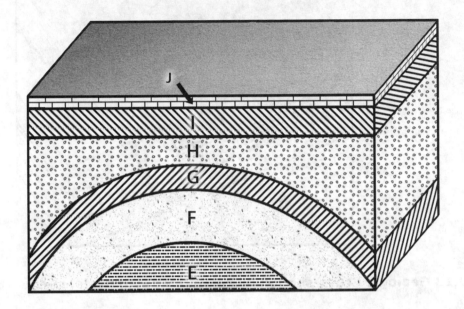

Figure 9.12 Geologic Cross-section of Relative Age Analysis. Illustration by Bob Dixon

5. _____ (youngest rock unit)
6. _____
7. _____
8. _____
9. _____
10. _____ (oldest rock unit)

List each of the rock units shown in the geologic cross section below (**Figure 9.13**) from youngest (11) to oldest (18). Unconformities (i.e., angular unconformity, disconformity, and nonconformity) are indicated by bold wiggly lines running across the geologic cross section. Faults are indicated with bold straight lines.

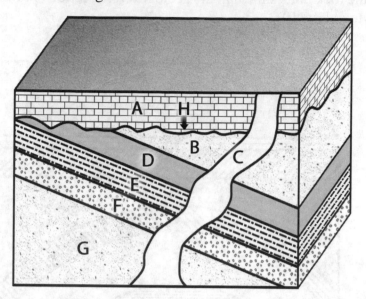

Figure 9.13 Geologic Cross-section of Relative Age Analysis. Illustration by Bob Dixon

11. _____ (youngest rock unit)
12. _____
13. _____
14. _____
15. _____
16. _____
17. _____
18. _____ (oldest rock unit)

List each of the rock units shown in the geologic cross section below (**Figure 9.14**) from youngest (19) to oldest (24). Unconformities (i.e., angular unconformity, disconformity, and nonconformity) are indicated by bold wiggly lines running across the geologic cross section. Faults are indicated with bold straight lines.

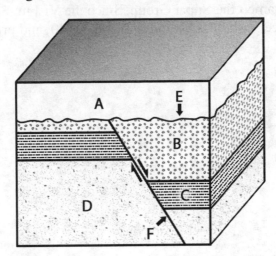

Figure 9.14 Geologic Cross-section of Relative Age Analysis. Illustration by Bob Dixon

19. _____ (youngest rock unit)
20. _____
21. _____
22. _____
23. _____
24. _____ (oldest rock unit)

25. What law states that in a sequence of sedimentary rocks, unless overturned, the oldest beds are at the bottom and the youngest beds are at the top?
   a. Principle of Cross Cutting
   b. Principle of Faunal Succession
   c. Principle of Inclusion
   d. Principle of Superposition
   e. Principle of Original Horizontality

26. What law states that fossils in a stratigraphic sequence succeed one another in a definite, recognizable order?
   a. Principle of Cross Cutting Relationships
   b. Principle of Faunal Succession
   c. Principle of Inclusion
   d. Principle of Superposition
   e. Principle of Original Horizontality

List each of the rock units shown in the geologic cross section of the Grand Canyon National Park (**Figure 9.15**) from youngest (27) to oldest (40). Unconformities (i.e., angular unconformity, disconformity, and nonconformity) are indicated by bold wiggly lines running across the geologic cross section. Faults are indicated with bold straight lines. Start with the sedimentary layer named the Supai Group. Since the Vishnu Schist is the oldest geologic event recorded, place Vishnu Schist on line number 40, and proceed to fill in the rest of the spaces provided.

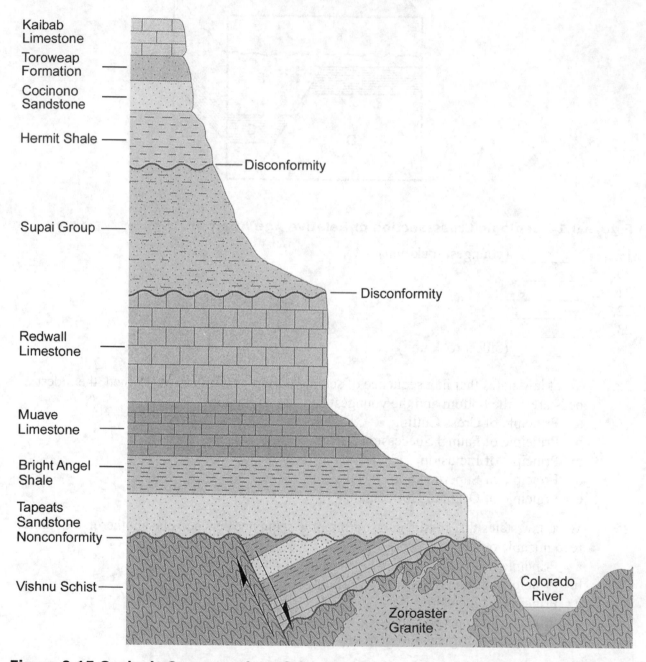

Figure 9.15 Geologic Cross-section of the Grand Canyon, Arizona. From *Planet Earth* by John J. Renton. Copyright © 2002 by John J. Renton. Reprinted by permission of Kendall Hunt Publishing Company.

27. _____ (youngest rock unit)
28. _____
29. _____
30. _____
31. _____
32. _____
33. _____
34. _____
35. _____
36. _____
37. _____
38. _____
39. _____
40. _____ (oldest rock unit)

41.   A _____ is evidence of past life through the remains or traces of prehistoric life of a plant or animal organism in strata.

42.   An _____ is a fossil of an organism that was common and had widespread geographic distribution during a certain time in Earth's history.

43.   Dinosaurs ruled Earth during
       a. the Paleozoic Era.
       b. the Mesozoic Era.
       c. the Cenozoic Era.
       d. the Precambrian Era.
       e. none of the above eras.

44.   During what geologic period did the first mammals appear?
       a. Tertiary
       b. Jurassic
       c. Permian
       d. Pennsylvanian
       e. Devonian

45.   During what geologic period did the first aquatic invertebrates (i.e., mollusks, etc.) appear?
       a. Permian
       b. Pennsylvanian
       c. Devonian
       d. Ordovician
       e. Silurian

46. The parent radioactive isotope that is used to date the age of human remains and artifacts is
    a. Rb^{87}.
    b. C^{14}.
    c. K^{40}.
    d. U^{238}.
    e. I^{131}.

47. If a sample of radioactive material has a half-life of 3 years, then at the end of 6 years
    a. all of the material remains.
    b. half of the same material remains.
    c. one-quarter of the same material remains.
    d. one-ninth of the same material remains.
    e. none of the same material remains.

48. The scientist that laid the foundation for all radioactive dating techniques by his or her discovery of the half-life of radioactive isotopes was
    a. Marie Curie.
    b. Lord Rutherford.
    c. Lord Kelvin.
    d. John Joly.
    e. William Smith.

49. Carbon-14 is radioactive and decays into
    a. carbon-12.
    b. carbon-13.
    c. oxygen-14.
    d. nitrogen-14.
    e. none of the above.

50. Uranium-235 is radioactive and decays into
    a. carbon-13.
    b. nitrogen-14.
    c. strontium-87.
    d. lead-207.
    e. lead-206.

51. Rubidium-87 is radioactive and decays into
    a. lead-207.
    b. strontium-87.
    c. cesium-137.
    d. argon-40.
    e. strontium-86.

52. The half-life of radon-222 is 3.8 days. How much of a 100 g sample is left after 15.2 days?
    a. 12.5 g
    b. 25 g
    c. 100 g
    d. 6.25 g
    e. 3.125 g

53. The half-life of iodine-131 is 8 days. How much of a parent sample of 75 g will remain after 48 days?
    a. 4.69 g
    b. 2.34 g
    c. 1.17 g
    d. 0.59 g
    e. 0.29g

54. The half-life of K-42 is 12.4 hours. How much of a 500 g sample of potassium-42 is left after 62 hours?
    a. 250 g
    b. 62.5 g
    c. 125 g
    d. 15.625 g
    e. 31.25 g

55. What is the half-life of a 200 g sample of nitrogen-16 that decays to 25 g of nitrogen-16 in 21.6 seconds? (Note: answer should be rounded to the nearest tenth decimal)
    a. 6.8 seconds
    b. 7.0 seconds
    c. 7.2 seconds
    d. 7.4 seconds
    e. 7.6 seconds

MASS WASTING

Lesson 10

AT A GLANCE

Purpose

Learning Objectives

Materials Needed

Overview

    Environmental Concerns Pertaining to Mass Wasting

    Water Infiltration into Slope

    Presence or Absence of Vegetation

Online Activities

Lab Exercise

    Lab Exercise: *Downslope Movement*

Quiz

Purpose

The activities in this lesson will lay the foundation for understanding and applying techniques in interpreting slope stability and how landslides are created. Each year, thousands of individuals are displaced by landslides that damage or destroy physical structures (i.e., homes, businesses, property, and so forth) and cost the individual taxpayer, insurance companies, and government organizations hundreds to millions of dollars. You will learn that mass movement of loose sediment, soils, and rocks moving down a slope is a natural disaster, but it can be predicted by modern technical knowledge and through public awareness of the slope conditions.

Learning Objectives

After completing this laboratory lesson, you will be able to:

- Describe the nature of mass wasting and distinguish the major factors involved in the movement of materials downslope.
- Differentiate the common types of mass wasting.
- Articulate the geologic hazards presented by slope instability and mass movement.

Materials Needed

- ❑ Pencil
- ❑ Eraser

Overview

Mass wasting (the downslope movement of rock materials by gravitational forces without being carried within, on, or under any other medium) is definitely the unsung hero of all geologic processes. Most individuals are totally unaware that some process of mass wasting is going on at Earth's land surface all the time and every place. Equally important is the fact that most of Earth's land topography is the result of the combined efforts of various mass wasting processes and stream erosion. While stream erosion is largely responsible for the deepening and widening of valley floors, the reduction of the highlands separating adjoining stream valleys is the result of the various agents of mass wasting (**Figure 10.1**).

From the moment that the regolith (i.e., the layer of unconsolidated material accumulated above bedrock) forms, a series of processes that remove the regolith materials, carry them off, and eventually deposit them into the ocean. The process that starts this journey is called mass wasting. The distance the regolith materials are carried by mass wasting is short, usually no further than from the tops of hills to the adjacent valley floor. Once the regolith materials reach the valley floor, the processes of mass wasting will have come to an end while one or more of the agents of erosion can pick up the materials and continue their journey to the sea. Of the three principal agents of erosion—streams, glaciers, and the wind—the major agent is streams. Anywhere water can exist, streams will be the major agent of erosion, including in the driest desert.

Most valleys contain a stream channel. While the channel may not always contain water, a stream channel will be present because most valleys are the result of stream erosion. Because most stream systems eventually flow to the ocean, once they pick up the materials transported to the valley floor by mass wasting, they complete the task of transporting the products of weathering to the ocean.

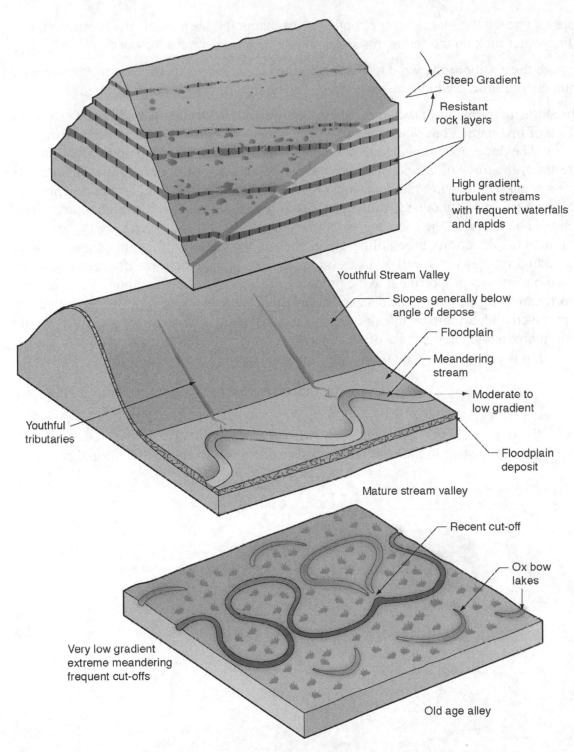

Figure 10.1 Stream Erosion. This image illustrates how stream erosion is largely responsible for the deepening and widening of valley floors; the reduction of the highlands separating adjoining stream valleys is the result of the various agents of mass wasting. Illustration © Kendall Hunt Publishing Company

Glaciers are also extremely effective agents of erosion, capable of picking up any loose material they may encounter regardless of particle size. While some glaciers do transport the products of weathering directly to the ocean, many melt and redeposit their loads of sediment before they reach the margin of the continent. At that point, the streams that form from the melting water pick up the sediments and continue their transport to the ocean.

Although the ability of the wind to erode is limited to sand-sized particles and smaller, under certain conditions the wind may carry off large volumes of fine-grained sediment.

Perhaps the major factor that distinguishes mass wasting from the other agents of erosion is the lack of involvement of other agents such as water, ice, or moving air in causing the changes. The downslope movement of the materials contained within the regolith is strictly the result of the force of gravity. The explanation of the concept of gravity was first developed by the seventeenth-century mathematician Sir Isaac Newton (1642–1727). Newton noted apples on a tree directly outside of the window in his study always fell straight down. From this simple observation, he soon conceived the presence of a force called gravity that determined the direction of the falling apple, but also the motions of the moon and all other celestial bodies. Newton specified in a simple relationship that the force of gravity between any two bodies was proportional to the product of the masses of the two bodies and inversely proportional to the square of the distance between their centers of gravity. This relationship was involved with a falling apple or the earth and the moon. The center of gravity of an object is a point around which the mass of the object is more or less uniformly distributed. His relationship is expressed by the following simple equation

$$Fg = \frac{kM_1 \times M_2}{D^2}$$

Because the relationship is applicable to any two bodies within the universe, the proportionality constant in the relationship, k, is called the universal gravitational constant.

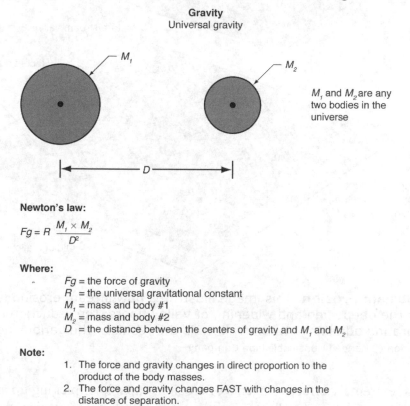

Gravity
Universal gravity

M_1 and M_2 are any two bodies in the universe

Newton's law:

$$Fg = R \frac{M_1 \times M_2}{D^2}$$

Where:

Fg = the force of gravity
R = the universal gravitational constant
M_1 = mass and body #1
M_2 = mass and body #2
D = the distance between the centers of gravity and M_1 and M_2

Note:

1. The force and gravity changes in direct proportion to the product of the body masses.
2. The force and gravity changes FAST with changes in the distance of separation.

Figure 10.2 Formula for Gravitational Forces. Illustration ©Kendall Hunt Publishing Company

Lesson 10/Mass Wasting

By definition, friction is the force resisting the relative lateral or tangential movement of solid surfaces, fluid layers, or materials in contact.

The word *cohesion* comes from the Latin word *cohaerere*, meaning "to stick or stay together." To a physicist, cohesion is "the molecular force between particles within a body or substance that acts to unite them." Simply put, cohesion is the state of cohering, uniting, or sticking together.

In all mass wasting processes, water is second only to gravity in importance. The major role of water is to serve as a lubricant that, by definition, is a substance, often a liquid, introduced between two moving surfaces to reduce friction and cohesion. In addition to its role as a lubricant, water added to slope materials tends to increase the total mass of the materials, which increases the force of gravity.

On a sloping surface, the force of gravity creates two other forces, one called the downslope component of gravity directed parallel to the surface, directed downslope and another called the force of cohesion and friction directed perpendicular to the surface (see **Figure 10.3**).

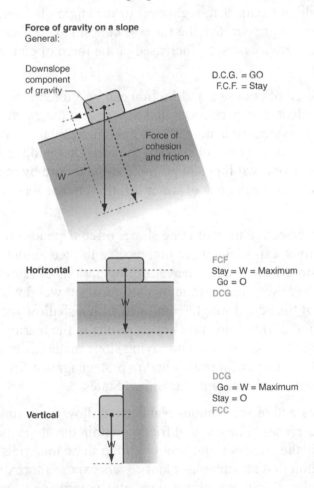

Figure 10.3 Force of Gravity on a Slope. Any object resting on a horizontal surface will not move of its own accord; because there is no force directed parallel to the surface, the entire force of gravity is directed perpendicular to the surface. On a horizontal surface, friction and cohesion between the surface and the object are at a maximum.
Illustration ©Kendall Hunt Publishing Company

As the angle of slope increases from the horizontal to the vertical, the relative magnitudes of the downslope component of gravity and the force of cohesion and friction progressively change. The downslope component of gravity increases from zero on a horizontal surface to the maximum, which is the full force of gravity on a vertical surface. While the force of cohesion and friction decreases from the maximum on a horizontal surface to zero on a vertical surface. Technically, a balance between the two forces is achieved at an angle of 45 degrees. Because of this balance, many particles will not move downslope at angles less than 45 degrees. While once the angle of slope exceeds 45 degrees, particles will begin to move downslope. The angle of repose is the angle up to which loose unconsolidated materials will be at rest; when the angle is exceeded, the materials will begin to slide and roll downslope.

Note that based on these relationships, particles resting on slopes of less than the angle of repose will **NOT** move downslope because the force of cohesion and friction is larger than that of gravity. However, the processes of mass wasting operate on **ALL** slopes, regardless of their slope angle. For any particle to move down a slope, gravity must exceed the force of cohesion and friction, which means that, regardless of the angle of slope, the downslope component of gravity can be greater than the force of cohesion and friction. Either the downslope component of gravity must be increased or the force of cohesion and friction must be decreased.

One way in which the force of cohesion and friction can be altered is the effect of vegetation on slope stability. This effect is very complex and depends on the extent and types of plant cover. In general, the root system of a more or less continuous plant cover promotes slope stability by increasing the friction and cohesion of the soil. On the other hand, a continuous plant cover may decrease slope stability and promote slope failure by reducing the amount of the surface runoff and increasing the rate of water infiltration that serves to decrease cohesion and friction within the soil.

Whether a plant cover is effective in stabilizing slopes often depends on the kind of vegetation. In many regions, especially those that receive limited amounts of precipitation, plants that take up and store water in their leaves during periods of rainfall are used as ground covers. Unfortunately, the absorption of water adds significant weight to the slope materials where the combination of the added weight combined with a shallow root system and increased water infiltration during rain events often results in the tearing of the plant cover and the initiation of slumping that exposes the underlying slope materials to erosion. Some succulent plants are used on slopes for beauty and to protect against fires—a very real danger in some developed regions in arid areas in the United States.

On the other hand, slopes with discontinuous plant cover allow more runoff because water that soaks into the ground decreases cohesion and friction within the slope materials. Deep root systems serve to increase the cohesion and friction of the slope materials helping to hold the hillside in place. Even though discontinuous plant covers expose more of the surface to surface erosion, tree- and bush-covered slopes generally experience a lower frequency of slope failure and maintain steeper slope angles than those covered with grasses.

Mass wasting processes are classified as flows, slides, and falls based on three parameters: (1) particle size, (2) rate of movement, and (3) amount of water involved. Of the three parameters, the amount of involved water is the basis for the classification scheme summarized in **Figure 10.4** below.

| Classification of Mass Wasting Processes | | | | |
Kind of Movement	Process	Amount of Water	Particle Size*	Rate of Movement
flow	mudflow	high	small-med	fast
flow	earthflow	mod.-high	small-med.	slow-mod.
flow	solifluction	high	small-large	slow
slide	slump	mod.	small-med.	mod.-fast.
slide	debris slide	mod.	small-med.	mod.-fast
slide	rock slide	mod.	med.-large	mod.-fast
slide	creep	low	small-med.	slow
fall	rock fall	low	med.-large	fast-freefall

Relative particle sizes:
small: cobble size (64–256 mm) and smaller
medium: cobble size (64–256 mm) to boulder size (>256 mm)
large: boulder size (>256 mm) and larger

Figure 10.4 Classification of Mass Wasting Processes

Creep involves the slow, downslope movement of the upper layers of the regolith. Typically, the rates of movement range from 2 millimeters to 3 millimeters per year. Of all the processes of mass wasting, creep is the most widespread and is responsible for the movement of the greatest mass of material.

Creep is caused by a number of factors. In humid, temperate regions, the combination of chemical and physical weathering results in a more or less continuous layer of regolith covering the bedrock surface. During the winter, when the regolith is subjected to repeated freeze-thaw cycles, frost heaving results in slow downslope movement of the uppermost layer of soil (see **Figure 10.5**). During the warmer months, soil containing clay minerals, which are capable of expanding and contracting as they take on and release water, may experience the same kind of downhill movement as frost heaving produces. Eventually, the materials are transported to the valley floor, where they are picked up by a stream and carried away. In arid regions, creep may be initiated by the cyclic growth and dissolution of water-soluble crystals in the upper layers of regolith. Evidence for creep includes fence posts tilted downslope, overturned stone walls, trees bent at the base of their trunks, leaning retaining walls and tombstones in cemeteries, and undulating slopes.

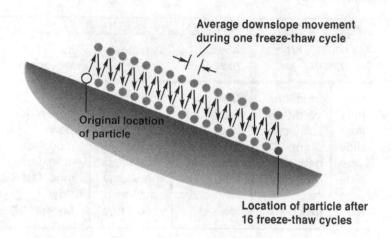

Average downslope movement
during one freeze-thaw cycle

Original location
of particle

Location of particle after
16 freeze-thaw cycles

Figure 10.5 Creep. In humid, temperate and tropic regions, the process of frost heaving is a very effective agent of mass wasting, including the slow downhill movement of the upper layers of regolith by a process called creep. From *Planet Earth* by John J. Renton. Copyright © 2002 by John J. Renton. Reprinted by permission of Kendall Hunt Publishing Company.

At higher latitudes and elevations where the regolith is frozen throughout the year except for a very short summer season, a type of creep called solifluction takes place when the uppermost layers of the regolith thaws (**Figure 10.6**). Because the regolith below the thawed layer remains permanently frozen, the water accumulates and saturates the thawed layer. This process essentially eliminates cohesion and friction between the individual particles, literally converting the materials into a viscous liquid. With no force to hold the materials in place, the surface materials slowly move downslope at rates ranging from 0.5 centimeters to 5 centimeters per year (0.25 to 2 inches) on slopes angles as low as 2 to 3 degrees.

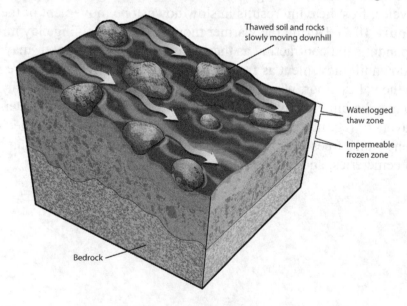

Thawed soil and rocks
slowly moving downhill

Waterlogged
thaw zone

Impermeable
frozen zone

Bedrock

Figure 10.6 Solifluction. Illustration by Don Vierstra

Earthflow is a type of mass wasting in which soil and loose rock material move over a laterally confined, basal shear zone oriented roughly parallel to the ground surface, with little rotation of the sliding materials. In temperate regions during the rainy seasons of the spring and early summer, slopes covered with grass sods result in the infiltration of water that tends to saturate the regolith and decreases cohesion and friction, accelerating the downslope movement of the materials. Unlike creep, which affects the entire hillside, earthflow usually only involves a limited area of the slope surface (**Figure 10.7**).

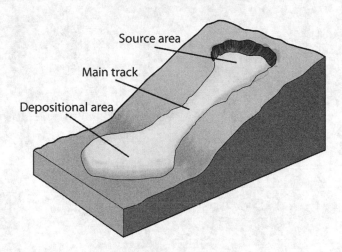

Figure 10.7 Earthflow. Illustration by Don Vierstra

Slumps are common mass wasting processes, especially in regions where the regolith is covered with a continuous layer of grass. Because of the vegetative cover, rainwater tends to infiltrate the regolith rather than running off, thereby increasing the overall mass of the regolith while at the same time decreasing cohesion and friction within the regolith. In a slump, a portion of the regolith, sometimes including bedrock, breaks away along curved fractures and rotates and moves downhill until enough water escapes to allow cohesion and friction to become reestablished within the mass (**Figure 10.8**).

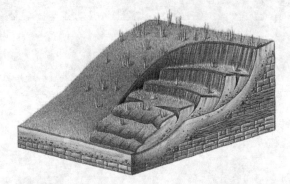

Figure 10.8 Slump. From *Planet Earth* by John J. Renton. Copyright © 2002 by John J. Renton. Reprinted by permission of Kendall Hunt Publishing Company.

Landslide is a general term for a variety of fast, gravity induced, downslope mass movements of rock and soil.

Mudflow is a type of mass wasting which is characterized by a flowing mixture of water and fine-grained materials possessing a high degree of fluidity during movement (**Figure 10.9**). With increased fluidity, mudflows grade into turbid and clear streams. With decreased fluidity, they grade into earthflows. The term is also used to describe a form of mass wasting following the deposition of the materials.

Figure 10.9 Mudflow. Shutterstock #30393142, credit Tomasz Parys

Lahar is a mudflow composed chiefly of volcanic materials originally accumulated on the flank of a volcano (**Figure 10.10**).

Figure 10.10 Lahar. The mudflow associated with a lahar is primarily composed of volcanic materials. Shutterstock #8542513, credit Dr. Morley Read

The origin of mudflows and debris flows are similar in that they are usually the result of torrential rains that soak slopes where the regolith exists at or near the angle of repose. The main difference between the two processes is that more than half of the material being carried by a debris flow consists of sand-sized and larger particles. Depending on the mass and viscosity of the flow and the angle of slope, debris flows can travel as slow as a few feet per year or as fast as 320 km per hour (200 mph) (see **Figure 10.11**).

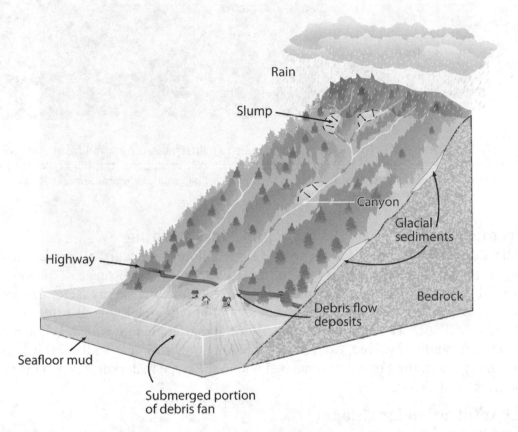

Figure 10.11 Debris Flow. As surface water moves downslope, it brings with it materials and debris that are deposited at the base of the mountain. Illustration by Don Vierstra

Rock falls may involve individual blocks of rocks of any dimension or large masses of rocks (see **Figures 10.12a** and **b**). Typically, the rocks exposed at the surface of steep cliffs or road cuts are subjected to various processes of weathering that slowly break the rock layers along natural fractures. In both arid and humid temperate climates, frost action dislodges blocks of rock from the faces of steep outcrops. Eventually, various processes of erosion may remove the remaining support from below, or the rock mass may be subjected to a local shock such as an earthquake that initiates the downward movement.

A debris slide is similar to a rockslide (a sudden and rapid movement of rock down a preexisting inclined surface such as a bedding plane or fault) except that the maximum particle sizes involved are not so large. Debris slides usually consist of a moderate-to-fast moving mixture of rock, regolith, and soil.

(a)　　　　　　　　　　　　**(b)**

Figure 10.12 Rock Fall. The drawing on the left (a) illustrates a rock fall from a steep cliff area. The photo on the right (b) shows an actual rock fall, where the slope of the hill could not hold the large boulders and debris in place. Illustration (a) courtesy California Geological Survey; Photo (b) Shutterstock #21928129, credit Timothy Epp

Environmental Concerns Pertaining to Mass Wasting

Regardless of where they occur or the type of slope failure that occurs, all processes of mass wasting result when the downslope force of gravity exceeds the resistance of movement, represented by the cohesion and friction within the slope materials. Any factor or combination of factors that increases the downslope component of gravity, relative to the force of cohesion and friction, will decrease the stability of the slope and promote movement. While many factors are potentially involved, two are of prime importance in nearly all mass wasting processes: (1) the amount of water contained within the slope materials, and (2) the presence or absence of vegetation.

Water Infiltration into Slope

Water infiltrating into slope materials promotes mass wasting in three ways: (1) by increasing the weight of the slope materials and thereby increasing the potential downslope component of gravity, (2) by decreasing the cohesion and friction within the slope materials, and (3) by dissolving cementing agents. Most mass wasting processes are the result of the water that accumulates within the slope materials. During periods of heavy rainfall, water may infiltrate and collect in the unconsolidated slope materials faster that it can permeate downward into the underlying bedrock. The mass of accumulated water adds weight to the slope materials and simultaneously reduces the cohesion and friction while increasing the hydrostatic pressure that tends to separate the particles. When the downslope component of gravity exceeds the resistance to movement represented by cohesion and friction, the surface materials will move.

Presence or Absence of Vegetation

Vegetation is a double-edged sword. While the roots of a continuous plant cover, such as various ground cover plants, serve to provide a certain amount of stability to the underlying slope materials, the plant cover minimizes runoff and enhances infiltration of water into the slope materials with the subsequent reduction in cohesion and friction, as well as increases the weight of the slope materials. Taken to the extreme, the increase in the downslope component of gravity coupled with the decrease in the force of cohesion and friction makes the slope unstable and prone to failure. While dispersed plants such as trees and bushes allow an increase in surface runoff and surface erosion, they also provide a degree of stability to the slope materials by minimizing the amount of water infiltration, while at the same time providing cohesion and friction by virtue of the root networks.

Lab Exercise

Lab Exercise: *Downslope Movement*

In this lab exercise, you will examine four photographs of developed areas that are suffering from creep. As you examine **Figures 10.13**, **10.14**, **10.15**, and **10.16**, list the types of features you see and should look for when determining whether a building or a particular landscape feature is susceptible to downslope movement (creep).

Make sure to save your results and observations. You will use the data to answer the questions at the end of this lesson.

Instructions

> **Step 1:** Observe **Figure 10.13**.

Figure 10.13 Houses on a Slope. Credit: American Geotechnical, Inc.

> In the space below, list the types of features you see in the photograph (**Figure 10.13**) and should look for when determining whether a house is susceptible to downslope movement/creep.

Step 2: Observe **Figure 10.14**.

Figure 10.14 Trees on a Slope. Shutterstock #41728024, credit Falex

In the space below, list the types of features you see in the photograph (**Figure 10.14**) and should look for when determining whether trees are susceptible to downslope movement/creep.

Step 3:   Observe **Figure 10.15**.

Figure 10.15 Cracks in a Wall. Shutterstock #63101599, credit homydesign

In the space below, list the types of features you see in the photograph (**Figure 10.15**) and should look for when determining whether a house is susceptible to downslope movement/creep.

Step 4: Observe **Figure 10.16**.

Figure 10.16 Fence Posts on a Slope. Shutterstock #5021846899, credit Evgeny Kovalev

In the space below, list the types of features you see in the photograph (**Figure 10.16**) and should look for when determining whether a fence is susceptible to downslope movement/creep.

Online Activities

As per your instructor's direction, go to the online lesson for this lab and complete the activities assigned.

Quiz

1. The characteristic of mass wasting processes is that they
   a. move materials very slowly.
   b. move materials relatively short distances.
   c. only operate on steep slopes.
   d. operate only during nonfreezing months of the year.
   e. do none of the above.

2. Slopes will be free of loose rock debris once the angle of slope exceeds about
   a. 10 degrees.
   b. 25 degrees.
   c. 45 degrees.
   d. 65 degrees.
   e. 75 degrees.

3. Of all the mass wasting processes, the one that operates over the largest area of Earth's land surface is
   a. slump.
   b. creep.
   c. debris flow.
   d. earthflow.
   e. none of the above.

4. Frost heaving is an important process in
   a. creep.
   b. slump.
   c. rock fall.
   d. earthflow.
   e. debris slide.

5. What are the three key agents of erosion? Which of these three is the major agent?

6. Which of the following agents of erosion is also highly effective, capable of picking up any loose material regardless of particle size and moving that material great distances over long periods of time?
   a. wind
   b. streams
   c. glaciers
   d. earthflow
   e. debris slide

7. The angle of repose is the angle
   a. of a slope covered with regolith.
   b. that any slope makes with the horizontal.
   c. at which loose regolith will begin to move downslope.
   d. above which processes of mass wasting will not operate.
   e. of a slope covered with earthflow.

8. What are the differences between slides, falls, and flows?

Figure 10.17 Mass Wasting Event. Credit: Shutterstock #21928129, Timothy Epp

9. The image above (**Figure 10.17**) was taken in California. What type of mass wasting event is taking place here?

10. The most important factor in the movement of regolith on slopes with angles less than the angle of repose is the
    a. thickness of the regolith.
    b. amount of water availability.
    c. mean particle size of the regolith.
    d. orientation of the slope relative to the sun.
    e. local shocks such as earthquakes

11. Bent tree bottoms and tipped fence posts are most likely the result of
   a. creep.
   b. solifluction.
   c. slump.
   d. rock fall.
   e. earthflow.

12. The destructive mass wasting process commonly associated with volcanic eruptions is
   _____.

13. The major driving force in all processes of mass wasting is _____.

14. The mass wasting process responsible for the movement of material in permafrost regions (areas in which water in the upper portion of the ground remains frozen for all or most of the time) on slopes of only a few degrees is called _____.

15. The mass wasting process that transports material for the greatest distance is called
   _____.

16. The mass wasting process that takes place under conditions of maximum downslope force of gravity and no force of cohesion and friction is known as
   _____.

17. The two factors involved in nearly all cases of slope instability are
   _____ and _____.

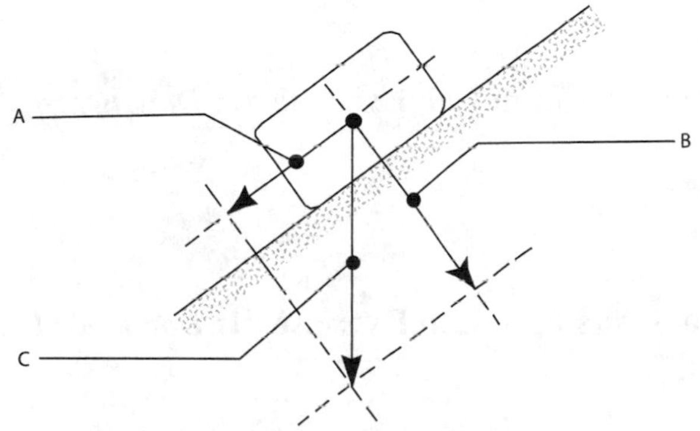

Figure 10.18

18. In **Figure 10.18** above, identify the three forces indicated at the lettered points.
   A. _____
   B. _____
   C. _____

19. Rank the following mass wasting processes in terms of the amount of water involved from the most water (a) to the least amount of water (e).
   ____ rock fall   ____ slump   ____ debris slide   ____ creep   ____ mudflow

20. _____ is the force that resists movement between two bodies.

21. _____ is the strength of a material derived from properties other than intergranular friction.

22. _____ is the accumulated product of weathering above bedrock.

23. How does water influence mass wasting?

24. Describe how a tree can help to stabilize a hillside that is at risk for a landslide.

For Questions 25 through 28, use your results from the **Lab Exercise:** *Downward Movement.*
25. Record your answers from **Lab Exercise #1:** *Downward Movement,* step 1.

26. Record your answers from **Lab Exercise #1:** *Downward Movement,* step 2.

27. Record your answers from **Lab Exercise #1:** *Downward Movement,* step 3.

28. Record your answers from **Lab Exercise #1:** *Downward Movement,* step 4.

Lesson 10/Mass Wasting

STREAMS AND GROUNDWATER

Lesson 11

AT A GLANCE

Purpose

Learning Objectives

Materials Needed

Overview

Hydrologic Cycle

> **Streams**

> **Groundwater**

Lab Exercises

> **Lab Exercise #1:** *Yosemite Valley*

> **Lab Exercise #2:** *Groundwater Flow*

Online Activities

Quiz

Purpose

The activities in this lesson will lay the foundation for understanding and applying techniques in interpreting stream features and how surface water is infiltrated underground and collected into large bodies of water.

Learning Objectives

After completing this laboratory lesson, you will be able to:

- Interpret different features of a stream such as how streams have shaped valleys, channel configurations, drainage patterns, and eroded the landscape.
- Explain the role of groundwater as it comes in contact with geologic materials.
- Calculate stream gradient, stream discharge, stream competence, and groundwater flow.
- Explain the development of karst topography.

Materials Needed

- ❏ Pencil
- ❏ Eraser
- ❏ Calculator
- ❏ Ruler (in lab kit)
- ❏ USGS Topographic Map Yosemite Valley (in lab kit)

Overview

Every year, nearly 4 billion tons of water precipitation falls on the earth's land surface—an average of about 40 inches for any one area. Most of this water is lost from the earth's surface through the following processes:

1. Some water is absorbed into the ground by infiltration.

2. A certain amount of the precipitation returns to the atmosphere by evaporation.

3. Plants use a portion of the precipitation during photosynthesis and some is returned to the atmosphere by transpiration.

Hydrologic Cycle

Approximately 25 percent of the precipitation falling on the land becomes surface water, or runoff, and flows to the sea in river and stream channels. Such gravity-driven down slope water flow and the resulting erosion and channel formation are among the most important agents sculpting Earth's land surface. The erosive power of running water highlights differences in bedrock (i.e., unweathered solid rock which is found underneath deposits of surface soil and rock debris) resistance. The resistance of bedrock to erosion by running water is governed by its mineralogy (how susceptible it is to chemical decomposition), its degree of lithification (how susceptible it is to mechanical disintegration), and the local climate.

Most of the water (97 percent) is contained within the ocean basins, which cover about 70 percent of Earth's surface. The oceans are both the source and the ultimate repository of the water that is continuously recycled in the hydrologic cycle (**Figure 11.1**). In this cycle, which is driven by the energy of the sun, water evaporates from the oceans and enters the atmosphere where it is carried by the prevailing winds in more or less fixed patterns over Earth's surface. As air masses in the lower atmosphere cool, the water vapor condenses and falls as precipitation. Most precipitation falls directly back into the ocean basins to complete the cycle. Water vapor that falls from the atmosphere in the form of snow may accumulate temporarily in snowfields or becomes glacial ice. Approximately 2 percent of Earth's water—about 80 percent of all the water outside the ocean basins—exists as glacial ice.

Of the rain that falls on the land, 70 percent returns to the atmosphere either through direct evaporation or by way of plants, which transpire water into the atmosphere through their leaves. The remaining surface water runs off into streams, accumulates temporarily in lakes or ponds, or infiltrates into the ground to become groundwater.

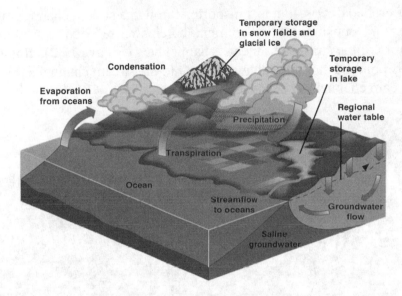

Figure 11.1 The Hydrologic Cycle. From *Planet Earth* by John J. Renton. Copyright © 2002 by John J. Renton. Reprinted by permission of Kendall Hunt Publishing Company.

Earth's freshwater is contained within lakes, rivers, groundwater, ice and snow, the atmosphere, and the biosphere. The biosphere reservoir refers to the very small amount of freshwater that is contained within the cells and tissues of plants and animals. The amount of water and the percentage of the total volume of freshwater contained within the various reservoirs outside the ocean basins on Earth are summarized in **Table 11.1**.

Distribution of Earth's Freshwater		
Reservoir	**Volume** (10⁶ km³)	**Percent of Total***
Glaciers	29	75.05
Groundwater	9.5	24.59
Lakes	0.125	0.32
Atmosphere	0.013	0.034
Rivers	0.0017	0.004
Biosphere	0.0006	0.002
Total	38.64	100

*Note: Numbers have been estimated and rounded.

Table 11.1: Distribution of Earth's Freshwater

Streams

Downslope water flow in channels (hereinafter referred to as streams) erodes the surface of the land by a combination of downcutting, headward erosion, and slope retreat. In the process of downcutting, the hydraulic action of the running water and the abrasive action of the transported debris progressively lower the bottom of the stream channel through the soil and/or bedrock. In the process of headward erosion, the source or headwater of a stream channel is progressively extended into higher-elevation areas, increasing the length of the stream channel in an upstream direction. In the process of slope retreat, erosion of the sides of the valley causes them to migrate laterally, increasing the width of the stream valley.

The sediment, or eroded debris, that is transported through a stream channel must ultimately deposit downstream. Deposition of the sediment, hereinafter referred to as alluvium, may take place on the bottom of the stream channel as channel bars (**Figure 11.2**), along the sides of the stream channel as point bars or natural levees, next to the stream channel as floodplains, or at the mouths of stream channels as deltas or alluvial fans.

Figure 11.2 Channel Bar. Whenever a stream flows across long surfaces with relatively flat surfaces, the larger particles of sediment settle out along the side of the stream called channel bars. Look at this photo of the Merced River in Yosemite Valley, Yosemite, California, and notice the channel bar on the right side of the river. Courtesy of Greg Gardiner

Drainage Patterns

A stream channel is part of a larger, complex network of channels called a drainage basin or watershed, which drains water from a specific geographic area. Within each drainage basin are smaller stream channels (tributaries) that feed water into the main stream channel. If the drainage basin is large, it may contain several orders of tributaries that systematically direct the gravity-driven flow of water downstream to progressively larger tributaries. Ultimately, the main stream channel is where the water flow is delivered to the mouth of the stream at the lowest elevation in the drainage basin.

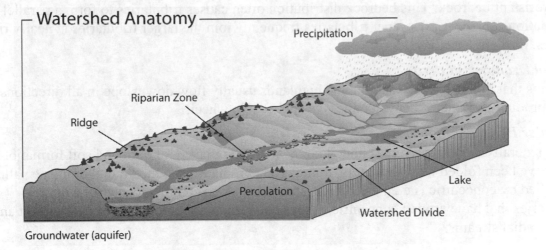

Figure 11.3 Watershed Anatomy. Illustration by Don Vierstra

Every stream is a member of a drainage basin that combines with other drainage basins to form a larger drainage area called a watershed (**Figure 11.3**). Drainage basins are separated by divides that are topographic highs, usually ridges between stream valleys. Divides direct the water flow into different drainage basins, or divide the runoff at hilltops, along ridge crests, or along the crests of mountain ranges. One control governing the water flow at the mouth of a stream is the surface area of the drainage basin, which is a function of the divide spacing. The best-known divide in the United States is the Continental Divide, which separates rivers that flow into the Atlantic Ocean and the Gulf of Mexico from those that flow into the Pacific Ocean and the Gulf of California.

The spatial distribution of streams within an area may display different geometric patterns in the channel networks (see **Figure 11.4**) that vary from region to region. The variations are the result of differences in the slope of the land, the bedrock lithology (i.e., study of rocks with a particular emphasis on their composition and classification), and the structure of the bedrock, as described below.

Dendritic Drainage Pattern

This is the most common type of drainage pattern. The drainage pattern form resembles that of tree branches—tributaries join the main channel (or small tributaries join larger tributaries) at an acute angle and the apex (top) of the acute angle always points downstream. This usually is controlled by the slope of the land surface. It generally develops in areas underlain by bedrock that uniformly resists erosion and lacks geologic structures such as faults, fractures, or folded formations.

Rectangular Drainage Pattern

This is generally found where streams flow along zones of weakened or weathered rock, such a fault lines or fracture lines. Because of this structural control and because fault lines and fracture lines often intersect at right angles, the streams generally meet at right angles and have right-angle bends.

Trellis Drainage Pattern

This generally develops where resistant ridges of bedrock alternate with valleys underlain by less-resistant bedrock. This bedrock distribution often causes tributaries to form a parallel orientation. Smaller and steeper tributaries frequently join the larger tributaries at nearly right angles, forming a trellis pattern.

Radial Drainage Pattern

Streams that drain isolated topographic highlands usually flow downslope in all directions. This produces a pattern that resembles the spokes of a wheel.

Annular Drainage Pattern

This generally develops in areas underlain by alternating layers of hard and soft formations that have been folded into a structural dome. They produce a subdued radial drainage pattern modified by concentric (i.e., these objects shared the same common center of a circle) tributaries that have eroded concentric valleys between concentric ridges at nearly right angles to the radial streams.

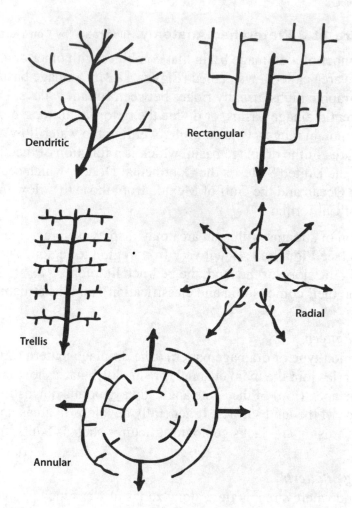

Figure 11.4 Drainage Patterns. Illustration by Mark Worden

Stream Gradient

Landforms produced by running water are created by stream erosion, stream deposition, or a combination of erosion and deposition. The gradient of a stream is the slope of the stream bed, or the slope of the surface of the stream in the case of larger rivers. The gradient, whether it is measured along an erosional segment of a stream or a depositional segment of a stream, is not measured in degrees, minutes, or seconds. Instead, the gradient of a stream is measured by the vertical difference in elevation between two points along the course of a stream per horizontal distance between the two points.

$$\text{Stream Gradient} = \frac{\text{Elevation of Point A} - \text{Elevation of Point B}}{\text{Horizontal distance from Point A to Point B}}$$

For example, if the elevation of point A along the course of a stream is 600 feet above sea level and the elevation of point B along the course of the same stream is 500 feet above sea level, and the points are separated by a horizontal distance of 4 miles, the stream gradient is:

$$\text{Stream Gradient} = \frac{600 \text{ feet} - 500 \text{ feet}}{4 \text{ miles}} = \frac{100 \text{ feet}}{4 \text{ miles}} = 25 \text{ feet per mile}$$

A longitudinal profile along the course of a stream shows that the gradient decreases in a downstream direction. A stream tends to erode its channel bottom in the upper, or headward, reaches and deposit alluvium or erode its channel walls in the lower reaches. Consequently, the headwater channel tends to be steep, narrow, straight, and V-shaped in cross section. In the lower reaches, the stream channel has a relatively gentle gradient, an often winding channel, and a broad, flat floodplain. Meander loops migrate on the floodplain by eroding their outer banks and depositing alluvium as point bars on their inner banks—often taking short cuts and creating oxbow lakes out of discarded or cast-off meander loops (**Figure 11.5**).

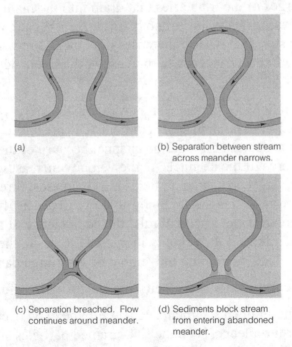

(a)

(b) Separation between stream across meander narrows.

(c) Separation breached. Flow continues around meander.

(d) Sediments block stream from entering abandoned meander.

Figure 11.5 Meandering River. An oxbow lake forms when a meander loop is cut off, usually during a flood, as the stream seeks a more direct route to its mouth along a steeper gradient. From *Planet Earth* by John J. Renton. Copyright © 2002 by John J. Renton. Reprinted by permission of Kendall Hunt Publishing Company.

Stream Discharge

A stream's discharge is the rate of stream flow at a given time and location, measured in volume of water per unit of time. Discharge is determined by measuring the width of the stream and the depth of the water in the stream at a given point, along with the velocity of the stream flow at the same point. First the stream width is multiplied by the stream depth to provide the cross-sectional area of the stream flow.

$$\text{Cross-sectional area of water flow} = \text{Width} \times \text{Depth}$$

Then cross-sectional area is multiplied by the stream velocity to provide the volume of the stream flow, or the discharge of the stream.

$$\text{Discharge} = \text{Width} \times \text{Depth} \times \text{Velocity}$$

For example, the discharge of a stream measuring 20 feet across and 4 feet in depth, and flowing at a velocity of 2 feet/second, would be:

$$\text{Discharge} = 20 \text{ feet} \times 4 \text{ feet} \times 2 \text{ feet/second}$$

$$\text{Discharge} = 160 \text{ cubic feet/second}$$

In this example, the cross-sectional area of water flow would be:

$$\text{Cross-sectional area of water flow} = 20 \text{ feet (width)} \times 4 \text{ feet (depth)} = 80 \text{ ft}^2$$

The discharge of a stream with tributaries always increases in a downstream direction because of the cumulative discharges of the tributaries that drain into the main stream channel. During flooding, discharge increases and streams often overrun their banks to increase their channel cross-sectional area. The stream flow also increases in velocity, moving greater volumes of water in a shorter time. Urbanization tends to increase in the frequency of flooding.

Sediment Transport

Stream capacity is the amount of sediment a stream is able to carry, which is proportional to the stream's discharge and the availability of sediment. The greater the discharge, the greater the volume of sediment transported through the channel because of the greater flow velocity and the greater sectional area of the channel. As the velocity increases, the ability of the flowing water to scoop up and carry large particles also increases. Stream competence is measured by the largest particle size the stream is able to carry, usually during flood stages when its velocity is the greatest. As a general rule, the competence of a stream increases as the square of its velocity. Therefore, if the velocity increases threefold, there is a nine-fold increase in stream competence, permitting movement of very large particles.

$$\text{Increase in stream competence} = (\text{velocity increase})^2 = \text{threefold squared} = 3^2 = 9$$

Suspension, usually of fine-grained sediment such as silt and clay, occurs where upward-directed eddy currents, or turbulence, keep the fine-grained particles suspended in the water column. Suspension usually occurs in high-velocity flow during high discharge, although finer-grained clay particles may remain in suspension during lower discharge as well. The bed load consists of the coarse-grained debris, primarily gravel, which is transported on the channel floor by rolling, sliding, or being bumped along. The coarse bed-load debris is confined to the channel bottom and is eventually abraded to smaller-sized particles as it works its way downstream. Saltation, a type of bed load, occurs when sand grains hop and skip along the channel floor, spending part of the time on the stream bed and part of the time in suspension. The net result is the progressive reduction in grain size and improved sorting in a downstream direction.

Sediment Deposition

Deposition of sediment by streams takes many forms. Alluvial fans are broad aprons of alluvium deposited at mountain bases in arid areas where steep-gradient streams emerge onto the gentle slopes of a plain, lose competence, and dump sediment **(Figure 11.6)**. During floods in humid areas, streams overflow their banks in the lower-gradient segments, lose competence, drop sand along channel margins, and create natural levees. Floodwaters spilling over the natural levees dump sediment behind the levees, blanketing flood plains with layers of upstream soil. As floodwaters subside, channel bars are created on stream beds and point bars are created at meander loops. Downstream in the lower reaches, streams that enter standing bodies of water suddenly stop, sediment drops from the loss of competence, and deltas build steadily outward.

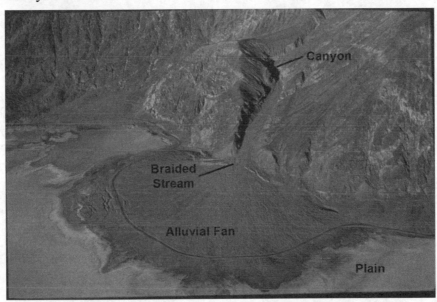

Figure 11.6 Alluvial Fan. Photo credit: Martin G. Miller

Groundwater

Groundwater is hidden and generally moves in response to pressure differences within the groundwater reservoir. Therefore, little is known about the details of its behavior. However, the volume of fresh water within the ground is estimated to be as much as forty times that of all the fresh water on the surface.

Groundwater is created when rainwater or melting snow infiltrates the ground, migrating through spaces in the soil and bedrock until all spaces are saturated with water. This water-saturated subsurface region is called the saturated zone, and its upper surface is called the water table. Water that stays in the saturated zone is called groundwater. Above the water table is the unsaturated zone, which consists of unsaturated sediment or bedrock with voids (spaces) occupied by air and small amounts of moisture held in place by surface tension. The position of the water table is variable. Its depth changes with the seasons and roughly mimics the surface topography, being slightly elevated under hills and depressed under valleys (see **Figure 11.7**).

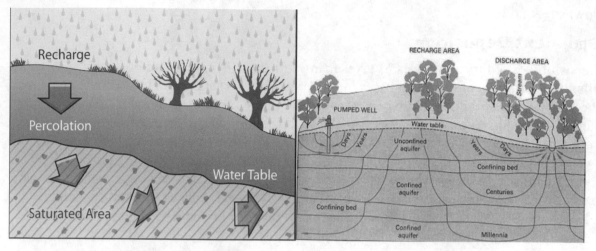

Figure 11.7 Water Table. Illustrations by Don Vierstra (left) and USGS (right)

Aquifers

Water filters into the ground from the surface and stays in the saturated zone within pores and fractures that exist in nearly all sediment and bedrock. Porosity (**Figure 11.8**) is the volume of void space in the sediment or bedrock expressed as a fraction of the volume of voids over the total volume (resulting in a number between 0 and 1 or as a percentage between 0% and 100%). The porosity increases when there are larger and more numerous void spaces between the grains. However, groundwater will not flow through sediment or bedrock with a high porosity if the individual voids are not interconnected. The degree of interconnection controls the permeability, which is a measure of how readily groundwater flows through the interconnected passageways in the sediment or bedrock.

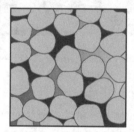 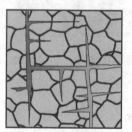

Figure 11.8 Porosity. The porosity of a rock is determined by the combined space between mineral grains (left) and within fractures (right). Illustration © Kendall Hunt Publishing Company

Different geologic materials have different porosities and permeabilities. Loose, unconsolidated sediment, such as sand, has a higher porosity and permeability than solidified sandstone, because the compaction and cementation that accompanies lithification reduces the amount of void space in the sandstone. Igneous rocks generally have a low porosity and permeability because of their intergrown crystals that leave few remaining void spaces. Shale also has low values of permeability and porosity because of the tight packing of its platy clay minerals, the small size of its pore spaces, and relatively few pore-space interconnections. In some circumstances, limestone can have high values of porosity and permeability because of interconnected solution cavities. Some crystalline rocks, which normally have low values, can have high values of porosity and permeability if extensively fractured. The degree of sorting in coarse-grained sediment, such as sand, also influences porosity and permeability, since a well-sorted sand (one with uniformity of grain size) will have higher values than poorly sorted sand.

Sediment and bedrock with high values of porosity and permeability are called aquifers. They have the capacity to store substantial volumes of groundwater and to produce considerable volumes of groundwater flow. Sediment and bedrock with low values of porosity and permeability are considered to be impermeable and are called confining beds. An example of a good aquifer would be a well-sorted and poorly cemented sandstone, whereas an example of a confining bed would be a shale which lacks interconnected fractures.

Unconfined Aquifer

An aquifer that lies directly beneath the water table and is not pressurized or sandwiched between confining beds is an unconfined aquifer. The saturated zone depicted in **Figure 11.7** is an example of an unconfined aquifer. A well drilled into an unconfined aquifer fills with water to the level of the water table, requiring a pump to lift the water to the surface. Excessive pumping may create a cone of depression in the water table, thus causing a lowering of the water table in the vicinity of the well (see **Figure 11.9**).

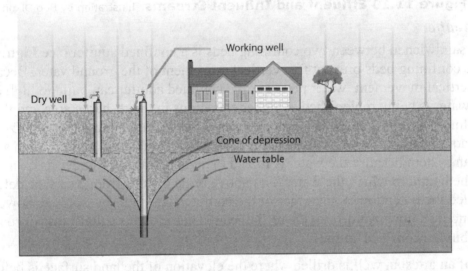

Figure 11.9 Cone of Depression in an Unconfined Aquifer. Illustration by Don Vierstra

If there is abundant rainfall and the water filters freely into the ground, the resulting groundwater will flow through the earth to low-lying areas, ultimately entering lakes and streams and creating an effluent (known as a gaining stream) condition. In times of drought or periods of excessive groundwater withdrawal, the elevation of the water table may fall below that of surface lakes and streams. The surface water may then flow downward into the groundwater system, thus creating an influent (known as a losing stream) condition (see **Figure 11.10**). If this condition persists, the surface water may disappear.

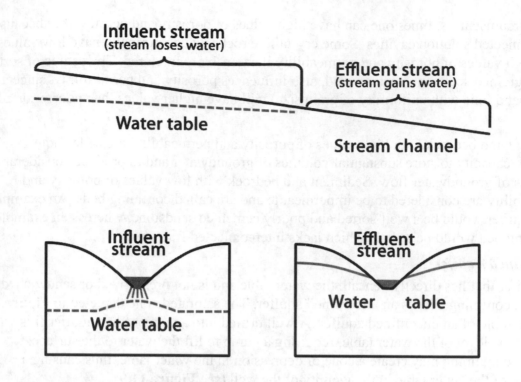

Figure 11.10 Effluent and Influent Streams. Illustration by Bob Dixon

Confined Aquifer

An aquifer sandwiched between two confining beds is a confined aquifer (see **Figure 11.11**), because the confining beds prevent free vertical movement of the groundwater. Because of restricted vertical movement, water pressure in a confined aquifer can build to high levels if the groundwater is being replenished at higher elevations in the recharge area and the confined aquifer is almost fully saturated with groundwater. A well drilled into the pressurized water of a confined aquifer fills with water to a height above the surrounding aquifer. Such a condition is an artesian system because the water is forced to higher elevations under its own fluid pressure. The height to which the water rises above or below the ground surface defines a horizon called the potentiometric surface of the confined aquifer. This surface, however, is not flat, but is inclined downward from the recharge area because of the head loss or retarding friction within the confined aquifer.

Therefore, if an artesian well is drilled where the elevation of the land surface is below the potentiometric surface, the result is a flowing artesian well. On the other hand, if the artesian well is drilled where the elevation of the land surface is above the potentiometric surface, the pressurized groundwater rises within the well just to the potentiometric surface, not the land surface. A pump must be used to lift the groundwater the remaining distance to the ground surface, resulting in a pumped artesian well.

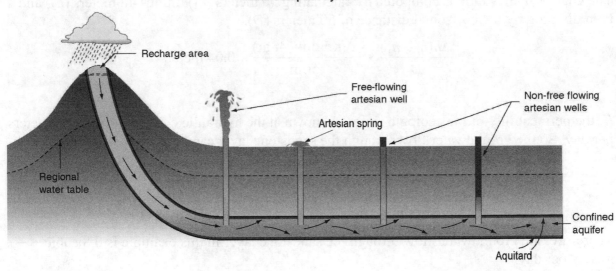

Figure 11.11 Artesian System. Illustration © Kendall Hunt Publishing Company

Groundwater Flow in Unconfined Aquifers

Although groundwater-flow velocities in unconfined aquifers are relatively low compared to the high-flow velocities of surface water, it is possible to gauge the rate of groundwater flow. Flow velocity and flow direction are controlled by the permeability of the saturated zone and the hydraulic gradient—slope of the water table.

Groundwater flow through permeable geologic materials can be quantified by *Darcy's Law*:

$$Q = KA\left(\frac{h\Delta(h_1 - h_2)}{D}\right)$$

Q is the discharge in terms of volume per unit of time.

K is the permeability of the geologic material known at the hydraulic conductivity.

A is the cross-sectional area through which the groundwater flows (width times depth).

h_1 is the elevation of water table at well 1.

h_2 is the elevation of water table at well 2.

$\frac{h\Delta(h_1 - h_2)}{D}$ is the hydraulic gradient or the change in elevation (Δh) divided by the flow horizontal distance (D).

For example, the cross-sectional area of a sandstone layer that is 20 meters wide and 5 meters deep is calculated as follows:

$$A = \textbf{20 meters (wide)} \times \textbf{5 meters (depth)} = \textbf{100 m}^2$$

The hydraulic gradient $\Delta h(h_1 - h_2)$ for the sandstone layer water table drops off to the west from well #1 at 50 meters (h_1) to well #2 at 48 meters (h_2). The horizontal distance is 50 meters (D).

The change in elevation is computed by calculating 50 meters (h_1) minus 48 meters (h_2) and then dividing by the horizontal distance of 50 meters (D).

$$\frac{\Delta h(h_1 - h_2)}{D} = \frac{\Delta h(50\text{m} - 48\text{m})}{50\text{m}} = 0.04 \text{ meters}$$

K, the permeability of the geologic material known at the hydraulic conductivity, is 0.2 meters per day. So the groundwater flow through the sandstone layer can be computed as follows:

$$Q = KA\left(\frac{h\Delta(h_1 - h_2)}{D}\right)$$

$$Q = 0.2 \text{ meters per day} \times 100 \text{ m}^2 \times 0.04 \text{ m} = 0.8 \text{ m}^3 \text{ per day}$$

Therefore, the groundwater flow through the sandstone layer in this example is 0.8 cubic meters per day.

In a permeable geologic material, such as sandstone, flow velocities might range from several feet per day to several feet per year. In less permeable geologic materials, such as shale, the groundwater-flow velocity might be only a few feet per thousand years. The groundwater flow is driven by relatively small differences in groundwater pressure, which cause the groundwater to flow along a pressure gradient. In most groundwater systems, the hydraulic gradient is essentially the same as the pressure gradient. Therefore, the groundwater simply moves along the pressure gradient or down the "slope" of the water table.

The groundwater-flow direction in the saturated zone is generally from the recharge area to the discharge area where the water table intersects the ground surface. The depth to the water table depends on the balance between the rate of recharge and the rate of discharge. Recharge areas include areas of high precipitation or areas occupied by influent streams, where water seeps through the stream bed into the ground and causes a rise in the water table. Lakes, ponds, and swamps are other common sources of influent recharge. Groundwater discharge, on the other hand, occurs in areas occupied by effluent streams, springs, or man-made wells. Groundwater flow into an effluent stream, for example, adds water to the stream's natural surface-water flow.

Karst Topography

As unconfined groundwater flows through the saturated zone within soluble bedrock, such as limestone, large amounts of the bedrock may be dissolved and carried away in solution by the groundwater. This process of groundwater solution forms underground cavities and connecting passageways. Ultimately, the roofs of these large underground voids collapse, leaving surface depressions called sinks or sinkholes. A terrain occupied by many sinkholes is called karst topography, a name derived from a pock-marked limestone region along the Dalmation Coast of what used to be Yugoslavia.

Limestone dissolves because rainwater (and ultimately groundwater) is slightly acidic from the atmospheric- and soil-derived carbon dioxide, which has been absorbed by the groundwater. The acidity results when water (H_2O) and carbon dioxide (CO_2) combine, resulting in carbonic acid (H_2CO_3). The dissolution of the limestone takes place, as follows: calcite (solid) and carbonic acid (liquid) combine into calcium ions and bicarbonate ions (both dissolved in water).

Karst topography is typically characterized by the following features:

Sinkholes—Surface depressions formed by the collapse of solution cavities or other large underground void spaces in limestone bedrock.

Solution valleys—Valley-like depressions formed by a linear series of adjacent sinkholes in limestone bedrock.

Springs—Locations where groundwater is discharged from limestone bedrock onto the land surface.

Disappearing streams—Streams that terminate abruptly by seeping into the ground through a sinkhole or fractures in limestone bedrock.

Much of the drainage in karst areas takes place underground through interconnected solution cavities or passageways rather than by surface runoff. Karst terrain is generally devoid of surface streams. However, lakes or ponds generally form where sinkholes intersect the water table, resulting in an abundance of water surfaces that coincide with the regional water table.

Although dissolution of limestone bedrock takes place in the saturated zone below the water table, limestone can be redeposited in the unsaturated zone above the water table in the form of stalactites and stalagmites. Stalactites are icicle-like masses of chemically precipitated limestone that hang from cave ceilings.

Stalagmites result from the buildup of chemically precipitated limestone where water drips onto the cave floor. If a stalactite and stalagmite join or grow together, the result is a *column* extending continuously from the cave ceiling to the cave floor.

Lab Exercises

Lab Exercise #1: *Yosemite Valley*

In this laboratory exercise you will apply what you have learned to calculate stream gradient, stream discharge, and stream competence. Follow the instructions below and record your results in the space provided or on a separate piece of paper. Make sure to save your results. You will use the data to answer the questions at the end of this lesson.

Instructions and Observations

Step 1: Lay out the USGS topographic map of Yosemite Valley found in your lab kit.

Step 2: Use a ruler to measure the distance along the Merced River from Leidig Meadow footbridge to El Capitan Bridge.

Step 3: Convert the measured distance from Step 2 above to distance expressed in miles. Refer to the bar scale provided along the left hand side above the topographic map.

Step 4: Compute the difference in elevation between Leidig Meadow footbridge (3,965 feet) and El Capitan Bridge (3,955 feet).

Step 5: Calculate the stream gradient of the Merced River between Leidig Meadow footbridge and El Capitan Bridge.

Step 6: Calculate the cross-sectional area of water flow if the channel width of the Merced River in the area is 35 feet and the average water depth is 3 feet.

Step 7: Calculate the discharge of the Merced River in this area if the velocity of water flow is 10 feet per second.

Step 8: Calculate what would happen to the stream competence of the Merced River if, during a flood, the flow velocity increased fourfold.

Lab Exercise #2: *Groundwater Flow*

In this laboratory exercise, you will apply *Darcy's Law* to compute groundwater flow. Follow the instructions below and record your results in the space provided or on a separate piece of paper. Make sure to save your results. You will use the data to answer the questions at the end of this lesson.

Use *Darcy's Law* to calculate the amount of groundwater (*Q*) flowing through a sandstone layer measuring 10 meters wide by 3 meters deep with hydraulic conductivity (*K*) of 0.2 meters per day and a water table that drops off to the east by 1 meter for every 20 meters of horizontal distance.

Instructions

Step 1: Calculate the cross-sectional area (A) through which the groundwater flows.

A = width × depth = _____ × _____ = _____

Step 2: Calculate the hydraulic gradient $\dfrac{\Delta h(h_1 - h_2)}{D}$.

$$\frac{\Delta h(h_1 - h_2)}{D} =$$

Step 3: Using the data provided in this exercise, what is the permeability of the geologic material known at the hydraulic conductivity (K)?

$K =$ _____

Step 4: Use the data from above to calculate the groundwater flow (Q).

$$Q = KA \left(\frac{h\Delta(h_1 - h_2)}{D} \right) =$$

Online Activities

As per your instructor's direction, go to the online lesson for this lab and complete the activities assigned.

Quiz

1. All of the following stream parameters generally increase downstream flow EXCEPT for
   a.   gradient.
   b.   discharge.
   c.   load.
   d.   capacity.
   e.   none of the above.

2. Downslope water flow in channels erodes the surface of the land by
   a.   downcutting.
   b.   headward erosion.
   c.   slope retreat.
   d.   all of the above.
   e.   none of the above.

3. The distance in miles along the Merced River from Leidig Meadow footbridge to El Capitan Bridge is
   a.   0.5 miles.
   b.   2.7 miles.
   c.   3.7 miles.
   d.   5.9 miles.
   e.   10.3 miles.

4. What is the difference in elevation between Leidig Meadow footbridge (3,965 feet) and El Capitan Bridge (3,955 feet)?
   a.   five feet
   b.   ten feet
   c.   twenty feet
   d.   forty feet
   e.   sixty feet

5. Calculate the stream gradient of the Merced River between Leidig Meadow footbridge (3,965 feet) and El Capitan Bridge (3,955 feet).
   a.   3.70 feet per mile
   b.   6.70 feet per mile
   c.   12.70 feet per mile
   d.   24.70 feet per mile
   e.   0.27 feet per mile

6. If the channel width of the Merced River in the area is 35 feet and the average water depth is 3 feet, the cross-sectional area of the water flow is
   a. 60 ft^2.
   b. 70 ft^2.
   c. 95 ft^2.
   d. 105 ft^2.
   e. 140 ft^2.

7. If the velocity of water flow is 10 feet per second, the discharge of the Merced River in this area is
   a. 750 ft^3 per second.
   b. 850 ft^3 per second.
   c. 950 ft^3 per second.
   d. $1,050 \text{ ft}^3$ per second.
   e. $1,150 \text{ ft}^3$ per second.

8. What would happen to the stream competence of the Merced River if, during a flood, the flow velocity increased fourfold?
   a.   It would double.
   b.   It would triple.
   c.   It would increase fourfold.
   d.   It would increase eightfold.
   e.   It would increase sixteenfold.

9. Describe how downslope waterflow in channels erodes the surface of the land to create stream meanders, point bars, and flood plains.

10. The type of stream pattern one would expect to find in regions underlain by horizontal, relatively homogenous rocks would be
    a. rectangular.
    b. dendritic.
    c. trellis.
    d. annular.
    e. none of the above.

Figure 11.12 Meander Loops. Photo © Science VU/Visuals Unlimited

11. In **Figure 11.12** above, the meander loops migrate on the floodplain by eroding their outer banks and depositing alluvium as point bars on their inner banks—often taking shortcuts and creating an _____.

12. Urbanization tends to _____ the frequency of flooding.
    a. decrease
    b. increase
    c. slow down
    d. have no impact on
    e. in wet climates only increase

13. What percentage of precipitation falling on the land becomes surface water, or runoff, and flows to the sea in river and stream channels?
    a. 5%
    b. 10%
    c. 15%
    d. 20%
    e. 25%

14. The volume of freshwater held beneath the earth's surface constitutes as much as _____ the freshwater contained in lakes, rivers, and streams.
    a. 10 times
    b. 20 times
    c. 40 times
    d. 80 times
    e. 160 times

15. An aquifer must be
    a. porous and impermeable.
    b. porous and permeable.
    c. impermeable and nonporous.
    d. just nonporous.
    e. just impermeable.

16. The best aquifer would be a
    a. well-sorted sand.
    b. well-cemented sandstone.
    c. soft clay.
    d. massive siltstone or shale.
    e. massive igneous rock such as granite.

17. A cone of depression is
    a. only associated with an unconfined aquifer.
    b. only associated with a confined aquifer.
    c. associated with both unconfined and confined aquifers.
    d. associated with a recession in the ice cream industry.
    e. none of the above.

18. A confined aquifer is always confined between
    a. the water table and earth's surface.
    b. the water table and bedrock.
    c. two impermeable layers.
    d. permeable layers.
    e. a permeable layer and impermeable layer.

19. What is the difference between an influent and an effluent stream?

20. What geologic conditions are necessary for artesian wells?

21. Karst topography frequently develops on
    a. basalt bedrock.
    b. shale bedrock.
    c. sandstone bedrock.
    d. granite bedrock.
    e. limestone bedrock.

22. Explain the development of karst topography and provide one example of karst topography.

Questions 23 through 26 are based on **Lab Exercise #2:** *Groundwater Flow*

23. The cross-sectional area of the sandstone layer is
    a. 12 m².
    b. 20 m².
    c. 30 m².
    d. 40 m².
    e. 60 m².

24. The hydraulic gradient for the sandstone layer is
    a. 0.01 meter.
    b. 0.05 meter.
    c. 0.10 meter.
    d. 0.50 meter.
    e. 1.0 meter.

25. The groundwater flow (*Q*) through the sandstone layer is
    a. 0.3 cubic meters per day.
    b. 0.8 cubic meters per day.
    c. 1.7 cubic meters per day.
    d. 2.9 cubic meters per day.
    e. 3.6 cubic meters per day.

26. The direction of groundwater flow through the sandstone layer is
    a.   to the north.
    b.   to the east.
    c.   to the south.
    d.   to the west.
    e.   none of the above.

OCEANS AND COASTLINES

Lesson 12

AT A GLANCE

Purpose

Learning Objectives

Materials Needed

Overview

> **Waves**
>
> **Currents**
>
> **Coastal Processes**

Lab Exercise

> **Lab Exercise:** *Tides*

Online Activities

Quiz

Purpose

Many urban cities have developed along our coastal regions and our populations are growing exponentially in such close proximity to our coastlines. Coastlines are dynamic features that are under constant change due to erosional and depositional processes, which are influenced by local tectonic movement and sea level changes. In this lesson, you will learn how coastlines are changing through tidal influence and wave action, and how marine storms can cause erosion of coastal zones.

Learning Objectives

After completing this laboratory lesson, you will be able to:

- Understand how erosional and depositional processes affect coastlines.
- Understand how wave action and tidal influence affects coastline areas.
- Understand how coastal currents work and how those currents affect coastal landforms.
- Calculate the tidal differential in a coastal zone community and wave frequency.

Materials Needed

❏ Pencil
❏ Eraser
❏ Calculator

Overview

The water molecules constantly move throughout all of the ocean basins. Most of us have enjoyed watching the seemingly constant arrival of waves at the shoreline. Everyone is familiar with the tides; those comings and goings of the water along the shoreline in response to the gravitational pull of the moon and the sun. Longshore currents carry sediments along and nearly parallel to the shoreline and are responsible for many coastal features. Most important are the various density currents (a gravity-induced flow dense where the density has been increased by changes in temperature, salinity, and suspended solids) that exist within the vast expanse of the ocean.

Waves

Waves are the major agents of change along the shorelines. In some cases, the change is destructive as the waves carve and erode the rocks, constantly undercutting the coast, driving sea cliffs landward, and removing the coastal sediments to the ocean depths. In other cases, the action of the waves is constructive as the waves build and modify beach deposits and construct offshore sand islands.

Wind-Driven Waves

Waves are created as wind moves across the surface of the water, transferring energy from the moving air mass to the water. Each wave is characterized by a wavelength (the distance between successive crests or troughs) and an amplitude (the distance from a midpoint to the crest or trough of the wave (**Figure 12.1**). Amplitude is sometimes expressed as wave height, the total distance from the top of a crest to the bottom of the adjacent trough.

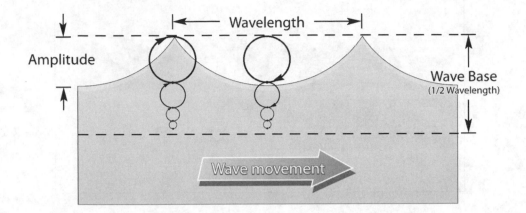

Figure 12.1 Wavelength. In water deeper than the wave base, a passing waveform results in no lateral motion of the water. Above that depth, the water is moved in circular paths that decrease in diameter as depth increases. Illustration by Don Vierstra

Once formed, the waves move in the wind direction with a frequency measured by the number of crests or troughs that pass a given point in a given amount of time. A passing wave will move water to a depth of approximately one-half its wavelength, referred to as the wave base, with the individual water molecules moving in circles that decrease in diameter with depth (refer to **Figure 12.1**). Two important aspects of wave motion are presented here: (1) waves do not move water at depths greater than the wave base (one-half the wavelength in depth); and (2) in water deeper than one-half the wavelength of the waves, there is no lateral motion of the water.

Waves are generated at a particular point of origin and they travel across the open ocean as successive wave crests above the wave base. Physical geologists are primarily interested in the portion of the original wave energy remaining when the waves reach the shore that is available to erode and modify the coastline. As the waves move into shallow water and the wave base "touches" or "feels" the sea bottom, the wavelength shortens, the wave height increases, and the cross section of the waves becomes increasingly asymmetric in the direction of the shoreline. Along the shore, the water begins to move laterally toward the shore (**Figure 12.2**). As the waves move shoreward, some of the original wave energy, E_O, is consumed increasing the amplitude of the waves, moving the water laterally, and eroding the offshore ocean bottom. As the waves approach the shore, the waves become increasingly asymmetric in cross section and form breakers that eventually collapse into the surf. Whatever energy remains in the surf drives the water up onto the beach, where all of the original energy is eventually consumed and gravity takes over, returning the water to the sea as backwash. It is also the energy remaining in the surf that drives coastal processes such as coastal erosion and deposition.

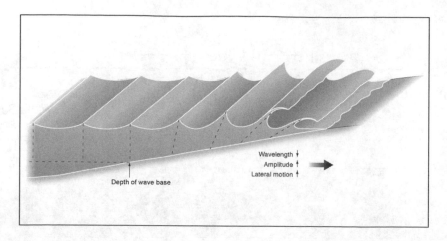

Figure 12.2 Wave Movement. When an arriving wave reaches a depth equivalent to its wave base, its wavelength shortens and its amplitude increases until it is no longer stable and breaks Illustration © Kendall Hunt Publishing Company

Whether a shore is subjected to dominantly erosional processes or to a combination of erosion and deposition depends primarily on the amount of energy remaining as the waves break on the land. In general, the longer and more gentle the offshore slope, the greater the amount of energy that will be used up in wave modification, the lateral movement of the water, and in coastal erosion as the waves make their way shoreward. As the slope of the offshore bottom increases, the distance between the point at which the waves "touch" bottom and the shoreline decreases. When less energy has been consumed between the point at which the wave base touches bottom and the shoreline, more energy becomes available in the surf zone. The extreme example is the pounding surf one observes where the ocean bottom drops precipitously just offshore.

Tsunami

Tsunami are long wavelength, low amplitude waves that are created by a number of events, perhaps the most common being the abrupt movement of the ocean floor (i.e., earthquakes deep within the oceanic crust) in the vicinity of a zone of subduction. Other sources of energy that create tsunami are the slumping of portions of volcanic islands and coastlines and earthquakes that occur along the margin of the ocean basin. The 1883 eruption of the volcanic island of Krakatau created a tsunami that overwhelmed all of the low-lying portions of the surrounding islands and carried an estimated 36,000 people to their deaths.

While the amplitudes of the waves associated with typical tsunami traveling across the ocean surface may be no more than 1 meter (3 feet) high, wavelengths may exceed 100 kilometers (60 miles). Because of the enormous amount of energy being transported, it is not uncommon for the velocity of a tsunami to be as fast as 750 kilometers per hour (470 miles per hour). As these waves come onshore and the wavelengths shorten, their amplitudes increase to as much as 30 meters (100 feet) high and drive inland, laying waste to everything in their path. Because of its location, Japan has probably experienced more devastating tsunami than any other place on Earth. For example, on June 15, 1889, a wall of water 25 to 30 meters (75 to 100 feet) high crashed onto the east shore of the Japanese main island of Honshu, sweeping away more than 10,000 homes and killing an estimated 26,000 people. In 1946, the Seismic Sea Wave Warning System (SSWWS) was established to warn the inhabitants of those regions located around the periphery of the Pacific Ocean basin of a potentially destructive tsunami.

Tides

Most individuals are aware that the tides are a type of wave caused by the gravitational attraction between the ocean's water and the moon but few are aware that the sun also plays a role. While the moon is many times less massive than the sun, the moon is so much closer to Earth that its gravitational effect on the tides is approximately twice that of the sun.

Spring and Neap Tides

Along most coasts, both high and low tides occur twice each day as Earth rotates through the two tidal bulges. Because Earth's hydrosphere is liquid and can flow with little resistance, the layer of water begins to deform into an oblong sphere with one tidal bulge facing toward the moon while another tidal bulge develops on the opposite side of Earth facing away from the moon. Because of the changing orientation of the sun, Earth, and moon during the monthly lunar cycle, the combined effects of the sun and moon change (**Figure 12.3**).

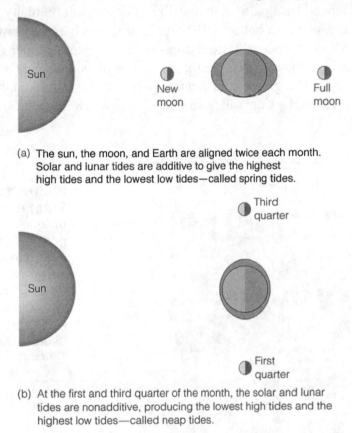

(a) The sun, the moon, and Earth are aligned twice each month. Solar and lunar tides are additive to give the highest high tides and the lowest low tides—called spring tides.

(b) At the first and third quarter of the month, the solar and lunar tides are nonadditive, producing the lowest high tides and the highest low tides—called neap tides.

Figure 12.3 Effect of the Sun and the Moon on Monthly Tidal Changes. The monthly tidal range is the result of the changing relationship between the sun, Earth, and the moon. When all three bodies are aligned along the same axis, as they are during the new and full phases of the moon, the tidal effects of the moon and sun are additive, resulting in the maximum tidal range, the so-called spring tide. When the moon is in either the first or third quarter phase, the tides are largely controlled by the moon and the tidal range will be at its minimum, the so-called neap tide.

From *Planet Earth* by John J. Renton. Copyright © 2002 by John J. Renton. Reprinted by permission of Kendall Hunt Publishing Company.

Tidal Range

When the sun, Earth, and the moon are aligned, as they are during the new and full phases of the moon, the effects of the solar and lunar tides are additive, resulting in the maximum tidal range, so-called spring tide. At these two times during the lunar cycle, the tidal range (the tidal range is the vertical difference between the high tide and the succeeding low tide. It is the difference in height between high and low water and will vary throughout the tidal cycle) is at a maximum, that is, the high tides are at their highest while the low tides are at their lowest. Such tides are called spring tides; the term having nothing to do with the season of the year. During the first and third phases of the moon when the sun and the moon are at right angles to Earth, the solar and lunar gravitational forces partially cancel each other, resulting in a decrease in the tidal range as the highest tides decrease while the lowest tides increase. Such tides are referred to as neap tides.

The tidal range experienced by a particular coastline is dependent on many factors, one of them being the slope of the ocean bottom offshore. In areas such as the Hawaiian Islands or off the Florida Keys where the ocean bottom drops off steeply into deeper water, the tidal range is relatively small. In locations where the ocean bottom slopes gently seaward, tidal ranges may be quite large. The greatest tidal range in North America is in the Bay of Fundy, Nova Scotia, Canada, where the tidal range can be as high as 18 meters (50 feet) (**Figure 12.4**).

Figure 12.4 Bay of Fundy Tidal Range. Because of its unique combination of a gentle offshore slope and confinement by the adjacent landmass, the Bay of Fundy, Nova Scotia, Canada, experiences the highest tidal range in North America.

Courtesy of Nova Scotia Tourism

The extreme tidal range within the Bay of Fundy is the result of both a gently sloping bottom within the bay as well as the funneling of the waters through a restricted channel that connects the bay with the open sea.

Currents

Longshore Currents

For the most part, waves approach the shoreline at an angle (**Figure 12.5**).

Figure 12.5 Surf Driving Waves to Shore. Because most waves approach the shoreline at an angle, they undergo refraction. As a result, the surf drives the water onto and along the shoreline, generating the longshore current, which is responsible for the lateral transportation of sand along the coastline. Photo credit: VU/© John D. Cunningham

As one end of the wave touches bottom, it enters water shallower than its wave base, the wave slows and bends, or refracts, becoming more parallel to the shoreline. As a result, the surf drives water both onto and along the beach, forming a longshore current within the surf zone (**Figure 12.6**). The velocity of the longshore current within the surf zone is dependent on the angle of wave approach with the velocity increasing with the angle of approach. The longshore currents are primarily responsible for the continuous movement of sand just offshore parallel to the beach, referred to as longshore transport.

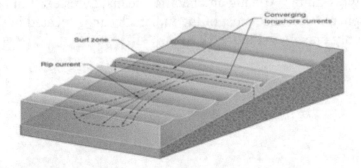

Figure 12.6 Longshore Current. Surf drives water both onto and along the beach, forming a longshore current within the surf zone. Illustration © Kendall Hunt Publishing Company

Longshore currents can also be created where the waves approach the shoreline at right angles by a process referred to as wave setup. The wave setup refers to piles of water along the shoreline within the surf zone. If the water slides off these piles in opposite directions parallel to the shoreline, this creates divergent longshore currents. In general, the higher the incoming breakers, the greater the amount of water contained within these piles of water, and the more powerful the subsequent divergent longshore currents are. Where two divergent longshore currents converge, the water flow will be diverted seaward to create a very strong rip current that transports the excess water that has been brought into the surf zone back to sea.

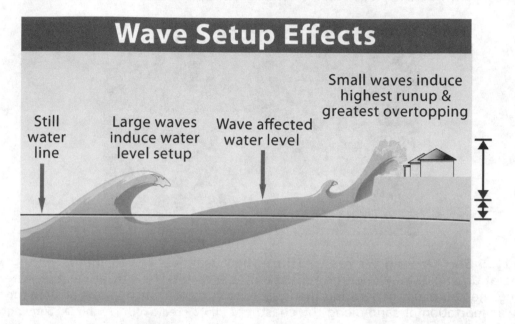

Figure 12.7 Wave Setup Effects. Longshore currents can also be created where the waves approach the shoreline at right angles by a process referred to as wave setup. The wave setup refers to piles of water along the shoreline within the surf zone. Illustration by Don Vierstra

Wind-Driven Currents

Within each ocean, surface and near-surface waters are set into motion as stresses develop between the wind and the ocean surface as energy is transferred from the wind to the water. Large-scale wind-driven ocean currents moving within each hemisphere in large circular patterns are called gyres. In the Atlantic and Pacific oceans, gyres exist in both the northern and southern hemispheres. Because most of the Indian Ocean is located in the Southern Hemisphere, it has only one gyre (**Figure 12.8**).

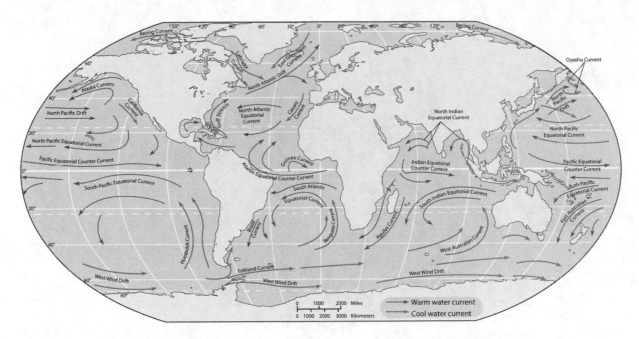

Figure 12.8 Gyres. Driven by energy provided by the winds, the surface waters of the ocean are driven in circular patterns called gyres, clockwise in the Northern Hemisphere and counterclockwise in the Southern Hemisphere. The Atlantic and Pacific oceans each have two gyres while the Indian Ocean, because it is almost totally located in the Southern Hemisphere, has a counterclockwise gyre. Illustration © Kendall Hunt Publishing Company

The winds primarily responsible for the creation of the gyres are the trade winds, which blow from east to west toward the equator between 5° and 25° north and south latitude, and the westerlies, which blow west to east. (**Figure 12.9**).

The trade winds create two warm water equatorial currents (currents just north and south of the equator that are driven by trade winds, southwestward or westward in the Northern Hemisphere and northward or westward in the South Hemisphere) that move westward parallel to the equator separated by an equatorial countercurrent (a narrow, surface ocean current near the equator that flows eastward between the westward-flowing equatorial currents) that flows eastward (see **Figure 12.9**). As the two warm equatorial currents reach the continents on the western margin of the ocean basins, they are deflected by Earth's rotation to the right and left and form a northern and southern equatorial current respectively that serve as heat pumps to transport heat from the tropical equatorial regions of Earth to the cooler, higher latitudes. As the warm currents move toward the poles along the continental margins, they eventually come under the influence of relatively cool, dry westerly winds which blow from the west between 35° and 60° both north and south latitude and are diverted eastward (see **Figure 12.9**). It is important to point out that as the heat brought to the higher latitudes by the gyres is transferred to the westerly winds, they are not only warmed but as a result of becoming warmed, acquire moisture from the ocean. Now warm and moist, the westerly winds continue eastward to determine the climate of the continent to the east. Upon encountering the continent on the eastern side of the ocean basin, the now cooled currents are deflected toward the equator where they join the equatorial currents to complete the gyre and become reheated. You may have learned in an elementary geography course that the relatively mild, but rainy, climate of Europe is a result of the landmass being bathed in the heat brought northward by the North Atlantic gyre from the warmer and moister tropical climates.

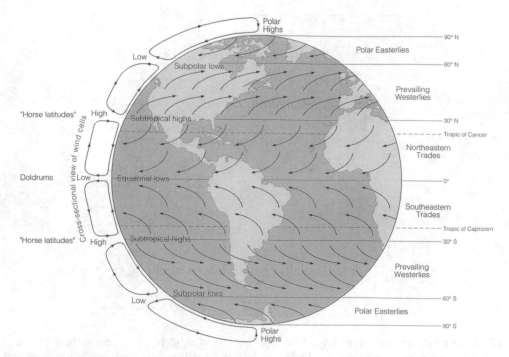

Figure 12.9 Trade Winds. Two dominant winds on Earth are the easterly trade winds and the westerly winds. The trade winds blow toward the equator from about 25 degrees north and south latitude and are primarily responsible for the generation of the gyres. The westerly winds blow from the west between about 35 degrees and 60 degrees north and south latitude and deflect the gyres away from the eastern continental coastlines, across the ocean basins and toward the western continental coastlines. From *Planet Earth* by John J. Renton. Copyright © 2002 by John J. Renton. Reprinted by permission of Kendall Hunt Publishing Company.

Because the equatorial countercurrent exists across the entire width of the Pacific Ocean, little or no exchange of surface water occurs between the Northern and Southern hemispheres. Within the Atlantic Ocean, some oceanic surface water moves from the Southern Hemisphere to the Northern Hemisphere as the south equatorial current is split by the landmass of Brazil (see **Figure 12.9**). The northern portion of the split continues into the Caribbean and the Gulf of Mexico where it joins with the northern equatorial current to become the part of the North Atlantic gyre, commonly referred to as the Gulf Stream.

Wind-Induced Currents

Ocean water is subdivided vertically into two masses, the upper water mass, which extends from the surface to a depth of about 1,000 meters (3,000 feet), and the deep water mass, which extends from the bottom of the upper water mass to the ocean bottom. Both of these zones experience vertical water movements. In the upper water mass, vertical movements are wind-induced. In areas where the water is carried away by one surface current and not replenished by another, replacement water moves up from below. Although such upwelling can occur anywhere within the ocean, it is most prevalent in four areas: (1) where equatorial currents deflect water away from the equator, (2) along western continental margins, where strong winds blowing off the land carry water away from the coastline, (3) where winds blow steadily in one direction and generate convection cells parallel to the wind flow (see **Figure 12.10**), and (4) in the north Atlantic and Pacific oceans, where the combination of winds, heat exchange, and salinity differences cause global convective currents that will be discussed below.

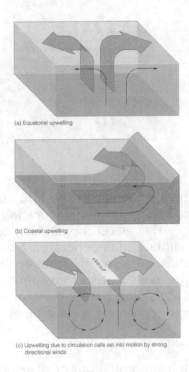

(a) Equatorial upwelling

(b) Coastal upwelling

(c) Upwelling due to circulation cells set into motion by strong
directional winds

Figure 12.10 Wind-induced Currents. Wind-induced currents form as surface water is removed from a portion of the ocean by a wind-driven surface current without being replaced by water brought in by another surface current. Three places where they are commonly found are: (1) along the equator; (2) parallel to western continental margins; and (3) anywhere at sea where winds blow steadily in one direction for long periods of time. A fourth scenario, not portrayed in this figure, involves areas in both the northern Atlantic and Pacific oceans, where currents are generated by the complex interaction of the wind, thermal gradients, and salinity differences. From *Planet Earth* by John J. Renton. Copyright © 2002 by John J. Renton. Reprinted by permission of Kendall Hunt Publishing Company.

Thermohaline Currents

Most of the vertical mixing of ocean water is the result of thermohaline currents, which affect the entire volume of ocean water. Thermohaline currents are density currents that originate in regions beyond 40° north and south latitude where masses of cold, dense, surface waters sink. Of the world's oceans, only the polar regions of the North and South Atlantic have surface waters with densities high enough to sink when surrounded by less dense water. Within the Pacific and Indian oceans, the relatively uniform conditions of temperature and salinity that characterize the surface and near-surface water masses apparently prevent the formations of density differentials large enough to cause surface water to sink.

The density of water increases with increasing salt content. Examples of salinity-induced density currents can be found wherever low-density freshwater enters the ocean and flows out across the surface of the higher-density, saline ocean waters until they are intermixed and dispersed by the waves. In many coastal areas, it is not uncommon for saline or brackish water to flow upstream along the bottoms of streams during the rising tides. The lack of vegetation along the downstream banks of many coastal streams is due to the infusion of toxic saltwater into the bank sediments. Perhaps the best example of a major salinity current is the one responsible for the continuous overturning of the water in the Mediterranean Sea
(**Figure 12.11**).

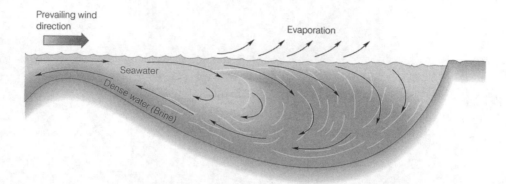

Figure 12.11 Salinity Currents. Each year, nearly 800 cubic miles of water move into the Mediterranean Sea to replace water lost by evaporation and not replaced by runoff from the surrounding landmasses. This water movement, combined with subsequent evaporation due to the hot, dry climate, has generated a density current within the Mediterranean Sea and has established a stratification at the Strait of Gibraltar as normal-salinity, normal-density, oceanic waters move into the Mediterranean Sea while, at the same time, the denser, more saline waters generated by evaporation move back out into the Atlantic Ocean. Illustration © Kendall Hunt Publishing Company

Turbidity Currents

Density currents resulting from high concentrations of suspended loads are called turbidity currents. Turbidity currents can commonly be seen wherever a silt- and clay-laden stream flows into the relatively clear larger body of water. As the sediment-laden water enters the larger body of water, it forms a turbidity flow that continues downward along bottom until currents within the larger body of water either dissipate the flow or until the sediment settles out (**Figure 12.12**)

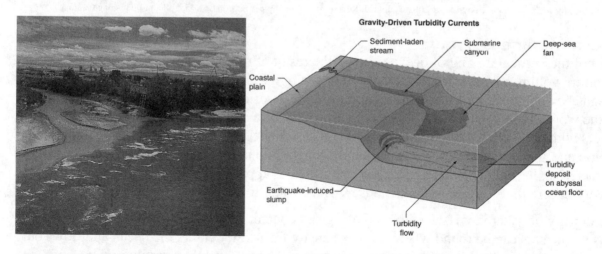

Figure 12.12 Turbidity Currents. Turbidity currents can commonly be seen wherever a silt- and clay-laden stream flows into the relatively clear larger body of water. Photo credit: VU/©Ron Spomer; illustration © Kendall Hunt Publishing Company

Coastal Processes

No two coastls are exactly alike. They exhibit differences in structure, rock types, or process. There are two basic types of coastlines: (1) the emergent or high-energy coastline typified by most of the U.S. Pacific coast and portions of the northeast Atlantic coast; and (2) the submergent or low-energy coastline found along most of the Atlantic and Gulf States.

Emergent or High-Energy Coastlines

Point Lobos, California, is not only an exceptionally scenic portion of the California coastline but also an example of an emergent, high-energy coastline (**Figure 12.13 a** and **b**).

Figure 12.13 Emergent Coastlines. An example of an emergent, high-energy coastline (left), Point Lobos, California, is thought by some to be the most beautiful meeting of the land and the sea on Earth. Eventually, the cliff fails by slumping or rock fall, and the debris is quickly removed to the wave-built terrace (right). From *Planet Earth* by John J. Renton. Copyright © 2002 by John J. Renton. Reprinted by permission of Kendall Hunt Publishing Company.

The scene at Point Lobos is repeated along most of the Pacific coast, where the continental edge is rapidly rising because of the tectonic activity associated with the transform boundary between the Pacific and North American plates. Because the offshore slope along coasts such as at Point Lobos is relatively steep, waves touch bottom close to the shore, the wave height builds rapidly, and little wave energy is dissipated before the waters reach the surf zone. Consequently, as the waves pound against the rocks within the surf zone, the rocks themselves see destruction from the high-energy environment (**Figure 12.13a**).

Because water is essentially incompressible (it is slightly compressible), each wave impacts the rock like a hammer, driving water under great pressure into fractures where mechanical weathering wears the rock away and undermines the cliff face. In some cases, fracture systems can form into sea caves that further undermine the wave-cut cliff (**Figure 12.13b**).

Submergent or Low-Energy Coastlines

In contrast to the emerging, high-energy, Pacific-style coastlines, most of the Atlantic and Gulf coastal shorelines are slowly subsiding in response to the combined effects of crustal cooling away from the oceanic ridges and the accumulation of thousands of feet of sediment within the tectonically quiet areas that border the edge of the continent. Along most of the Atlantic and Gulf coast, the coastal plain extends seaward as the long, gently sloping continental shelf. Because incoming waves touch the sea bottom relative far from the shore, water movement and bottom erosion consume much of their energy before they reach the shoreline. As a result, the amount of energy remaining in each wave upon arriving in the surf zone is significantly less than in waves approaching the typical Pacific coastline.

Slight topographic relief in the coastal plain is amplified into the irregularities that are commonly seen along Atlantic-type coastlines (**Figure 12.14**).

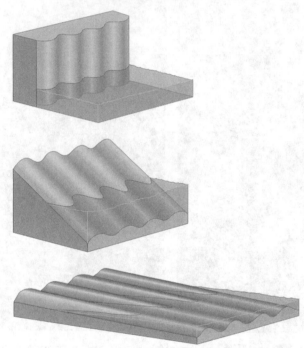

Figure 12.14 Highly Irregular Coastlines. In locations where the land enters the water at a steep angle, the coastline can be highly irregular. If the land enters the water at a shallow angle, the shoreline is initially highly irregular, but over time, erosional and depositional forces tend to straighten out the coastline. From *Planet Earth* by John J. Renton. Copyright © 2002 by John J. Renton. Reprinted by permission of Kendall Hunt Publishing Company.

Along such coastlines, erosion by the incoming waves is concentrated at the seaward ends of the promontories (a prominent mass of land which overlooks lower lying land or a body of water and it may be called a peninsula or headland). As the promontories are eroded and retreat, the sediments generated are simultaneously deposited in an adjacent area (see **Figure 12.15**).

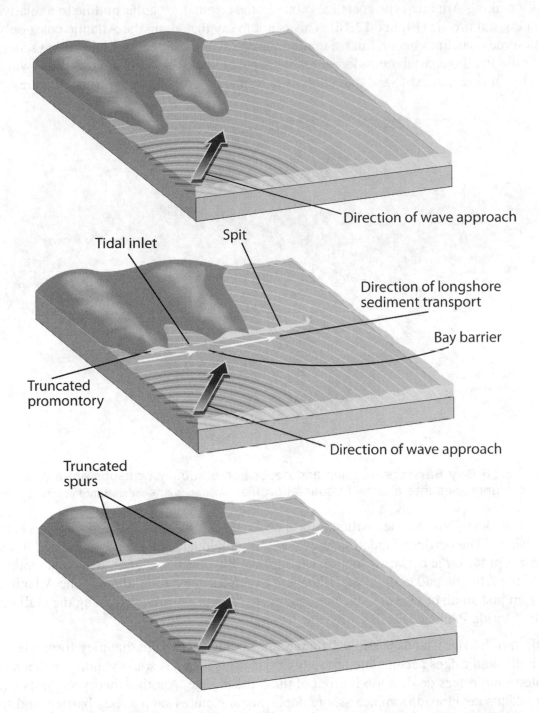

Figure 12.15 Submergent Coastline. Although submergent coastlines are initially irregular in outline, the shoreline straightens as waves erode the promontories and deposit the debris as bay barriers and spits. Illustration © Kendall Hunt Publishing Company

Longshore currents carry the sediments, mostly sand-size, parallel to the shoreline and deposit them between adjacent retreating headlands, creating bay barriers or baymouth bars (a narrow strip of deposited sand that crosses the mouth of a bay), which in turn create sheltered bays and lagoons. As sand moves parallel to the coast, long narrow deposits called spits are created that are attached to the retreating headland at one end, extend parallel to the shore, and commonly terminate with a characteristic inward curl. The combined processes of erosion and deposition along Atlantic-type coastlines convert the original irregular outline to a relatively straight coastal profile (**Figure 12.16**). This is not to say that along the Atlantic coast only Atlantic-type coastlines occur, but the conditions do favor these features barrier bays and sand spits. Some Pacific coastal areas do have what appear to be Atlantic-type coastlines, which are caused by an abundance of sand that allows the formation of these depositional features.

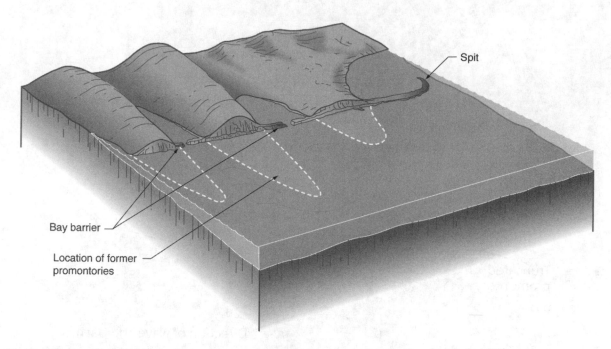

Figure 12.16 Bay Barriers. Erosion and deposition gradually transubstantiate the former promontories into a straight coastal profile. Illustration © Kendall Hunt Publishing Company

Perhaps the most dominant depositional form observed along Atlantic-type coastlines is the barrier island. The barrier island system consists of individual sand islands separated by tidal inlets. Except for large estuaries such as Chesapeake Bay, barrier islands are found along much of the Atlantic and Gulf coasts. Excellent examples can be found along the Atlantic coast from just south of Ocean City, New Jersey, to Miami, Florida, and along the Gulf coast from the Florida Panhandle to Brownsville, Texas.

The origin of barrier islands is still debated. Some geologists believe that they form when storm-built sand ridges accumulate above high tide. This idea has some validity in that storm-generated sand ridges do develop in front of the breaker zone. Another theory suggests that the barrier islands developed from near-shore depositional features such as bay barriers and spits that migrated landward as sea level rose. Other geologists believe that the present system of barrier islands along the Atlantic and Gulf coasts originated as sand beaches and beach ridges formed far out on the exposed portion of the continental shelf at the low stand of the ocean during the last glacial episode. According to this theory, as the ice melted and sea level rose, the beaches and beach ridges combined to form sand ridges that moved progressively landward and increased in height (see **Figure 12.17**).

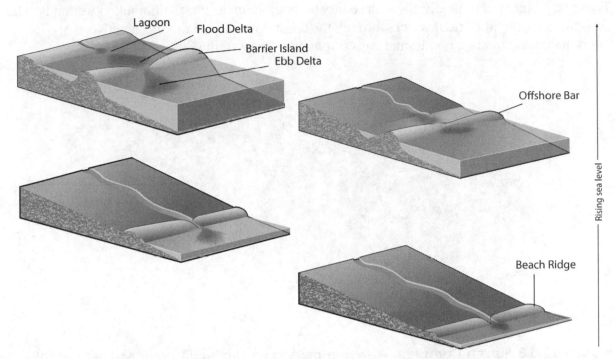

Figure 12.17 Creation of Barrier Islands. Although barrier islands can form by a number of processes, most of those associated with the Atlantic and Gulf coasts are thought to have formed as sea level rose following the retreat of the last glacial episode. Illustration © Kendall Hunt Publishing Company

Eventually sea level rose to the point that seawater flooded the low-lying area landward of the sand ridges, creating lagoons (a shallow body of water open to the sea but protected from the energy of the open sea by organic reefs or sand barriers) or bays (surrounded by land on three sides; it is a shallow body of water and is protected from the energy of the open sea). As the lagoons or bays became interconnected, the sand ridges became isolated as offshore barrier islands.

Once the barrier islands formed, the bays began to fill with sediment from the land as deltas built into the bays. Sand that was transported through the tidal inlet separating the individual islands takes place during the incoming tides (known as flood tides) and deposited on the bay side of the tidal inlet as flood deltas. During the outgoing or ebb tide, some of the material deposited in the bay is carried back through the tidal inlet and deposited on the seaward side of the tidal inlet as the delta (low triangular area where alluvial deposits enter into the river which divides before entering a larger body of water). Because the wave energy of the incoming tide is always greater than that of the ebb tide, the amount of sediment deposited in the flood delta always exceeded that deposited in the ebb delta. Over time, the bays behind the barrier islands begin to fill with sediment. The first sign that bays are beginning to fill with sediment is the exposure of the bay bottom at low tide called a mudflat.

Salt-tolerant grasses begin to grow on the exposed mudflat that trap sediments that normally would be flushed through the system. In time, the grass-covered mudflat builds above high tide to form a saltwater marsh.

As the marsh continues to expand, trees may begin to grow within portions of the marsh, converting the marsh into a swamp. In time, much of what had been open bays is converted into a swamp-marsh complex.

These bays never completely fill with sediment, but remain as water-dominated wetlands. The constant movement of tidal waters through the coastal wetland maintains a network of interconnected streams, ponds, and bays throughout the system (**Figure 12.18**).

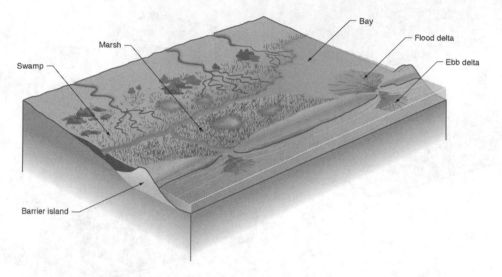

Figure 12.18 Marsh Complex. A swamp-marsh complex, infiltrated by a network of water features. Illustration © Kendall Hunt Publishing Company

Most of the water that enters through a tidal inlet during the flood tide circulates through the wetland and exits the wetland through a different tidal inlet. This circulation of water through the system is essential for the survival of the wetland and for the offshore fisheries for which the wetland is a major source of food.

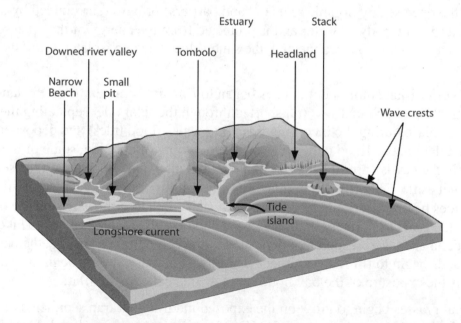

Figure 12.19 Major Coastal Regions. Major features found along a coastal region.
Illustration by Don Vierstra

In **Figure 12.19** above, each coastal feature has a distinct meaning and definition. These coastal features are created by natural forces acting upon one another, and are a result of erosional, wave action, and ocean current movements.

Beach a mixture of gravel or sand paralleling and declining towards a shoreline.

Estuary–a flooded ocean or lake resulting in a river valley.

Longshore current–a water current driven by wind-caused waves parallel to the shoreline.

Headland–an extension of land extending into a body or water, commonly with cliffs on the water boundary.

Spit–an extension into the mouth of a bordering bay by a sand bar extending from a beach.

Stack–a small island of rock isolated from the mainland and near a headland cliff.

Saltmarsh– a marsh of salt water comprising flooded ocean water, which is exposed at low tide.

Tide island–an island that, through a tombolo, is attached to another piece of land.

Tombolo–a sand bar serving to unite an island with another piece of land.

Wave crest–the highest part of a wave.

Wave Frequency

Wave frequency is calculated by the speed of the wave (velocity) divided by the wavelength (**Figure 12.20**).

$$\text{Wave Frequency} = \frac{\text{Speed of Wave}}{\text{Wavelength}}$$

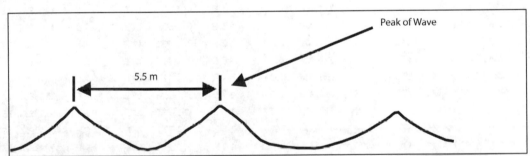

Figure 12.20 Wavelength. The two marks indicate the distance between the peaks of the wave. In this figure, the wavelength is 5.5 m/w. Illustration by Mark Worden

For example, an incoming ocean wave has a velocity of 6.5 meters per second (m/s) and a wavelength of 5.5 meters per wavelength (m/w). Find the frequency of the wave.

$$\text{Frequency} = \frac{\text{Speed of Wave}}{\text{Wavelength}} = \frac{6.5 \text{ m/s}}{5.5 \text{ m/w}} = \textbf{1.18 w/s}$$

Answer: **The frequency of the wave between the two wave peaks is 1.18 wavelengths per second (w/s).**

Lab Exercise
Lab Exercise: *Tides*

In this laboratory exercise, you will use a tide chart to find high and low tide readings and calculate the difference between them. This exercise will demonstrate the immense gravitational forces the moon has upon our tidal fluctuations along the coastal regions of our world. Follow the instructions below and record your results in the space provided or on a separate piece of paper. Make sure to save your results. You will use the data to answer the questions at the end of this lesson.

2010 NOAA Tide Predictions: El Segundo, Santa Monica Bay

(Reference station: Los Angeles, Corrections Applied: Times: High 0 hr. 13 min., Low 0 hr. 13 min., Heights: High *0.96, Low *0.96)

January - El Segundo, Santa Monica Bay

Date	Day	Time		Height	Time		Height	Time		Height	Time		Height
01/01/2010	Fri	02:44AM	LST	1.8 L	08:59AM	LST	6.8 H	04:13PM	LST	-1.6 L	10:45PM	LST	4 H
01/02/2010	Sat	03:35AM	LST	1.7 L	09:46AM	LST	6.5 H	04:55PM	LST	-1.4 L	11:28PM	LST	4.2 H
01/03/2010	Sun	04:31AM	LST	1.6 L	10:35AM	LST	6 H	05:37PM	LST	-1.1 L			
01/04/2010	Mon	12:13AM	LST	4.4 H	05:34AM	LST	1.6 L	11:28AM	LST	5.3 H	06:19PM	LST	-0.5 L
01/05/2010	Tue	01:02AM	LST	4.6 H	06:47AM	LST	1.6 L	12:28PM	LST	4.4 H	07:03PM	LST	0.2 L
01/06/2010	Wed	01:55AM	LST	4.8 H	08:14AM	LST	1.5 L	01:44PM	LST	3.6 H	07:51PM	LST	0.9 L
01/07/2010	Thu	02:52AM	LST	4.9 H	09:51AM	LST	1.2 L	03:28PM	LST	3 H	08:46PM	LST	1.5 L
01/08/2010	Fri	03:51AM	LST	5.1 H	11:18AM	LST	0.7 L	05:27PM	LST	2.8 H	09:52PM	LST	2 L
01/09/2010	Sat	04:49AM	LST	5.3 H	12:24PM	LST	0.1 L	06:57PM	LST	3 H	11:02PM	LST	2.3 L
01/10/2010	Sun	05:42AM	LST	5.5 H	01:15PM	LST	-0.3 L	07:55PM	LST	3.3 H			
01/11/2010	Mon	12:03AM	LST	2.3 L	06:29AM	LST	5.6 H	01:56PM	LST	-0.6 L	08:36PM	LST	3.5 H
01/12/2010	Tue	12:53AM	LST	2.3 L	07:10AM	LST	5.7 H	02:32PM	LST	-0.8 L	09:08PM	LST	3.6 H
01/13/2010	Wed	01:34AM	LST	2.2 L	07:46AM	LST	5.8 H	03:03PM	LST	-0.8 L	09:35PM	LST	3.6 H
01/14/2010	Thu	02:09AM	LST	2.1 L	08:20AM	LST	5.8 H	03:32PM	LST	-0.8 L	10:01PM	LST	3.6 H
01/15/2010	Fri	02:43AM	LST	2 L	08:52AM	LST	5.7 H	03:59PM	LST	-0.7 L	10:26PM	LST	3.7 H
01/16/2010	Sat	03:16AM	LST	1.9 L	09:22AM	LST	5.5 H	04:26PM	LST	-0.5 L	10:52PM	LST	3.8 H
01/17/2010	Sun	03:51AM	LST	1.8 L	09:53AM	LST	5.2 H	04:51PM	LST	-0.3 L	11:19PM	LST	3.9 H
01/18/2010	Mon	04:28AM	LST	1.8 L	10:24AM	LST	4.8 H	05:16PM	LST	0.1 L	11:47PM	LST	4 H
01/19/2010	Tue	05:10AM	LST	1.9 L	10:57AM	LST	4.3 H	05:41PM	LST	0.5 L			
01/20/2010	Wed	12:18AM	LST	4.1 H	06:01AM	LST	1.9 L	11:34AM	LST	3.7 H	06:04PM	LST	0.9 L
01/21/2010	Thu	12:52AM	LST	4.1 H	07:07AM	LST	1.9 L	12:23PM	LST	3.2 H	06:29PM	LST	1.3 L
01/22/2010	Fri	01:34AM	LST	4.3 H	08:40AM	LST	1.7 L	01:47PM	LST	2.5 H	06:57PM	LST	1.7 L
01/23/2010	Sat	02:27AM	LST	4.4 H	10:26AM	LST	1.2 L	04:35PM	LST	2.3 H	07:43PM	LST	2.1 L
01/24/2010	Sun	03:31AM	LST	4.7 H	11:41AM	LST	0.7 L	06:39PM	LST	2.6 H	09:21PM	LST	2.4 L
01/25/2010	Mon	04:37AM	LST	5.1 H	12:33PM	LST	-0.1 L	07:25PM	LST	2.9 H	10:57PM	LST	2.4 L
01/26/2010	Tue	05:36AM	LST	5.6 H	01:16PM	LST	-0.7 L	07:58PM	LST	3.3 H			
01/27/2010	Wed	12:06AM	LST	2.2 L	06:29AM	LST	6 H	01:55PM	LST	-1.2 L	08:29PM	LST	3.6 H
01/28/2010	Thu	01:02AM	LST	1.8 L	07:19AM	LST	6.4 H	02:34PM	LST	-1.5 L	09:01PM	LST	3.9 H
01/29/2010	Fri	01:53AM	LST	1.4 L	08:06AM	LST	6.6 H	03:11PM	LST	-1.7 L	09:35PM	LST	4.2 H
01/30/2010	Sat	02:43AM	LST	1.2 L	08:53AM	LST	6.6 H	03:48PM	LST	-1.5 L	10:10PM	LST	4.6 H
01/31/2010	Sun	03:33AM	LST	0.9 L	09:40AM	LST	6.2 H	04:25PM	LST	-1.2 L	10:47PM	LST	4.8 H

All times are listed in Local Standard Time(LST) or, Local Daylight Time (LDT) (when applicable). All heights are in feet referenced to Mean Lower Low Water (MLLW).

Figure 12.21 Tide Chart. Chart by Mark Worden.

The tide chart (**Figure 12.21**) describes the high and low fluctuations of the tide in the Santa Monica Bay near the City of El Segundo in Southern California. A tide table, sometimes called a tide chart, is used for tidal prediction and shows the daily times and height of high water and low water for a particular location. Tide charts are published for major commercial ports for the shipping industry so large commercial transport vessels can move safely in and out of a port.

The tidal difference within a 24-hour period is determined by the highest tide in a 24-hour period minus the lowest tide in the same 24-hour period.

Tidal difference =   Highest tide – lowest tide

Example:
Using the tide chart above (**Figure 12.21**), January 5, 2010, had the following tide predictions.

Date: 01/05/10

Time	Height	Tide (Low or High)
1:02 a.m.	4.6 feet	High tide
6:47 a.m.	1.6 feet	Low tide
12:28 p.m.	4.4 feet	High tide
7:03 p.m.	0.2 feet	Low tide

The highest tide in the 24-hour period (on 01/05/10) = 4.6 feet

The lowest tide in the 24-hour period (on 01/05/10) = 0.2 feet

The tidal difference = 4.6 feet – 0.2 feet = 4.4 feet in a 24-hour period

Instructions and Observations

Step 1:   Use the tide chart (**Figure 12.21**) to record the tide predictions for January 20, 2010.

Date:

Time	Height	Tide (Low or High)

Step 2:   Record the highest tide in the 24-hour period.

Step 3:   Record the lowest tide in the 24-hour period.

Step 4:   Calculate the tidal difference within the 24-hour period.

Step 5:   Looking at the entire month of January, 2010, record the highest tide in the month.

Step 6:   Looking at the entire month of January, 2010, record the lowest tide in the month.

Step 7:   Calculate the tidal difference with the one-month period.

Online Activities

As per your instructor's direction, go to the online lesson for this lab and complete the activities assigned.

Quiz

1. An incoming ocean wave is traveling at 8.2 m/s and the wavelength is 4.4 m/w. Find the frequency of the wave. Show your work.

2. An incoming ocean wave has a velocity of 10.4 m/s and the wavelength is 2.4 m/w. Find the frequency of the wave. Show your work.

3. How are wind-driven waves created through our oceans? Draw and label a diagram of how wind-driven waves are created. Submit your work as directed by your instructor.

4. What are the two most important aspects of wave motion?

5. The 1883 eruption of the volcanic island of Krakatau created what type of massive wave that overwhelmed all of the low-lying portions of the surrounding islands and carried an estimated 36,000 people to their deaths? How is this massive wave created in the ocean?

6. Tides are a type of wave caused by what type of natural force between the ocean's water and the moon?

7. What type of celestial object other than the moon in our solar system plays a role in how the tides are formed?
   a. Jupiter
   b. Saturn
   c. Mercury
   d. Sun
   e. Mars

8. While the moon is many times less massive than the sun, the moon is so close to Earth, 383,000 kilometers (~ 238,000 miles) as opposed to the 1.5 billion kilometers (92 million miles) to the sun, that its gravitational effect on the tides is approximately _____ that of the sun.
   a. twice
   b. triple
   c. quadruple
   d. quintuple
   e. sextuple

Questions 9 and 10 are based on the **Lab Exercise:** *Tides*.

9. Provide your results for January 20, 2010.

   Highest tide in the 24-hour period =
   Lowest tide in the 24-hour period =
   Tidal difference within the 24-hour period =

10. Provide your results for the month of January, 2010

    Highest tide for the month of January, 2010 = _____

    Lowest tide for the month of January, 2010 = _____

11. The surface waters of the ocean are driven by the wind into huge circular patterns called _____.

12. What are the two dominant winds found on Earth? How are those winds generated across Earth's surface?

13. The density currents that originate beyond 40° north and south latitude and sink to the ocean bottom and are responsible for most of the vertical mixing of ocean waters are called _____ currents.

14. Describe salinity currents and provide an example of salinity current.

15. What are the two types of coastlines found along eastern and western coastlines of the United States?

16. Describe the process of what is happening with the sediments that are generated and deposited along the coastal area.

17. Longshore currents carry what type of small-sized particles along shores and deposit them between adjacent retreating headlands, creating bay barriers or baymouth bars that create sheltered bays and lagoons?

18. As sand moves parallel to the coast, long narrow deposits called _____ are created that are attached to the retreating headland at one end, extend parallel to the shore, and commonly terminate with a characteristic inward curl.
    a. sandbars
    b. spits
    c. baymouth bars
    d. barrier islands
    e. groins

19. What shoreline features result from deposition of sediments?

20. Sand that was transported through the tidal inlet separating the individual islands takes place during the incoming tides (known as flood tides) and deposited on the bay side of the tidal inlet as a(n)
    a. ebb delta.
    b. mudflat.
    c. flooded delta.
    d. salt marsh.
    e. salt marsh complex.

21. The first sign that bays are beginning to fill with sediment is the exposure of the bay bottom at low tide, which is called a _____.

22. Salt-tolerant grasses begin to grow on the exposed mudflat that trap sediments that normally would be flushed through the system. In time, the grass-covered mudflat builds above high tide to form a(n)

    a. ebb delta.
    b. mudflat.
    c. flooded delta.
    d. salt marsh.
    e. salt marsh complex.

23. As the marsh continues to expand, trees may begin to grow within portions of the marsh, converting the marsh into a swamp. In time, much of what had been open bays is converted into a(n)

    a. ebb delta.
    b. mudflat.
    c. flooded delta.
    d. salt marsh.
    d. salt marsh complex.

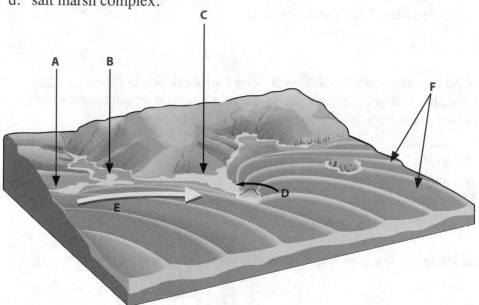

Figure 12.22 Coastal Features. Illustration by Don Vierstra

24. Referring to the labels on **Figure 12.22** above, identify the major coastal features in the diagram from a through f.

A. _____

B. _____

C. _____

D. _____

E. _____

F. _____

GLACIERS

Lesson 13

AT A GLANCE

Purpose

Learning Objectives

Overview

    Formation of Glacial Ice

    The Movement of Glacial Ice

    Dry-Based and Wet-Based Glaciers

    Zone of Accumulation

    Zone of Ablation

    Processes of Glacial Erosion

    Erosion by Alpine Glaciers

    Glacial Lakes

    Glacial Load

    Moraines

Online Activities

Quiz

Purpose

The two largest glaciers in the world are located on the continent of Antarctica and Greenland. These large masses of sheet ice, known as glaciers, have been accumulating snow over very long periods of time. Glaciers are being studied to provide baseline information for air and water pollution. By analyzing air entrapped in glaciers and the trace elements composition of ice, Scientists are able to establish the composition of the atmosphere before the impact on human lives.

Learning Objectives

After completing this laboratory lesson, you will be able to:
- Understand the characteristics and processes of how glaciers are formed.
- Identify different types of glaciers.
- Understand how glaciers move and what happens to a glacier when it encounters a lake or sea.
- Understand how glaciers have changed the landscape.
- Understand how glaciers carry sediments, boulders, and other large objects and deposit them along the landscape.

Overview

Glacial ice covers about 15.6 million km^3 (5 million mi^2) of Earth's present-day surface. About 90 percent of the total is located over the continent of Antarctica where the ice sheet reaches thicknesses of more that 4,700 m (15,000 feet) in places. The second largest ice mass on Earth, the Greenland ice sheet, covers about 80 percent of the island or subcontinent, an area of about 1.8 million km^2 (700,000 mi^2) with a maximum ice thickness of about 3,000 m (10,000 feet) (**Figure 13.1**). The Antarctic and Greenland ice sheets are examples of continental glaciers (a glacier of considerable thickness that covers a large part of a continent, or an area of at 20,000 square miles (50,000 km^2), and obscures the topography of the underlying surface).

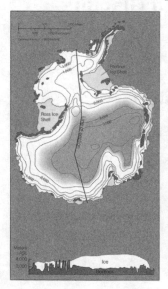

Figure 13.1 Continental Glaciers. About 90% of Earth's glacial ice covers the continent of Antarctica and Greenland. From *Planet Earth* by John J. Renton. Copyright © 2002 by John J. Renton. Reprinted by permission of Kendall Hunt Publishing Company.

This is the same force involved in pulling apart dough or stretching a rubber band. The remaining 648,000 km^2 (250,000 mi^2) of glacial ice is scattered throughout the mountains of the world as alpine or valley glaciers and piedmont glaciers. Alpine glaciers form in the upper reaches of high mountain stream valleys and flow down slope following the stream valley (**Figure 13.2**).

Figure 13.2 Alpine or Valley Glaciers. Alpine or valley glaciers form on mountain summits and their flow paths follow former stream valleys. Shutterstock 45808435, credit Dongliu

Piedmont glaciers form where alpine glaciers emerge from mountain valleys and spread out into the lowland beyond (**Figure 13.3**).

Figure 13.3 Piedmont Glaciers. Piedmont glaciers form when alpine glaciers flow beyond the mouth of a mountain valley and out onto the adjoining valley floor. Courtesy of P. Carrara/USGS

Formation of Glacial Ice

The formation of glacial ice requires the accumulation and preservation of massive volumes of snow. Glaciers are therefore restricted to regions that receive adequate precipitation and that are located either at high elevations or at high latitudes where large volumes of snow can be preserved from year to year. The elevation above which snow can accumulate and be preserved over a single year is called the snow line. In the polar regions, the snow line is located at sea level, approximately at the latitudes of the Arctic and Antarctic Circles. Toward the lower latitudes, the snow line rises, except it is not necessarily at the highest elevations near the equator, because of the combination of high levels of precipitation and cloud cover. The snow line is generally highest surrounding the latitudes of the Tropics of Cancer and Capricorn, about 23° north and south latitude.

The conversion of snow to glacial ice begins with the sublimation of the ice within snowflakes (**Figure 13.4**).

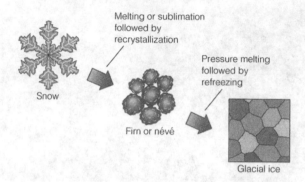

Figure 13.4 Formation of Glacial Ice. The first step in the formation of glacial ice is the transformation of snow into granular ice called névé or firn. With burial and compaction, the firn undergoes pressure melting and the individual ice crystals are cemented together as the water freezes in the pores between the grains. From *Planet Earth* by John J. Renton. Copyright © 2002 by John J. Renton. Reprinted by permission of Kendall Hunt Publishing Company.

Sublimation is the process by which water ice can go between the solid and gaseous phases without going through the liquid phase. Once the water vapor has formed by the sublimation of the snow, it crystallizes back into the solid phase in the form of grains of granular ice called névé or firn. Once the granular ice is buried and compacted, the grains of ice undergo pressure melting (the melting of ice due to increased pressure favoring the higher density phase. Example: a trail of water left behind the blade of an ice skate) at their points of contact. You will remember from previous discussions that pressure affects the melting point/freezing point by favoring liquid water because it is the denser of the two phases. Once the water forms at the points of grain contact, it flows into the void spaces between the grains where it eliminates the air from within the pores, then freezes and cements the granules of ice together to form glacial ice.

The rate at which snow is converted to glacial ice depends in large part on the climate and on the amount of accumulated snow. The snow and ice may approach the melting point during the warmer seasons of the year in temperate regions at high elevations. The availability of water allows the transformation of snow to ice to take place within just a few years. In the Polar Regions with temperatures constantly below the freezing point, this process may take hundreds of years.

The Movement of Glacial Ice

The movement of glacial ice is dependent on: (1) the *thickness* of the ice, (2) the *temperature* of the ice, and (3) the *slope* of the underlying bedrock and the surface elevation of the ice. At atmospheric pressure, ice is a brittle solid, as the jab of an ice pick can easily prove. Once the ice accumulates to a thickness of more than 46 m (150 feet), the pressure of the overlying ice combined with the directional forces developed within the ice mass cause the ice mass below 46 m (150 feet) to respond as a plastic material and begin to flow (**Figure 13.5**).

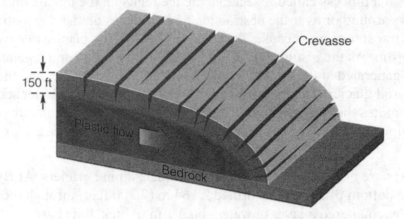

Figure 13.5 Glacial Ice Movement (plastic flow). Once the thickness of glacial ice exceeds 150 feet (46 m), the lower portion of the ice begins to undergo plastic flow. The brittle surface ice breaks into fractures called crevasses as it is carried along by the flowing ice below.
From *Planet Earth* by John J. Renton. Copyright © 2002 by John J. Renton. Reprinted by permission of Kendall Hunt Publishing Company.

The mechanism of plastic flow is not fully understood. If the temperature of the ice is near the melting point, the process of plastic flow may involve pressure melting and recrystallization of the ice. When the temperature of the ice is far below the melting point, the plastic flow may be the result of solid-state recrystallization or inter- and intra-granular movements.

While the ice below 46 m moves by plastic flow, the ice above 46 m becomes increasingly brittle nearer to the surface of the ice (refer to **Figure 13.5**). As a result, fractures called crevasses form in the upper layers of ice that widen toward the surface. Wind-blown snow commonly spans crevasses in the form of snow bridges. Because the presence of a snow bridge is difficult to detect at the surface of the ice, they become a danger to those who venture out onto the ice surface.

Glacial ice is usually described as being an ice cap or an ice sheet. An ice cap is usually a dome-shaped mass of ice covering the summit of mountains or a flat landmass with an area of less than 50,000 km^2 (20,000 mi^2). An ice sheet is a glacier of considerable thickness that forms a continuous cover over a land surface with an area of more than 50,000 km^2.

Ice Temperature
The temperature of glacial ice increases with depth at an average rate of 0.7°C/1,000 m (1.2°F/3,300 feet). Heat within the glacier may come from a number of sources including internal friction, geothermal heat being conducted upward from the underlying bedrock and, in some cases, underlying hot springs and near-surface magmas.

Dry-Based and Wet-Based Glaciers
In most polar ice caps and ice sheets, the temperature at the base of the ice is far below the freezing/melting point of ice and, as a result, the ice is frozen to the bedrock. Such glaciers, called dry-based glaciers, move primarily by plastic flow. Nearly all continental glaciers are dry-based glaciers.

If the temperature of the ice at the base of the glacier has been elevated to near the melting point, the ice can undergo pressure melting as it moves and encounters irregularities in the bedrock surface. In a process called regelation, the ice melts on the up-stream side of the obstruction, flows around or over the obstruction and refreezes on the down-stream side of the obstruction. The transfer of mass causes the ice at the base of the glacier to move by a process called regelation slip. As the result of the combination of regelation and regelation slip, a film of water may be generated at the contact between the base of the glacier and the bedrock, creating a wet-based glacier. The layer of water beneath a wet-based glacier serves as a lubricant and promotes the movement of the glacier by basal sliding. It is estimated that at least half of all alpine glaciers move by a combination of plastic flow, regelation slip, and basal slip.

Wet-based glaciers are not restricted to temperate-climate alpine glaciers. At Byrd Station in the Antarctic, the bottom of a borehole drilled 2,164 m (7,100 feet) through the Antarctic ice sheet to bedrock encountered a layer of water about 1 mm thick at its base.

At the margins of glaciers where the ice is too thin for either plastic flow or basal sliding, the ice may move as a result of brittle fracture. At the headwaters of alpine glaciers, the down slope movement of the ice may be the result of masses of ice rotating along arcuate (curved) fractures in much the same fashion that regolith moves during slumping. At the margins and terminus (lower end) of glaciers, compressive forces create fractures that allow masses of ice to be driven up and over the underlying stagnant ice (**Figure 13.6**).

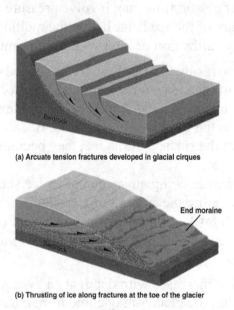

(a) Arcuate tension fractures developed in glacial cirques

(b) Thrusting of ice along fractures at the toe of the glacier

Figure 13.6 Creation of Glacial Ice Fractures. Toward both the headwaters and terminus of the glacier where the ice thins to less than 150 feet (46 m), it reacts as a brittle material and forms fractures along which the ice moves. In the headwaters (a), gravity drives the ice downward along curving fractures while in the terminus (b), the pressure exerted by the moving ice thrusts layers of ice forward and over the underlying ice. From *Planet Earth* by John J. Renton. Copyright © 2002 by John J. Renton. Reprinted by permission of Kendall Hunt Publishing Company.

Alpine Glaciers

In addition to plastic flow, regelation slip, and basal sliding, the rate of downhill movement of alpine glaciers is affected by the slope of the bedrock surface. Movements of alpine glaciers have been measured at 150 to 180 meters per year (500 to 600 feet per year) with some glaciers in Alaska moving as much as 3 m (10 feet) per day. The highest recorded speeds of alpine glaciers have occurred during *surges* where short-term movements of as much as 300 m (21,000 feet) per day have been observed. Most glaciologists believe that surges are the result of pressures that develop in the upstream ice mass as a combination of restricted down-stream flow and the rapid accumulation of new ice in the source area. One study of a surge involving the Variegated Glacier in Alaska indicated that an abnormal buildup of water generated by regelation at the base of the glacier resulted in an accelerated rate of basal slippage. Once thought to be rare events, surges are now known to be common events. Surges of the glaciers in Glacier Bay National Monument, for example, occur every 20 years.

Continental Glaciers

The movement of glaciers resting on gentle slopes, such as all continental glaciers, is affected only by the slope of the ice surface, not by that of the bedrock surface. As long as the thickness of the ice is greater than the relief of the underlying bedrock, the doming (an accumulation of ice and material) of the ice at the point of origin of ice caps or ice sheets produces a surface that slopes toward the margin of the ice mass. The effect of gravity on the ice mass causes the ice to simultaneously collapse at the highest point and generate the horizontal forces necessary to move the ice laterally by plastic flow. As a result, continental ice sheets can ride up and over hills and obstructions within their paths as well as into and out of depressions in the bedrock surface. An example of the former is the fact that, during the last Ice Age, the ice sheet moving out of Canada overran the Adirondack Mountains and gouged out the river valleys that became the Great Lakes and New York's Finger Lakes.

Because of the dry-based character of continental glaciers combined with the horizontal surfaces across which they move, the rates of movement of continental glaciers are significantly slower than those of alpine glaciers. The ice sheet presently forming at the South Pole is moving toward the edge of Antarctica at a rate of about 9 m (27 feet) per year. Even though their average rates of movement are quite slow, continental glaciers are also subjected to surges. Portions of the Greenland ice sheet have been recorded as moving through buried mountain passes at rates of nearly 8 km (5 miles) per year.

Zone of Accumulation

The size of a glacier and whether it advances or retreats depends on the relative rates of ice accumulation and ablation (wastage). For most glaciers, ice accumulation dominates during the winter season when the precipitation of snow is the highest. Although snow may fall over the entire surface of the glacier, the transformation of snow into glacial ice will only occur in the zone of accumulation (**Figure 13.7**). In alpine glaciers, the zone of accumulation is located in the source area, while in continental glaciers it is located in the interior of the ice sheet.

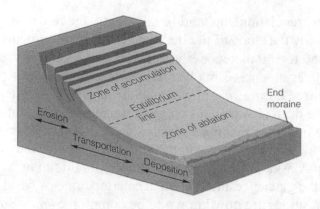

Figure 13.7 Zone of Accumulation of Glacial Ice. Whether a glacier is advancing or retreating depends upon whether the mass of ice being formed in the zone of accumulation is greater or less than the amount of ice being lost in the zone of ablation. From *Planet Earth* by John J. Renton. Copyright © 2002 by John J. Renton. Reprinted by permission of Kendall Hunt Publishing Company.

Zone of Ablation

Beyond the zone of accumulation, in the zone of ablation, the ice mass of the glacier experiences a net loss of volume. In the case of alpine glaciers, the primary cause of ablation is the melting of the ice as the glacier moves into regions where the temperature is too high and the ice melts. In the case of continental glaciers where the temperatures are consistently below the freezing point, the dominant process of ablation is sublimation. Sublimation is the process in which a solid vaporizes without going through a liquid state. An example of sublimation is the vaporization of dry ice (solid CO_2). Glaciers that flow into the sea or an inland body of water can undergo ablation by breaking off or calving at the terminus (**Figure 13.8**).

Figure 13.8 Calving of Glacial Ice. Where a glacier flows into a body of water and loses support from below, it abates (ice mass of the glacier experiences a net loss of volume) by breaking off masses of ice, a process called calving. Shutterstock 31885780, credit Anthony Ricci

The equilibrium line separates the zones of accumulation and ablation (refer to **Figure 13.7**). In the case of alpine glaciers, the equilibrium line is called the firn line. From the point of origin to the equilibrium or firn line, the ice mass is constantly increasing while from the firn line to the terminus of the glacier, the mass of ice is constantly decreasing.

Glacial Ice Advance
When the rate of ice accumulation exceeds the rate of ablation, the glacier will advance. When the rates of accumulation and ablation are in balance, the glacier will come to a "stop." The word "stop" is placed within quotation marks to emphasize the point that the ice mass never stops moving forward. The glacier appears to come to a stop at the terminus of a glacier because the rate of forward movement is offset by the rate of ablation.

Glacial Ice Retreat
When the rate of ablation exceeds the rate of accumulation, the glacier will retreat. During retreat, the loss of ice is not necessarily concentrated at the terminus of the ice. Much of the ablation occurs within the ice sheet upstream from the terminus as the ice sheet thins. As the ice sheet thins, blocks of ice may separate from the main glacier, become stranded, and be buried by the sediments being released from the melting ice.

Processes of Glacial Erosion
Glacial and stream erosion processes are similar in many ways. For example, both glaciers and streams erode the land by the combined processes of bed load abrasion and direct lifting. The major difference between the erosional styles of glaciers and streams is due to the relative viscosities of ice and water. Because of its higher viscosity, the competence of ice is much greater than that of water, resulting in glaciers being able to carry larger particles and greater volumes of material than an equal volume of water. The higher viscosity of ice also prevents the sorting of materials during the erosion, transportation, and deposition processes.

Quarrying or Plucking
As a glacier advances, the ice is not selective at all in terms of the particle size that it can carry. It strips the entire regolith from the bedrock by direct lifting. Water generated at the base of wet-based glaciers penetrates into fractures within the bedrock, refreezes and disrupts the rock by the process of frost wedging. The ice rotates and pulls blocks of rock out of their original positions in a process called quarrying or plucking. These rock mix with the regolith materials stripped from the original bedrock surface and becomes embedded in the bottom few tens of feet of the ice as a part of the glacial bedload (**Figure 13.9**).

Figure 13.9 Glacial Process: Quarrying or Plucking. Credit: USGS.

Because continental glaciers erode almost exclusively by quarrying, most of their load is transported as bedload in the lower portions of the ice. In the case of alpine glaciers, rock and debris slides from the adjacent valley walls fall on the ice and become a major portion of the glacial load.

Abrasion

As glaciers move, the bottom surface of the ice with the embedded rock debris moves over the bedrock surface like a gigantic piece of sandpaper and abrades (to wear away by physical or mechanical means) the bedrock (**Figure 13.10**).

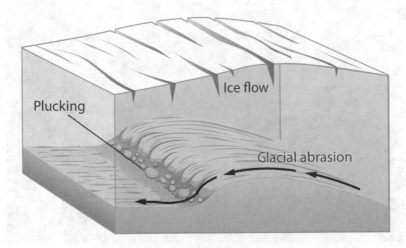

Figure 13.10 Glacial Abrasion. Illustration by Don Vierstra

Striations and Grooves

Depending on the size of the embedded material and the thickness of the ice, the moving glacier may generate a variety of abrasion features from smooth polish, to hairline striations, to deep grooves (**Figure 13.11**). Striations and grooves are commonly used to map the direction of ice movement.

Figure 13.11 Glacial Striations. As wet-based glaciers move, rock debris in the bottom of the ice abrades and gouges the rock surface, forming striations that allow geologists to determine the direction of movement of former glaciers. Courtesy of Walter Siegmund

Facets

As the rock particles in the ice abrade the bedrock, they also abrade each other as they are moved within the plastic ice, producing flat surfaces called facets on pebble-sizes and larger particles.

Erosion by Alpine Glaciers

Much of the spectacular mountain scenery around the world is the product of alpine glaciations (**Figure 3.12**).

Figure 13.12 Alpine Glacier. This photograph illustrates spectacular mountain scenery, which was created by an alpine glacier. Shutterstock 49848541, credit javarman

Cirques

At the source of the glacial ice in the former headwaters of a mountain stream, the ice erodes the underlying bedrock by quarrying. The result is a bowl-shaped depression called a cirque (**Figure 13.13**). While the glacier is active, ice occupies the bottom of the cirque basin. Once the ice has melted, the cirque depressions commonly become the sites of mountain lakes.

Figure 13.13 Cirque. As glacial ice melts from a cirque, the basin commonly becomes filled with water to form a mountain lake called a tarn. Shutterstock 34693321, credit Herr Petroff

Arêtes

As individual alpine glaciers occupying cirques located along both sides of a mountain ridge, the cirques on both sides of the ridge begin to overlap and steepen their upper slopes. In time, the steep slopes from opposite sides of the ridge intersect along the summit of the ridge to form a knife-edged mountain ridge called an arête (**Figure 13.14**).

Figure 13.14 Arêtes. Results of alpine erosion include sharp mountain ridges called arêtes. Courtesy of W. B. Hamilton/USGS

Cols

As two cirques erode toward each other from opposite sides of a ridge, they eventually carve through the ridge. With no support from below, the overlying rock collapses to form a high mountain pass through the ridge called a col (**Figure 13.15**).

Figure 13.15 Cols. This photograph illustrates erosion by alpine glaciers in high mountain passes called cols. Courtesy of W. B. Hamilton/USGS

Horns

One of the most spectacular erosional features created by alpine erosion is the horn. Horns form as multiple cirques carve around a mountain peak and produce a sharp mountain spire. Perhaps the best-known example of a horn is the Matterhorn in the Swiss Alps (**Figure 13.16**). Equally impressive examples of horns can be seen throughout the Northern Rockies, in particular the beautiful Grand Tetons just west of Jackson Hole, Wyoming (**Figure 13.17**).

Figure 13.16 Matterhorn in the Swiss Alps. Shutterstock 29014780, credit kohy

Figure 13.17 Horns. The Grand Tetons located west of Jackson Hole, Wyoming, are excellent examples of horns. Shutterstock 13708960, credit Theresa Martinez

U-Shaped Valleys

Once an alpine glacier leaves the cirque, it flows down the slope following the V-shaped stream valley in which it formed. As the glacier moves down the valley, it begins to scour and abrade the floor and walls of the valley, straightening the course of the valley and converting the V-shaped valley of a youthful mountain stream into the diagnostic U-shaped valley of a glacier. One of the best examples of a U-shaped valley in the United States is Yosemite Valley in the Sierra Nevada of eastern California (**Figure 13.18**).

Figure 13.18 U-shaped Valley. Yosemite Valley in Yosemite National Park is an excellent example of a U-shaped valley, which was carved by a glacier. Photo courtesy of Greg Gardiner

Hanging Valleys

Tributary glaciers to main alpine glaciers carve their own U-shaped valleys, but not to the depth of the valley occupied by the main glacier. After the retreat of the ice, the valleys carved by the tributary glaciers become located high on the wall of the main valley as hanging valleys. The hanging valleys are often sites of spectacular waterfalls where tributary streams plunge hundreds of feet to the main valley floor (**Figure 13.19**).

Figure 13.19 Small Tributary Glaciers. One of the most characteristic topographic features formed by glaciations is the U-shaped valley carved by a main valley glacier with its tributary hanging valleys carved by smaller tributary glaciers. Photo courtesy of N. K. Huber/USGS

Glacial Lakes

Tarns

After the final retreat of alpine glaciers, erosional basins and depressions in the debris laid down by the retreating glacier often become the sites of glacial lakes. One spectacular example of such lakes is the tarns that occupy the lower portion of abandoned cirques (**Figure 13.20**).

Figure 13.20 Tarn. Lake Louise in Alberta, Canada, is an example of a tarn. Shutterstock 39396052, credit Zap Ichigo

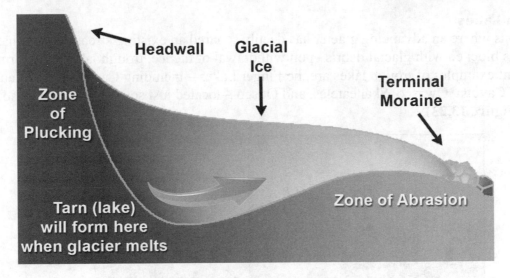

Figure 13.21 Process of a Glacial Tarn. Illustrates how a glacial tarn is formed after the glacier has receded. Illustration by Marie Hulett

Paternoster Lakes

Another example of glacial lakes are strings of lakes that commonly form in thc lowcr reaches of major U-shaped valleys. Because the lakes are interconnected as each lake drains into the next lower lake, they are called paternoster lakes, in reference to a string of prayer beads. (**Figure 13.22**).

Figure 13.22 Paternoster Lakes. Glacial lakes are strings of lakes that commonly form in the lower reaches of major U-shaped valleys called paternoster lakes. Courtesy of John Johnston

Trough Lakes

In regions where an advancing glacier has deeply scoured an existing stream valley that becomes blocked with glacial debris upon withdrawal of the ice, trough lakes may form. Excellent examples of trough lakes are the Finger Lakes—including Canandaigua, Keuka, Seneca, Cayuga, Owasco, Skaneateles, and Otisco—located just south of Lake Ontario in New York (**Figure 13.23**).

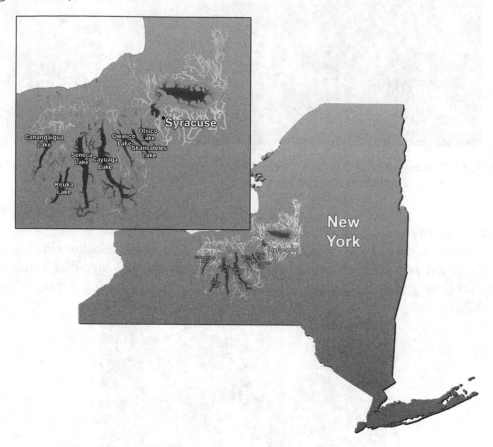

Figure 13.23 Trough Lakes. An example of trough lakes are the Finger Lakes located south of Lake Ontario near the city of Syracuse, New York. Illustration by Marie Hulett

Glacial Load

Glacial ice does not have the ability to discriminate between particle size during erosion, transportation, or deposition; this causes the poorly sorted nature of most glacial deposits. Because of this, glaciers may mix huge boulders, sand, and clay-sized particles in the same deposit. Two terms, drift and till, are used to describe glacial deposits. The term drift dates back to the days when geologists thought that the material was a flood deposit. Today, the term drift refers to any material deposited directly or indirectly from glacial ice. Till is a general term that refers to any poorly sorted, unstratified (unlayered) material deposited from a glacier. Most glacial deposits consist of till.

Moraines

The most common glacial deposit is moraine, which is any mound, ridge, or other distinct accumulation of unsorted, unstratified material (till) deposited directly from glacial ice. There are five types of moraines: (1) terminal or end, (2) ground, (3) recessional, (4) lateral, and (5) medial (**Figure 13.24**).

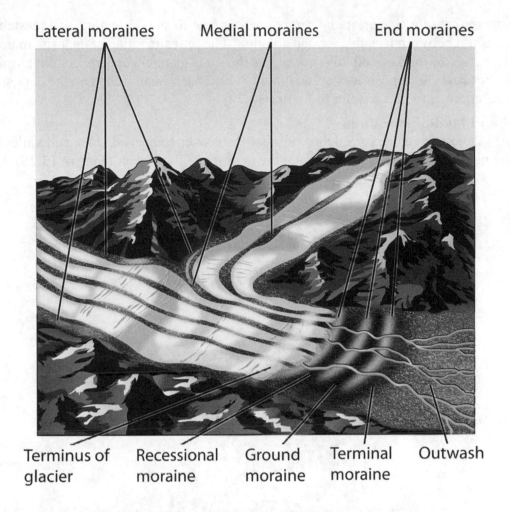

Figure 13.24 Parts of a Glacier. Glaciers deposit a variety of moraines, as the energy to keep the sediment from being deposited is lost. All glaciers deposit a *terminal* or *end moraine* recording the point of maximum advance. As all glaciers retreat, they deposit *ground moraine* in much the same fashion as icing is spread on a cake. *Recessional moraines* record hesitations in the retreat of any glacier. *Lateral* and *medial moraines* are associated only with alpine glaciers and consist of materials that fell from the steep walls of the valley. Illustration by Don Vierstra

Terminal or End Moraine

When an advancing glacier reaches the point where it comes to a "stop" and remains stationary for a period of time, the debris released from melting accumulates along the leading edge of the ice as a terminal or end moraine. Should the glacier begin to once again advance, the material that had accumulated in the terminal moraine is picked up by the glacier and carried as bedload to the next point of ice stability where it is again deposited. Ultimately, a glacier will reach a point of maximum advance and a final terminal moraine will be deposited (refer to **Figure 13.24**).

Ground and Recessional Moraines

During the retreat of a glacier, the material released from the melting ice is spread over the surface of the ground forming a deposit called a ground moraine. This is similar to the way that gravel is spread by a moving dump truck leaving behind a thin layer. The gently rolling topography of much of Ohio and Indiana, has been subjected to continental glaciations and is in part the result of a ground moraine filling of the ice-gouged valleys as the glacier retreated.

During the retreat of a glacier, it may temporarily appear to stop retreating as it reestablishes the equilibrium between ice advance and ablation. The retreating glacier deposits materials at the leading edge of the ice, and this deposit has the same general appearance of a terminal moraine. Because the deposit was accumulated during the retreat of the ice, the deposit is called a recessional moraine (refer to **Figure 13.24**).

Lateral and Medial Moraines

As alpine glaciers advance, rock debris falling off the over-steepened U-shaped valley walls often accumulates on the ice surface along the margins of the glacier (**Figure 13.25**).

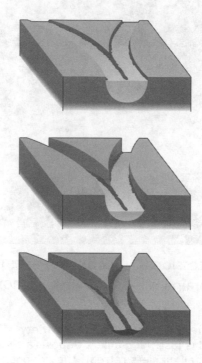

Figure 13.25 Evolution of a Lateral and Medial Moraine. Illustration © Kendall Hunt Publishing Company

When the glacier melts, this material is deposited as a ridge along the sides of the valley called a lateral moraine. Not uncommonly, lateral moraines may be plastered high on the valley walls.

A medial moraine is carried upon or in the middle of a glacier parallel to the valley walls formed by coalescing of two inner lateral moraines below the junction of two alpine glaciers.

When two tributary glaciers flow together into a main glacier, the rock debris collected on the outside margins of the converging tributary glaciers join to form a single deposit down the middle of the main glacier (refer to **Figures 13.25**, **13.26**, and **13.27**).

Figure 13.26 Lateral Moraine. When the glacier retreats, material falls from the valley walls and accumulates on the surface of an alpine glacier. This sediment will eventually be deposited along the sides of the valley as a lateral moraine. Shutterstock 17979844, credit Fedor Selivanov

Figure 13.27 Medial Moraine. When two tributary glaciers flow together into a main glacier, the rock debris collected on the outside margins of the converging tributary glaciers join to form a single deposit down the middle of the main glacier. Courtesy of Joe Donovan

Lab Exercises

There are no hands-on lab exercises for this lesson. See the *Online Activities* section for this lesson.

Online Activities

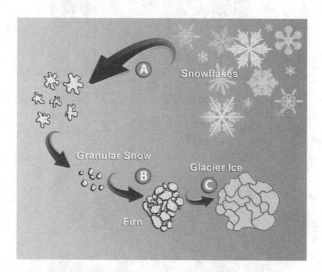

As per your instructor's direction, go to the online lesson for this lab and complete the activities assigned.

Quiz

1. How much glacial ice presently covers Earth's surface?
   a. 10 million km^3
   b. 12 million km^3
   c. 13 million km^3
   d. 15 million km^3
   e. 17 million km^3

2. Name the two continents where most of the glacial ice sheets are found?

3. The Antarctic and Greenland ice sheets are examples of _____.

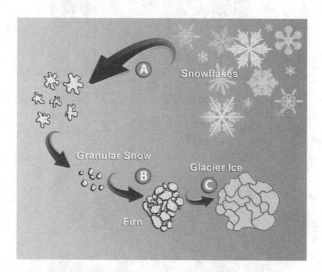

Figure 13.28 Glacial Ice Formation. Illustration by Marie Hulett

4. In **Figure 13.28** above, identify the processes—**accumulation**, **compaction** and **refreezing**, and **recrystallization** happening at each of the corresponding arrows.

   a. _____

   b. _____

   c. _____

5. The movement of glacial ice is dependent on three important integral points. In your own words, describe those three points and the process of glacial ice movement.

6. Plastic flow will be initiated in the lower portions of a glacier once the thickness of ice exceeds about
   a. 50 feet.
   b. 150 feet.
   c. 500 feet.
   d. 1,000 feet.
   e. 1,500 feet.

7. The characteristic of most glacial deposits is that they are
   a. extremely fine-grained.
   b. poorly sorted.
   c. very thick.
   d. found only in cold climates.
   e. none of the above.

8. The pressure of melting ice at the base of a moving glacier is called
   a. solifluction.
   b. regelation.
   c. calving.
   d. sublimination.
   e. recrystallization.

9. Describe how a wet-based glacier is created and provide an example of a wet-based glacier.

10. The process by which a solid may convert to a gas without going through a liquid phase is called

    a. solifluction.
    b. regelation.
    c. calving.
    d. sublimination.
    e. recrystallization.

11. When alpine glaciers emerge from a mountain valley and spread out beyond the base of the mountain, they form a _____ glacier.

    a. alpine or valley
    b. piedmont
    c. u-shaped
    d. horn
    e. cirque

12. Dry-based glaciers are mostly restricted to _____ regions.

    a. polar
    b. tropical rainforest
    c. sub-tropical desert
    d. temperate desert
    e. boreal wet rainforest

13. The most common glacial deposit is the

    a. moraine.
    b. calving.
    c. till.
    d. firn.
    e. sublimination.

14. Explain the process of glacial ice advance.

15. Which of the following is **NOT** true of glaciers?

    a. originate on land
    b. exist only in the Northern Hemisphere
    c. show evidence of past or present flow
    d. form from the recrystallization of snow
    e. a, b, c, and d are all true statements

16. Which of the moraines listed below is **NOT** characteristic of continental glaciation?

    a. Lateral moraine
    b. Ground moraine
    c. Terminal moraine
    d. Recessional moraine
    e. Medial moraine

17. What are the major processes of glacial erosion? Explain each process.

18. A _____ is likely to host a waterfall or steep rapids.

    a. horn peak
    b. paternoster
    c. calving
    d. hanging valley
    e. surging

19. A "bowl-shaped mountain depression" describes a(n)

    a. arête.
    b. col.
    c. horn.
    d. cirque.
    e. calving.

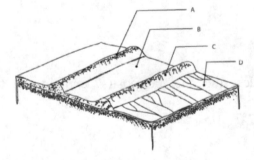

Figure 13.29 Glacial Moraine. Illustration by Mark Worden

20. In **Figure 13.29** above, identify the glacial features of a moraine.

    A. _____

    B. _____

    C. _____

    D. _____

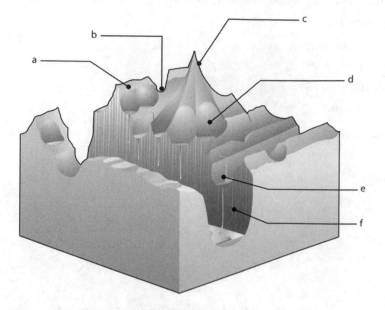

Figure 13.30 Glacial Features of a Moraine. Illustration by Don Vierstra

21. **Figure 13.30** above depicts different types of alpine glaciers that have undergone tremendous erosion. Identify each glacier in the diagram from a through f.

a. _____

b. _____

c. _____

d. _____

e. _____

f. _____

22. Explain how glacial ice does not have the ability to discriminate between particle sizes.

23. What two terms describe glacial deposits? Explain each term.

Figure 13.31 Franz Josef Glacier. Shutterstock 32304529, credit Pichugin Dmitry

24. Look at **Figure 13.31**. On a separate piece of paper, sketch this glacier and label the **zone of accumulation**, **equilibrium line** (**firn line**), and **zone of ablation**. Submit your work as directed by your instructor.

Figure 13.32 Nunavut Glacier on Bylot Island, Canada. Reproduced with permission of Natural Resources Canada 2010, courtesy of Geological Survey of Canada Photo 2002_217, photo by Ron DiLabio.

25. Look at **Figure 13.32**. On a separate piece of paper, sketch this glacier and label the **medial moraine**, **terminal moraine**, **lateral moraine**, **outwash**, and **ground moraine**. Submit your work as directed by your instructor.

ECONOMIC GEOLOGY AND RESOURCES

Lesson 14

AT A GLANCE

Purpose

Learning Objectives

Materials Needed

Overview

> **The Origin of Petroleum**
>
> **The Subsurface Entrapment of Petroleum**
>
> **Finding Oil and Gas Traps**
>
> **The Structure Contour Map**
>
> **The Isopach Map**
>
> **Coal**
>
> **Mining of Coal**

Lab Exercise

> **Lab Exercise: *Structure Contour Map***

Online Activities

Quiz

Purpose

This laboratory lesson will familiarize you with the procedures and techniques used to interpret subsurface geology as it applies to the exploration for and production of fossil fuels.

Learning Objectives

After completing this laboratory lesson, you will be able to:

- Understand how oil and natural gas have formed under the earth.
- Understand how subsurface processes turn organic material into oil and natural gas.
- Interpret subsurface contour maps.
- Understand how oil and natural gas have been trapped under folded layers of rock.
- Learn how to recognize structural and stratigraphic traps based on subsurface contour maps.
- Understand how coal is formed under the earth.
- Understand how coal is mined, transport, and used throughout the planet for energy.

Materials Needed

- ❑ Pencil
- ❑ Eraser
- ❑ Calculator

Overview

Fossil fuels are essential to our civilization. Fossil fuels account for more than 85 percent of the energy used in the United States and they will comprise the major energy sources for the near future. Because the geologic conditions for the formation of oil, coal, and gas did not exist everywhere, fossil fuels do not occur evenly throughout the world. All fossil fuels are derived from organic materials that were preserved in unusual geologic circumstances. Oil and natural gas are fluids that form by alteration of aquatic organic material and terrestrial plant material that then migrate into porous and permeable reservoir rocks and are trapped underground. The exploration for these fluids consists of a series of techniques designed to locate these subsurface reservoirs.

Coal forms by burial and alteration of terrestrial organic material. In the eastern United States the coals are mined by underground methods, while strip mining is common in the western part of the country. The United States has the largest deposits of coal that will continue to be mined if the environmental problems associated with burning of coal are resolved.

The use of petroleum products spread slowly in what has been called the "kerosene" age (1860–1900), but the development of the internal combustion engine near the beginning of the twentieth century set off a phenomenal growth of the petroleum industry. Consequently, we are now in what might be regarded as the "gasoline age," for gasoline is the chief product being derived from petroleum. In addition, thousands of chemical compounds, called petrochemicals, are made from petroleum. Petroleum, therefore, has become one of the most important natural resources of modern civilization.

The Origin of Petroleum

Ever since E. L. Drake drilled the first oil well in Pennsylvania in 1859, and especially since the beginning of this century, the geology of petroleum became increasingly important. As the petroleum industry grew and developed, new geological concepts relating to petroleum evolved. Large amounts of new data were made available to prove or disprove many established principles. For example, a biogenic origin for petroleum is now accepted by most geologists in the form of multitudes of microscopic, one-celled plankton that floated along on the surface of ancient bodies of water. Therefore, the environment of deposition for most of petroleum's organic raw material is believed to involve the following:

1. Upwelling nutrient-rich ocean currents created superficial planktonic blooms, resulting in the production of huge amounts of organic matter, which ultimately settled to the seafloor.

2. An oxygen-deficient seafloor environment discouraged bottom scavengers and preserved the precipitated organic matter.

3. Fine-grained sediment entombed the organic matter in impermeable organic-rich sediment.

Although most petroleum organic matter is believed to have a marine origin, some is believed to have originated in ancient saline or alkaline lakes. In such localized occurrences, the organic matter is believed to have been derived from multitudes of microscopic plankton nourished by drainage into the lakes of nutrient-rich surface-water runoff.

As organic-rich sediment, marine or otherwise, is buried to progressively greater depths and ultimately solidifies into organic-rich shale, it is transformed into a source rock for petroleum. However, liquid or gaseous hydrocarbons cannot evolve from the deeply buried, organic-rich source rock until the latter is subjected to sufficient forces. There has to be enough confining pressure and geothermal heat to literally cook the organic matter, convert a substantial amount into hydrocarbons, and drive the hydrocarbons out of the source rock, apparently through microfractures created by the evolving and abnormally pressured hydrocarbons themselves. The hydrocarbons then become free to migrate through more permeable strata to their final resting places.

The Subsurface Entrapment of Petroleum

The fundamental geologic requirements for the entrapment of oil and gas are simple. A porous and permeable formation, the reservoir rock, is overlain by an impermeable formation, the cap rock. The reservoir rock is deformed or obstructed in such a manner to form a subsurface hydrocarbon trap.

Any formation that is porous and permeable may become a reservoir rock, but those properties are most commonly found in sedimentary rock, especially sandstones. A trap is usually formed by deformation involving faulting, folding, or both. However, some traps are formed by stratigraphic variations in the reservoir rock. These may be primary—the result of changes in porosity and permeability brought about during sedimentation—or secondary, such as fracturing, solution, or truncation and overlap along unconformities. Some traps are the result of complex combinations of structural and stratigraphic variations that are difficult to unravel and evaluate.

But because oil and natural gas are less dense than formation water, which is usually saline, the hydrocarbons always rise above the water. Consequently, gas in any hydrocarbon trap is generally encountered in the highest part, oil is generally found beneath the gas, and the formation water is generally found in the lowest part (see **Figure 14.1**). Few rocks are completely solid but rather contain spaces between the individual grains called pores. In addition, most rocks are broken by fractures that generate additional space within the rock. This explains how solid rocks can hold fluids such as water, oil, and gas; as a result instructors have compared rocks to sponges. The total accumulation of oil and gas trapped in the reservoir rock is called a pool.

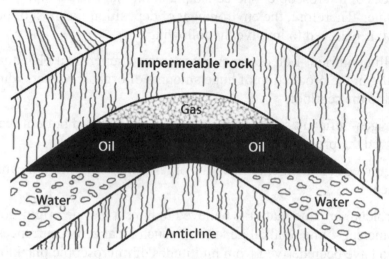

Figure 14.1 Hydrocarbon Trap. Illustration by Bob Dixon

There are two major types of hydrocarbon traps: structural traps, which are produced by folding and/or faulting, and stratigraphic traps, which are produced by changes in lithology, including unconformity-related entrapment mechanisms (see **Figures 14.2**, **14.3**, **14.4**, and **14.5**).

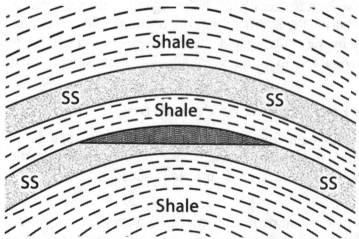

Figure 14.2 Fold-related Structural Trap. The strata are deformed into an anticlinal fold, causing the hydrocarbons to migrate updip from both sides and accumulate in the reservoir rock at the top of the anticlinal fold. In order for petroleum to remain in the reservoir, the rock must be overlain by a low-permeability rock layer, appropriately called a cap rock. It should come as no surprise to find that the most common cap rock is shale. Illustration by Bob Dixon

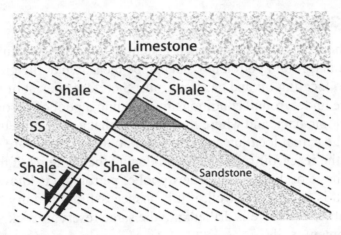

Figure 14.3 Fault-related Structural Trap. The strata are tilted and faulted, causing the hydrocarbons to migrate updip to the right and accumulate in the reservoir rock against the impermeable barrier created by the displaced shale on the other side of the fault. Structural traps are far more common than stratigraphic traps, probably because the former are easier to find than the latter. Illustration by Bob Dixon

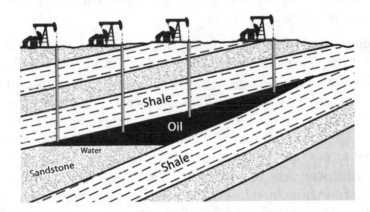

Figure 14.4 Simple Stratigraphic Trap. The reservoir rock has pinched-out or shaled-out in an updip direction, causing the hydrocarbons to migrate updip to the right and accumulate within the pinched out reservoir rock confined by surrounding impermeable rock. Illustration by Bob Dixon

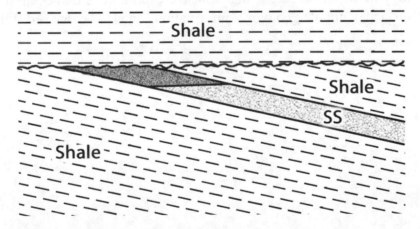

Figure 14.5 Unconformity-related Stratigraphic Trap. The reservoir rock has been tilted and truncated in an updip direction, causing the hydrocarbons to migrate updip to the right and accumulate against the impermeable barrier created by the cap-rock overlap at the angular unconformity, in this case shale. Illustration by Bob Dixon

Lesson 14/Economic Geology and Resources **273**

Finding Oil and Gas Traps

There is no direct method of locating subsurface accumulations of petroleum, nor is there a physical property of underground petroleum that can be measured at the ground surface. The geologist's approach to locating oil and gas traps must therefore consist of indirect methods. Test wells are located where underground conditions for trapping a pool of oil or gas are suspected from the available geologic data, and where it is believed that a pool of petroleum can be produced at a profit. The actual location and size of a pool of oil or gas are determined only by drilling test wells into the reservoir rock and by producing the contents of the reservoir rock. A test well drilled in the hope of discovering a new pool of petroleum is known as a wildcat well. If the well is successful, it is a discovery well; if it is unsuccessful, it is a dry hole (see **Figure 14.6**). On the other hand, wells drilled into the same reservoir rock after a discovery has been made are development wells.

As the search for petroleum goes deeper into the earth, the geology becomes more complex and uncertain, and the data upon which the geologist must base a conclusion becomes less reliable. Therefore, every scrap of information must be squeezed out of the record and put to use, and the data from each record must be projected outward in all directions. If conditions are favorable, such efforts may result in locating an oil or gas prospect that will geologically and economically justify the drilling of a wildcat well.

The first step in developing an oil or gas prospect is to assemble all available information from previously drilled oil wells, gas wells, water wells, and so forth in the prospect area. This generally consists of well records, or well logs, that include descriptions of the rock formations encountered in each well and the depths at which they occur. Such rock formations may be identified and correlated from one well to another by the mineralogical content or fossil content of rock samples recovered at the surface or by means of the in-hole physical properties of the penetrated rock formations as determined by geophysical logs (a record of the structure and composition of the earth encountered when drilling a well, test hole, or bore hole). Additional data might consist of information on oil shows or gas shows encountered during drilling operations, records of previous oil or gas production in the prospect area, or the results of geophysical surveys in the prospect area. The most helpful geophysical surveys are seismic traverses in which man-made seismic tremors, created at the ground surface, are used to interpret the structural geology in the subsurface. If the same rock formations that occur in the subsurface are visible at the surface, valuable geological information can also be derived from the surface exposures.

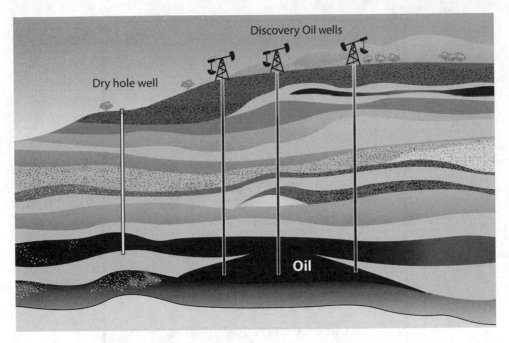

Figure 14.6 Oil Well. Illustration by Don Vierstra

The Structure Contour Map

If the prospect area is endowed with good source rock and good reservoir rock, the first step in the development of a prospect is to look for regions in the subsurface where oil or gas might be trapped. This usually entails the creation of a structure contour map showing the configuration of the top of a good reservoir rock, such as porous and permeable sandstone, that might be overlain by a nonporous and impermeable cap rock, such as tight shale. The structure contour map is contoured like a topographic map except that the control points for the structure contour map are subsurface elevations of the top of the reservoir rock being contoured, not spot elevations of the ground surface.

A structure contour map, therefore, shows the structurally high parts and the structurally low parts of a prospect area. Because oil or gas tends to accumulate in structurally high regions, such as anticlinal folds, the structurally low regions can be eliminated from consideration. Therefore, the structurally high areas should get top consideration as prospective drill sites. The flanks of the structural highs might be considered as well, because oil or gas could be trapped against faults or updip pinchouts at those sites.

The Isopach Map

If the structure contour map of the top of the reservoir rock reveals favorable structural conditions for trapping oil or gas, it is often desirable to also create an isopach map of the reservoir rock. (see **Figure 14.7**) An isopach map, also called a "thickness map," is a contour map, too, but the contour lines connect points of equal thickness rather than points of equal elevation. A good entrapment mechanism, such as an anticlinal fold, would not be a good drilling prospect if the reservoir rock was so thin in the anticlinal region that the produced oil's potential revenue would not cover the drilling costs.

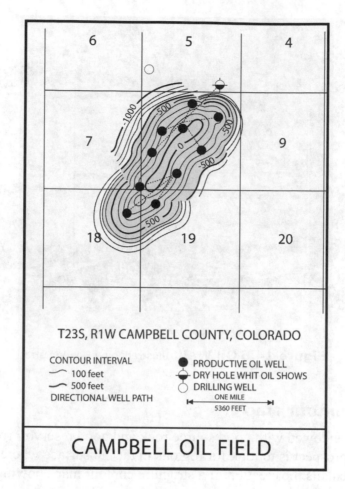

Figure 14.7 Isopach Map. Illustration by Don Vierstra

An isopach map would show variations in thickness of the reservoir rock and would allow the areas where the reservoir rock is too thin to be eliminated from consideration, even though the structural geology might be favorable. An isopach map might also direct the geologist to off-structure regions where thicker parts of the reservoir rock might thin and pinch out updip along the flanks of a structurally high region, resulting in the stratigraphic entrapment of oil or gas.

Coal

Coal consists primarily of the preserved remains of the woody tissue of land plants. Under normal conditions, any plant debris that falls to the ground is quickly attacked by a combination of microbial activity, bacteria and fungi, and oxidation that converts the plant debris to humus and soluble compounds that return to the soil to provide food for the living plants. In order to preserve plant remains in sufficient quantity to produce coal, it must accumulate in an environment in which the oxygen content is very low and the microbial activity is suppressed. The environment that serves that purpose is the swamp.

A swamp is a wetland dominated by wood-rich land plants in which the water is both oxygen deficient and acidic. The oxygen content of the water is low because the currents within the swamp are so slow that the water is not naturally aerated and because of the abundance of carbon available to remove the oxygen as carbon dioxide, CO_2. The microbial activity is controlled by the acidity of the water. Microbes are most active at pH of about 7. As the pH decreases (the water becomes more acidic), the activity of the microbes decreases. Above a pH of about 3, there may be enough organic material preserved to stain the swamp sediments black, giving rise to black shales. Below pH3, the level of microbial activity is reduced to the point where enough woody tissue may be preserved to create a coal-forming peat. Coal-forming peat differs from the peat used in gardens in that it contains more woody tissues. Most of the peat purchased for gardening is made from sphagnum moss and other nonwoody plants.

After the plant debris within the swamp is converted into peat, the peat is buried either by floodplain deposits as the sediments subside and streams meander across the swamp or by marine deposits as sea level rises and the sea transgresses onto the land. As the thickness of the overlying sediments increase, the peat is subjected to compaction that reduces the thickness of the original peat by about 90 percent; in other words, about 10 feet of peat produces 1 foot of coal. In addition to the pressure applied by the weight of the overlying sediments, the peat also begins to be heated as a result of the geothermal gradient, initiating a process called coalification that converts the peat into other forms of coal (coal geologists consider peat to be a type of coal). Subjected to modest pressures and temperatures of no more than about 150°C (300°F), compositional changes begin to occur within the peat, the chemical details of which are not precisely understood. The major change that takes place is the conversion of the woody tissues into the material that makes up most of the mass of coal. Plant parts, such as spores, pollen, and the cuticles of leaves, survive relatively intact and can be identified by microscopic examination of the coal.

The coalification process creates the various ranks of coal, starting with peat, the lowest rank of coal (**Figure 14.8**).

Rank	Coal type	Weight % Dry, ash-free carbon	Heat potential in (BTU/lb.)
High	Anthracite		
		91	15,500
	Bituminous		
		77	12,600
	Subbituminous		
		71	9.900
	Lignite		
		60	
Low	Peat		

Figure 14.8 Coal Rank Series. The various members of the coal rank series change from an organic portion of peat during the burial process and changes to the different types of coal such as lignite, subbituminous, bituminous, and anthracite.

Coal quality is determined by: (1) the amount of ash (mineral matter) in the coal and (2) the sulfur content. All plants contain minerals within their tissues; the ash remaining after a log has been burned in a fireplace or campfire is the mineral matter originally contained in the dead wood cells. As the woody tissues are converted to coal, some of the original mineral matter is incorporated into the coal and, when burned, remains behind as ash. While of no environmental concern, increases in mineral matter reduce the energy potential of the coal by not contributing to the production of heat. Following combustion, the ash must be collected from the firebox of a power plant and disposed of.

The source of sulfur in coal is the original plant materials. Sulfur is one of the six essential elements of life as we know it along with carbon, C; hydrogen, H; oxygen, O; phosphorous, P; and nitrogen, N. In unweathered coal, sulfur is found in two forms: (1) organic sulfur and (2) pyritic sulfur. Organic sulfur is that sulfur which is part of the organic components of the coal while pyritic sulfur is that contained in the mineral pyrite, FeS_2. As a rule of thumb, organic sulfur is the dominant form of sulfur in coals containing less than 1 weight percent sulfur; when the sulfur content exceeds 1 weight percent, the increase is the result of the introduction of pyrite. Sulfate sulfur in the form of $FeSO_4$ indicates that the coal has been subjected to chemical weathering. In general, ash and sulfur content increase and decrease together. Based on ash and sulfur content, coals are arbitrarily classified as high, medium, and low quality. High-quality coals are those containing less than 10 weight percent ash and 1 weight percent sulfur. The division between medium- and low-quality coal is less definite and depends more upon the intended mode of utilization. In general, however, coals with more than 25 to 30 weight percent ash and 3 to 4 weight percent sulfur would be considered low-quality.

Today, nearly all of the coal mined in the United States is used to generate electricity in coal-burning power plants. According to 2008 figures, Wyoming is the leading producer of coal in the United States, producing about 39.9 percent of the total U.S. output of 1,171,809 short tons. Kentucky and West Virginia are tied for second, each producing about 11.9 percent of the total. In the United States, about 60 percent of all the coal is obtained from surface mines with nearly 99 percent of all the coal produced from western states being open pit surface mines. Most of the eastern coals are deep-mined with surface mines only accounting for 25 percent of the production.

The coals of the United States are divided into western and eastern coal-producing areas. In general, the eastern coal fields contain low- to high-quality, high-rank, bituminous coal, while the western fields contain high-quality coal, mostly lignite and subbituminous in rank. (see **Figure 14.9**) The western coals are distributed among many relatively small basins throughout the Rocky Mountains and western Great Plains, while the eastern coals occur in four relatively large basins. The western coals are mostly low-rank subbituminous coals and lignites but are all of high quality with ash contents less that 10 weight percent and total sulfur contents under 1 weight percent. As a result, all of the western coals meet EPA compliance standards without any type of treatment. In comparison, except for a small area of anthracite in eastern Pennsylvania, all of the eastern coals are bituminous in rank. They range in quality, however, from high-quality in the southern Appalachian Basin (southern West Virginia and Kentucky), to medium quality in the northern Appalachian Basin (northern West Virginia, western Pennsylvania, and eastern Ohio). Except for a few individual coal beds, most of the coals in the Illinois Basin are noncompliance coals, even with treatments. Most of the coals in the Mid-Continent Basin are low quality. There is no commercial coal production from the Michigan Basin.

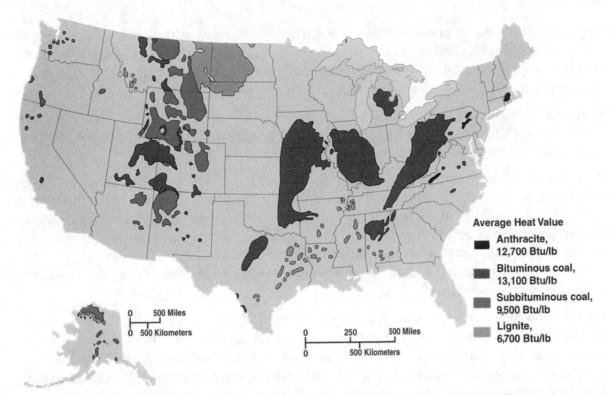

Average Heat Value	
Anthracite, 12,700 Btu/lb	
Bituminous coal, 13,100 Btu/lb	
Subbituminous coal, 9,500 Btu/lb	
Lignite, 6,700 Btu/lb	

Figure 14.9 Distribution of Coal-producing Areas in the Western and Eastern United States. From *Planet Earth* by John J. Renton. Copyright © 2002 by John J. Renton. Reprinted by permission of Kendall Hunt Publishing Company.

Because of the distances involved, the western power-generating industry builds mine-mouth power plants where the coal is taken from the mine, pulverized, and fed directly into the firebox (**Figure 14.10**).

Figure 14.10 Power Plant. To minimize the overall costs of power production, most western coals are burned in nearby power plants, such as this plant in Rosebud County, Montana, and the power is shipped by way of the national electrical grid. Courtesy of E. N. Hinrichs, USGS

Rather than selling and shipping coal, the western utilities sell and ship electricity, although some western coal is shipped to the east to serve as high-quality coal for blending. In contrast, eastern power-generating plants are usually supplied with coal from several distant sources by rail or a combination of rail, barge, and truck.

Mining of Coal

Coal deposits are extracted through a series of mining processes. These mining processes include strip mining (or open-pit mining) and underground mining.

In strip mining. coal beds are close enough to the surface (i.e., surface to approximately 200 feet below ground surface) that conventional modern mining equipment can remove the top layer of soil and mine the coal bed and transport the coal to any power plant facility in the continental United States or to any other country around the world. Strip mining or open-pit mining causes serious environmental damage because native vegetation is removed and the remaining overburden (topsoil material) is easily erodible, thus increasing the erosion rate where sediments can impact stream biodiversity.

In underground mines, coal beds are located at a depth of 200 feet to 1,000 feet below ground surface. Modernized mining machinery and manpower are used to mine the coal. Decisions a mining company must make in order to mine the coal are the following—the thickness of the coal seam, the quality and rank of the coal, the difficulty of removing the rock material to the surface, transportation costs, and the price of coal. Underground coal mines can also cause environmental damage through acid mine drainage to subsurface groundwater reservoirs thus creating contamination into drinking water sources, and abandoned underground coal mines become structurally weakened over time and collapse, causing subsidence in surrounding localities.

Lab Exercise

Lab Exercise: *Structure Contour Map*

In this exercise, you will use a structure contour map to identify where oil is found in subsurface strata. Follow the steps below and record your observations in the space provided or on a separate piece of paper. Make sure to save your observations. You will use the data to answer questions in the quiz at the end of this lesson.

Step 1: Locate **Figure 14.11**, a structure contour map. Notice that it is similar to a topographic map except that the points represent subsurface elevations (as indicated by the negative numbers). For example, –3950 indicates that the point is 3,950 feet below the surface of the ground.

Step 2: Using a 50-foot contour interval, draw the contours of the map on **Figure 14.11**.

Step 3: As indicated on the map legend, open circles represent dry holes and the black dots represent oil-producing wells. The depths of the oil and dry wells range from 3,900 feet to 4,250 feet below ground surface. Use the structure contours on the map to assist you in identifying the approximate location of the oil boundary. Use a dashed line to mark this area.

Step 4: Shade the area that contains the oil-producing wells on the structure contour map. Submit your work as directed by your instructor.

Step 5: How many oil wells are producing oil and at what range of depth below ground surface are the wells producing oil?

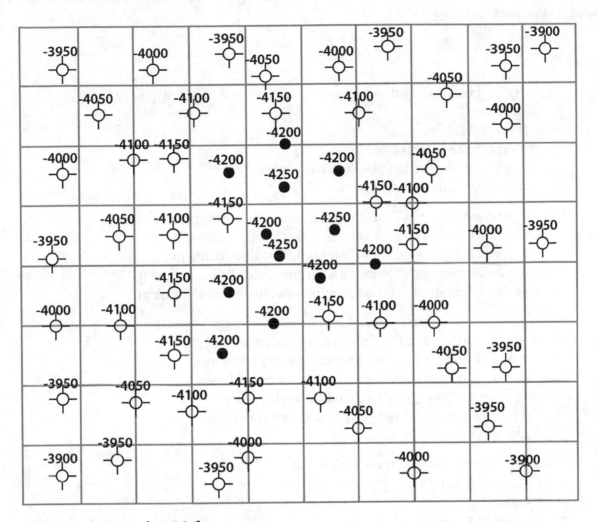

Contour Interval = 50 ft.

-ϕ- = Dry holes - not oil producing wells, may contain water within the well.

● = Oil well - oil producing well.

Figure 14.11 Structure Contour Map. Illustration by Bob Dixon

Online Activities

As per your instructor's direction, go to the online lesson for this lab and complete the activities assigned.

Quiz

1. The organic matter, or hydrocarbon raw material, is derived primarily from
    a. dinosaurs.
    b. sea serpents.
    c. mammoths and mastodons.
    d. microscopic one-celled planktonic organisms.
    e. macroscopic clams and oysters.

2. The organic matter, or hydrocarbon raw material, is best preserved in
    a. oxygenated environments with an influx of fine sediment.
    b. oxygenated environments with no influx of fine sediment.
    c. oxygen-deficient environments with an influx of fine sediment.
    d. oxygen-deficient environments with no influx of fine sediment.
    e. none of the above.

3. Hydrocarbons are generated from organic matter in
    a. shallow, low-pressure, low-temperature environments.
    b. shallow, high-pressure, high-temperature environments.
    c. deep, low-pressure, low-temperature environments.
    d. deep, high-pressure, high-temperature environments.
    e. none of the above.

4. The best hydrocarbon reservoir rock is
    a. a massive granite.
    b. a banded gneiss.
    c. a massive siltstone.
    d. an organic-rich shale.
    e. a poorly cemented sandstone.

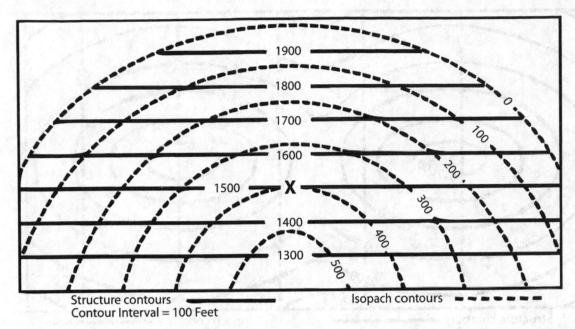

Structure contours ———————
Contour Interval = 100 Feet

Isopach contours — — — — —

Figure 14.12 Structure contours on top of the Bonanza sandstone with isopach-contour overlay.
Illustration by Mark Worden

Use Figure 14.12 to answer Questions 5 and 6.

5. Which type of hydrocarbon trap is depicted in **Figure 14.12**?
    a. a simple stratigraphic trap (updip pinchout)
    b. an unconformity-related stratigraphic trap
    c. a fold-related structural trap
    d. a fault-related structural trap
    e. none of the above

6. The elevation of the *bottom* of the Bonanza sandstone at point X in **Figure 14.12** is
    a. 400 feet above sea level.
    b. 1,500 feet above sea level.
    c. 1,100 feet above sea level.
    d. 1,900 feet above sea level.
    e. none of the above.

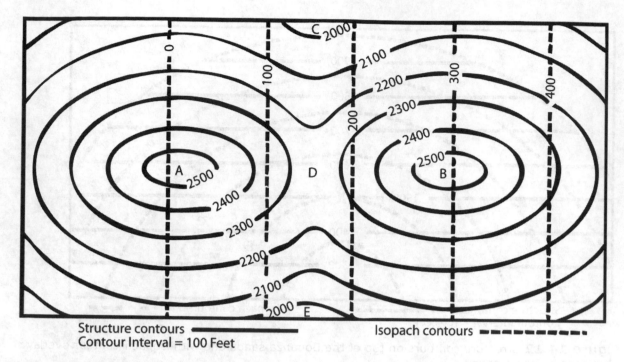

Structure contours ━━━━━━━
Contour Interval = 100 Feet

Isopach contours ━ ━ ━ ━ ━

Figure 14.13 Structure contours on top of the Bonanza sandstone with isopach-contour overlay.
Illustration by Mark Worden

Use Figure 14.13 to answer Questions 7 and 8.

7.　The best hydrocarbon trap depicted in **Figure 14.13** is at location
　　a.　A.
　　b.　B.
　　c.　C.
　　d.　D.
　　e.　E.

8.　The best hydrocarbon trap depicted in **Figure 14.13** is
　　a.　a simple stratigraphic trap (updip pinchout).
　　b.　an unconformity-related stratigraphic trap.
　　c.　a fold-related structural trap.
　　d.　a fault-related structural trap.
　　e.　none of the above.

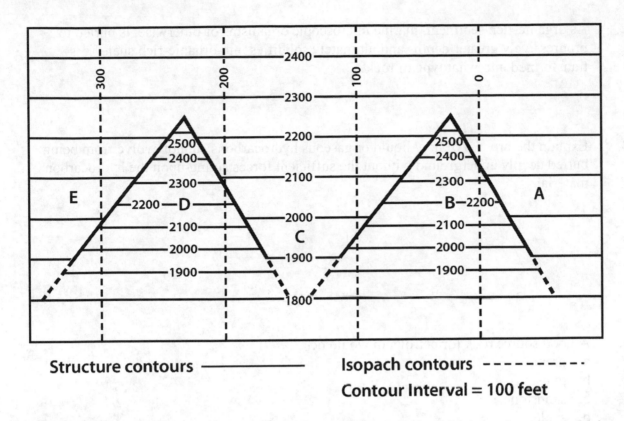

Structure contours ——————— Isopach contours - - - - - - - - -

Contour Interval = 100 feet

Figure 14.14 Structure contours on top of the Bonanza sandstone with isopach-contour overlay.

Illustration by Bob Dixon

Use Figure 14.14 to answer Questions 9 and 10.

9. The best hydrocarbon trap depicted in **Figure 14.14** is at location
    a. A.
    b. B.
    c. C.
    d. D.
    e. E.

10. The best hydrocarbon trap depicted in **Figure 14.14** is
    a. a simple stratigraphic trap (updip pinchout).
    b. an unconformity-related stratigraphic trap.
    c. a fold-related structural trap.
    d. a fault-related structural trap.
    e. none of the above.

11. Although most petroleum organic matter is believed to have a marine origin, some scientist believed that some petroleum has originated in _____ or

    _____.

    Describe how the microscopic plankton came to be found in this region.

12. As organic-rich sediment, marine microscopic organisms or otherwise, is buried to progressively greater depths and ultimately solidifies into organic-rich shale, it is transformed into what type of rock?

13. Explain the process of how liquid or gaseous hydrocarbons cannot evolve from being buried deeply underground without the sufficient forces acting upon the hydrocarbon material.

14. A good source rock for petroleum would be
    a. granite.
    b. gypsum.
    c. sandstone.
    d. shale.
    e. none of the above.

15. A good reservoir rock for petroleum would be a porous
    a. granite.
    b. gypsum.
    c. sandstone.
    d. shale.
    e. none of the above.

16. How do geologists locate oil and gas traps deep within the earth?

17. Explain the difference between a wildcat well, a discovery well, and a development well.

18. Describe the process of how coal is formed.

19. The evolution of coal (where 1 = lignite, 2 = anthracite, 3 = peat, and 4 = bituminous) by increasing heat content is
    a. 1, 2, 3, 4.
    b. 4, 3, 2, 1.
    c. 3, 1, 2, 4.
    d. 3, 1, 4, 2.
    e. none of the above.

20. The fossil fuel with the greatest reserves in the United States is
    a. coal.
    b. tar sands.
    c. onshore oil.
    d. offshore oil.
    e. all oil.

21. The eastern coal fields contain low- to high-quality, high-rank, _____ coal, while the western fields contain high quality coal, mostly_____ and _____ in rank.

22. Where is most of the western part of the United States coalfields distributed?

23. What is meant by coal rank?

24. What are the two forms of mining for coal in the United States? Describe the process of mining for the coal.

Question 25 is based on the Lab Exercise: *Structure Contour Map*
25. Record you answer from the Lab Exercise, step 5.

Appendix

Tables for Reference

I. Conversion Factors

Convert From	To	Multiply by
Centimeters	Feet	0.0328
Centimeters	Inches	0.394
Meters	Inches	39.37
Meters	Feet	3.2808
Meters	Yards	1.0936
Meters	Miles	0.0006214
Kilometers	Miles	0.621
Inches	Centimeters	2.54
Inches	Meters	0.0254
Feet	Centimeters	30.48
Feet	Meters	0.3048
Yards	Meters	0.9144
Miles	Kilometers	1.609
Miles	Feet	5280
Miles	Yards	1760
Square miles	Square kilometers	2.59
Square miles	Square acres	640
Grams	Ounces	0.03527
Grams	Pounds	0.002205
Kilograms	Ounces	35.27
Kilograms	Pounds	2.2046
Ounces	Grams	28.35
Pounds	Grams	453.6
Pounds	Kilograms	0.4536

II. Prefixes for System Units

Prefix	Power	Equivalent
Tera	10^{12} = 1,000,000,000,000	Trillion
Giga	10^{9} = 1,000,000,000	Billion
Mega	10^{6} = 1,000,000	Million
Kilo	10^{3} = 1,000	Thousand
Hecto	10^{2} = 100	Hundred
Deca	10^{1} = 10	Ten
	10^{0} = 1	One
Deci	10^{-1} = .1	Tenth
Centi	10^{-2} = .01	Hundredth
Milli	10^{-3} = .001	Thousandth
Micro	10^{-6} = .000001	Millionth
Nano	10^{-9} = .000000001	Billionth
Pico	10^{-12} = .000000000001	Trillionth

III. Scientific Notation

Scientific notation is a shorthand way of designating numbers and is especially useful when dealing with very large or very small numbers, both of which are difficult to read and equally difficult to notate. For example, the distance from the sun to Pluto is three billion, six hundred and sixty-seven million miles (five billion, nine hundred million kilometers). Even if we reduce the distances to numerical notation, one still has to write 3,667,000,000 miles (5,900,000,000 km). Scientific notation reduces such numbers to a number greater than 1 and less than 10, called the real constant, times 10 to an exponent. When the original number is larger than 1, the exponent of 10 is positive; when it is smaller than 1, the exponent is negative. The exponent tells how many powers of ten are needed to convert the real constant to the original number.

Let us first consider a simple case. The real constant for the number 100 would be 1. (Remember, the real constant is a number between 1 and 10.) The real constant, 1, must be multiplied by two powers of ten (10×10) to equal 100. The scientific notation for 100 would therefore be 1 (the real constant) $\times$ 10 raised to a power of two (the exponent). The scientific notation for 100 would therefore be 1×10^{2}. Similarly, the real constant for the number 1,000 is also 1, but it would have to be multiplied by three powers of ten ($10 \times 10 \times 10$) to equal 1,000. The scientific notation for 1,000 would therefore be 1×10^{3}.

Now let's convert the distance to Pluto in miles, 3,667,000,000, to scientific notation. The real constant, which would be 3.667, needs to be multiplied by nine powers of ten or 1 billion to equal the original number. The scientific notation would therefore be 3.667×10^9) miles. The scientific notation is a much easier way to both record and convey the distance from the sun to Pluto.

The same procedure is applied to determine the scientific notation of very small numbers. For example, the diameter of the carbon atom is 0.000,000,000,154 meters. The real constant would be 1.54. Because the number is less than 1, the exponent of 10 will be negative and will be equal to the number of digits the decimal point was shifted to the right to arrive at the real constant. Note that to arrive at 1.54, the decimal point is shifted 10 places. The scientific notation for the diameter of a carbon atom in meters would be 1.54×10^{-10}.

IV. Summary of the Scientific Notation Method

10^6	=	1,000,000
10^5	=	100,000
10^4	=	10,000
10^3	=	1,000
10^2	=	100
10^1	=	10
10^0	=	1
10^{-1}	=	.1
10^{-2}	=	.01
10^{-3}	=	.001
10^{-4}	=	.0001
10^{-5}	=	.00001
10^{-6}	=	.000001